METHUEN LIBRARY REPRINTS

SBN/416 32510 6/33

THE COMPLETE WORKS

OF

WALTER SAVAGE LANDOR

———

VOLUME IV

LANDOR'S BIRTHPLACE AT WARWICK.

THE
COMPLETE WORKS
OF
WALTER SAVAGE
LANDOR

EDITED BY
T. EARLE WELBY

VOLUME IV

BARNES & NOBLE, Inc.
New York
METHUEN & CO. Ltd
London

This edition, published in 1969

by Barnes & Noble, Inc., New York
and Methuen & Co., Ltd. London

is reproduced from the edition
published by Chapman & Hall, Ltd.
between 1927 and 1936

Manufactured in the United States of America

CONTENTS

IMAGINARY CONVERSATIONS

ENGLISH

IMAGINARY CONVERSATIONS

ENGLISH

I. LEOFRIC AND GODIVA

(*Imag. Convers.*, v., 1829 ; *Wks.*, i., 1846 ; *Wks.*, v., 1876.)

GODIVA. There is a dearth in the land, my sweet Leofric ! Re-member how many weeks of drought we have had, even in the deep pastures of Leicestershire ; and how many Sundays we have heard the same prayers for rain, and supplications that it would please the Lord in his mercy to turn aside his anger from the poor pining cattle. You, my dear husband, have imprisoned more than one malefactor for leaving his dead ox in the public way ; and other hinds have fled before you out of the traces, in which they and their sons and their daughters, and haply their old fathers and mothers, were dragging the abandoned wain homeward. Although we were accompanied by many brave spearmen and skilful archers, it was perilous to pass the creatures which the farm-yard dogs, driven from the hearth by the poverty of their masters, were tearing and devour-ing ; while others, bitten and lamed, filled the air either with long and deep howls or sharp and quick barkings, as they struggled with hunger and feebleness or were exasperated by heat and pain. Nor could the thyme from the heath, nor the bruised branches of the fir-tree, extinguish or abate the foul odor.

LEOFRIC. And now, Godiva, my darling, thou art afraid we should be eaten up before we enter the gates of Coventry ; or perchance that in the gardens there are no roses to greet thee, no sweet herbs for thy mat and pillow.

GODIVA. Leofric, I have no such fears. This is the month of roses : I find them everywhere since my blessed marriage : they, and all other sweet herbs, I know not why, seem to greet me wherever

I look at them, as though they knew and expected me. Surely they can not feel that I am fond of them.

LEOFRIC. O light laughing simpleton ! But what wouldst thou ? I came not hither to pray ; and yet if praying would satisfy thee, or remove the drought, I would ride up straightway to Saint Michael's and pray until morning.

GODIVA. I would do the same, O Leofric ! but God hath turned away his ear from holier lips than mine. Would my own dear husband hear me, if I implored him for what is easier to accomplish ? what he can do like God.

LEOFRIC. How ! what is it ?

GODIVA. I would not, in the first hurry of your wrath, appeal to you, my loving lord, in behalf of these unhappy men who have offended you.

LEOFRIC. Unhappy ! is that all ?

GODIVA. Unhappy they must surely be, to have offended you so grievously. What a soft air breathes over us ! how quiet and serene and still an evening ! how calm are the heavens and the earth ! shall none enjoy them ? not even we, my Leofric ! The sun is ready to set : let it never set, O Leofric, on your anger. These are not my words ; they are better than mine ; should they lose their virtue from my unworthiness in uttering them !

LEOFRIC. Godiva, wouldst thou plead to me for rebels ?

GODIVA. They have then drawn the sword against you ! Indeed I knew it not.

LEOFRIC. They have omitted to send me my dues, established by my ancestors, well knowing of our nuptials, and of the charges and festivities they require, and that in a season of such scarcity my own lands are insufficient.

GODIVA. If they were starving as they said they were——

LEOFRIC. Must I starve too ? Is it not enough to lose my vassals ?

GODIVA. Enough ! O God ! too much ! too much ! may you never lose them ! Give them life, peace, comfort, contentment. There are those among them who kissed me in my infancy, and who blessed me at the baptismal font. Leofric, Leofric ! the first old man I meet I shall think is one of those ; and I shall think on the blessing he gave, and (ah me !) on the blessing I bring back to him. My heart will bleed, will burst—and he will weep at it ! he will weep, poor soul! for the wife of a cruel lord who denounces vengeance on him, who carries death into his family.

LEOFRIC. We must hold solemn festivals.

GODIVA. We must indeed.

LEOFRIC. Well then.

GODIVA. Is the clamorousness that succeeds the death of God's dumb creatures, are crowded halls, are slaughtered cattle, festivals? are maddening songs and giddy dances, and hireling praises from party-coloured coats? Can the voice of a minstrel tell us better things of ourselves than our own internal one might tell us; or can his breath make our breath softer in sleep? O my beloved! let everything be a joyance to us: it will, if we will. Sad is the day, and worse must follow, when we hear the blackbird in the garden and do not throb with joy. But, Leofric, the high festival is strown by the servant of God upon the heart of man. It is gladness, it is thanksgiving; it is the orphan, the starveling, pressed to the bosom, and bidden as its first commandment to remember its benefactor. We will hold this festival; the guests are ready: we may keep it up for weeks, and months, and years together, and always be the happier and the richer for it. The beverage of this feast, O Leofric, is sweeter than bee or flower or vine can give us: it flows from heaven; and in heaven will it abundantly be poured out again, to him who pours it out here [1] unsparingly.

LEOFRIC. Thou art wild.

GODIVA. I have indeed lost myself.[2] Some Power, some good kind Power, melts me (body and soul and voice) into tenderness and love. O my husband, we must obey it. Look upon me! look upon me! lift your sweet eyes from the ground! I will not cease to supplicate; I dare not.

LEOFRIC. We may think upon it.

GODIVA. Never say that [3]! What! think upon goodness when you can be good? Let not the infants cry for sustenance! The mother of our blessed Lord will hear them; us never, never afterward.

LEOFRIC. Here comes the bishop: we are but one mile from the walls. Why dismountest thou? no bishop can expect it. Godiva!

---

[1] 1st ed. reads: "here abundantly."

[2] 1st ed. reads: "myself: the words are not mine: I only feel and utter them. Some," etc.

[3] 1st ed. reads: "that word: those who utter it are false ones. What!... cry for food: the mother," etc.

my honour and rank among men are humbled by this : Earl Godwin will hear of it : up ! up ! the bishop hath seen it : he urgeth his horse onward : dost thou not hear him now upon the solid turf behind thee ?

GODIVA. Never, no, never will I rise, O Leofric, until you remit this most impious tax, this tax on hard labour, on hard life.

LEOFRIC. Turn round : look how the fat nag canters, as to the tune of a sinner's psalm, slow and hard-breathing. What reason or right can the people have to complain, while their bishop's steed is so sleek and well caparisoned ? Inclination to change, desire to abolish old usages.—Up ! up ! for shame ! They shall smart for it, idlers ! Sir bishop, I must blush for my young bride.

GODIVA. My husband, my husband ! will you pardon the city ?

LEOFRIC. Sir bishop ! I could not think you would have seen her in this plight. Will I pardon ? yea, Godiva, by the holy rood, will I pardon the city, when thou ridest naked at noontide through the streets.

GODIVA. O my dear cruel Leofric, where is the heart you gave me ! It was not so ! can mine have hardened it !

BISHOP. Earl, thou abashest thy spouse ; she turneth pale and weepeth. Lady Godiva, peace be with thee.

GODIVA. Thanks, holy man ! peace will be with me when peace is with your city. Did you hear my lord's cruel word ?

BISHOP. I did, lady.

GODIVA. Will you remember it, and pray against it ?

BISHOP. Wilt *thou* forget it, daughter ?

GODIVA. I am not offended.

BISHOP. Angel of peace and purity !

GODIVA. But treasure it up in your heart : deem it an incense, good only when it is consumed and spent, ascending with prayer and sacrifice. And now what was it ?

BISHOP. Christ save us ! that he will pardon the city when thou ridest naked through the streets at noon.

GODIVA. Did he not swear an oath ?

BISHOP. He sware by the holy rood.

GODIVA. My Redeemer ! thou hast heard it ! save the city !

LEOFRIC. We are now upon the beginning of the pavement : these are the suburbs : let us think of feasting : we may pray afterward : to-morrow we shall rest.

4

LEOFRIC AND GODIVA

GODIVA. No judgments then to-morrow, Leofric ?

LEOFRIC. None : we will carouse.

GODIVA. The saints of heaven have given me strength and confidence : my prayers are heard : the heart of my beloved is now softened.

LEOFRIC (*aside*). Ay, ay—they [1] shall smart though.

GODIVA. Say, dearest Leofric, is there indeed no other hope, no other mediation ?

LEOFRIC. I have sworn : beside, thou hast made me redden and turn my face away from thee, and all the knaves have seen it : this adds to the city's crime.

GODIVA. I have blushed too, Leofric, and was not rash nor obdurate.

LEOFRIC. But thou, my sweetest, art given to blushing ; there is no conquering it in thee. I wish thou hadst not alighted so hastily and roughly : it hath shaken down a sheaf of thy hair : take heed thou sit not upon it, lest it anguish thee. Well done ! it mingleth now sweetly with the cloth of gold upon the saddle, running here and there, as if it had life and faculties and business, and were working thereupon some newer and cunninger device. O my beauteous Eve ! there is a Paradise about thee ! the world is refreshed as thou movest and breathest on it. I can not see or think of evil where thou art. I could throw my arms even here about thee. No signs for me ! no shaking of sunbeams ! no reproof or frown or wonderment—I *will* say it—now then for worse—I could close with my kisses thy half-open lips, ay, and those lovely and loving eyes, before the people.

GODIVA. To-morrow you shall kiss me, and they shall bless you for it. I shall be very pale, for to-night I must fast and pray.

LEOFRIC. I do not hear thee ; the voices of the folk are so loud under this archway.

GODIVA (*to herself*). God help them ! good kind souls ! I hope they will not crowd about me so to-morrow. O Leofric ! could my name be forgotten ! and yours alone remembered ! But perhaps my innocence may save me from reproach ! and how many as innocent are in fear and famine ! No eye will open on me but fresh from tears. What a young mother for so large a family ! Shall my youth

---

[1] From " they " to " though " added in 2nd ed.

5

harm me ! Under God's hand it gives me courage. Ah, when will the morning come ! ah, when will the noon be over !

The [1] story of Godiva, at one of whose festivals or fairs I was present in my boyhood, has always much interested me ; and I wrote a poem on it, sitting, I remember, by the *square pool* at Rugby. When I showed it to the friend in whom I had most confidence, he began to scoff at the subject ; and on his reaching the last line, his laughter was loud and immoderate. This conversation has brought both laughter and stanza back to me, and the earnestness with which I entreated and implored my friend *not to tell the lads* ; so heart-strickenly and desperately was I ashamed. The verses are these, if anyone else should wish another laugh at me.

> In every hour, in every mood,
> O lady, it is sweet and good
>   To bathe the soul in prayer,
> And, at the close of such a day,
> When we have ceased to bless and pray,
>   To dream on thy long hair.

May the peppermint be still growing on the bank in that place !—W. S. L.

---

[1] 1st ed. introduces the note with the following words : "This Conversation was suggested by the *Indicator*, an excellent book, stored with sound criticisms, and what are better still, with manly, just, and generous reflexions."

6

II. RICHARD I. AND THE ABBOT OF BOXLEY

(Imag. Convers., i., 1824 ; i., 1826 ; *Wks.*, i., 1846 ; *Wks.*, iii., 1876.)

THE abbot of Boxley was on his road to Haguenau in search of Richard, and [1] the appearance of the church-tower in the horizon had begun to accelerate his pace, when he perceived a tall pilgrim at a distance, waving his staff toward some soldiers who would have advanced before him : [2] they drew back.

" He may know something of the Lion-heart," [3] said the abbot, spurred his horse onward,[4] and in an instant threw [5] himself at the pilgrim's feet, who raised and embraced him affectionately.

ABBOT. O my king ! my king ! the champion of our faith at the mercy of a prince unworthy to hold his stirrup ! the conqueror of Palestine led forth on foot ! a captive ! a captive of those he commanded and protected ! Could Saladin see it [6]——

RICHARD. The only prince in the universe who would draw his sword for me against the ruffian of Austria. He alone is worthy to rescue me who hath proved himself worthy to fight me. I might have foreseen this insult.[7] What sentiment of [8] magnanimity, of honour, of humanity, ever warmed an Austrian bosom ?

Tell me, declare to me, abbot, speak it out at once—is this the worst of my misfortunes ? Groans burst from me ; they cleave my heart ; my own English, I hear, have forsaken me : my brother John is preferred to me—I am lost indeed. What nation hath ever witnessed such a succession of brave kings,[9] two hundred years together, as have reigned uninterruptedly in England ? Example formed them, danger nurtured them, difficulty instructed them, peace and war in an equal degree were the supporters of their throne. If John

---

[1] From " and " to " pace " added in 2nd ed.
[2] Period instead of colon in 1st ed.   [3] 1st ed. reads : " Cœur de Lion."
[4] 1st ed. reads : " on."
[5] 1st ed. reads : " he threw . . . who embraced," etc.
[6] 1st ed. reads : " this."   [7] 1st ed. reads : " result."
[8] 1st ed. reads : " of glory, of magnanimity, of honour, of gratitude, of humanity," etc.
[9] 1st ed. reads : " monarchs."

succeed to me, which he never can by virtue, never shall by force, and I pray to God never may by fortune, what will remain to our country but the bitter recollection of her extinguished glory ? I would not be regretted at so high a price : I would be better than the gone, presumptuous as is the hope, but may the coming be better than I ! Abbot, I have given away thrones, but never shall they be torn from me : rather than this, a king of England shall bend before an emperor of Germany,[1] * but only to rise up again in all his majesty and strength.

[1] 1st ed. reads : " Germany ; but shall bend as an oak before the passing wind, only," etc.

* Opinions have changed on most things, and greatly on titles and dignities.[1] A consul is appointed to reside in a seaport : a Roman senator was often, in political weight and in landed property, beneath the level of an English gentleman ; yet not only a Roman senator, but a Roman citizen, held himself superior to kings. It might well be permitted our Richard to assume a rank above any potentate of his age. If almanacks and German court-calendars are to decide on dignities, the emperors of Morocco [2] and Austria shall precede the kings of England : learned men have thought otherwise. On this subject hear Leonardo Aretino.

" Quid enim mea refert quemadmodum barbari loquantur, quos neque corrigere possum si velim, neque magnopere velim si possim ? De rege tamen et imperatore idem sentio quod tu, et jampridem ridens barbariem istam, hoc ipsum notavi atque redargui. Tres enim gradus majorum dignitatum apud Romanos, de quorum principe loquimur, fuere : rex, dictator, imperator. Ex his suprema omnium potestas rex est ; post regem verò secundum tenuit dignitatis locum dictatura ; post dictaturam imperium *tertio gradu* consequitur. Hujusce rei probatio est, quod Octaviano imperatori optime se gerenti Senatus Populusque Romanus dignitatem augere, pro imperatore dictatorem facere decrevit, quod ille non recepit, sed flexo genu recusavit, quasi majoris statûs majorisque invidiæ dignitatem existimans, Imperatoris nomen modicum ac populare, si ad Dictatoris fastigium comparetur. Majorem vero esse regiam potestatem quam dictaturam ex eo potest intelligi, quia Julius Cæsar, Dictator cum esset, affectavit Regem fieri." [3]

The dignity of a sovereign does not depend on the title he possesses, which he may with equal arrogance and indiscretion assume, but on the valour, the power, the wealth, the civilisation, of those he governs. This view of the subject the Aretine has not taken.[4]

Rank pretends to fix the value of everyone, and is the most arbitrary of all things. Roman knights, corresponding for the most-part in condition with our wealthier yeomanry and inferior esquires, would have disdained to be considered as no better or more respectable than the kings they hired. In our days, an

[1] 1st ed. reads : "dignities. Who has not seen a consul appointed to reside in a fishing town ? Who has not given a shilling to a marquis, a sixpence to a knight? A Roman senator was often beneath," etc.
[2] 1st ed. reads : "of Morocco, of Austria, and, since last August, of Mexico, should," etc.
[3] *Epist.* ix., 6. 1st ed. reads on : "Many acute arguments follow. The dignity," etc.
[4] 1st ed. reads : "taken, and which undoubtedly Richard took."

RICHARD I. AND THE ABBOT OF BOXLEY

ABBOT. God grant it ! Abandoning a king like Richard, we abandon our fathers and children, our inheritance and name : far from us be for ever such ignominy ! May the day when we become the second people upon earth, Almighty God ! be the day of our utter extirpation !

RICHARD. I [1] yet am king, yea, king am I more than ever, who even in this condition rule over hearts like thine.

Genii [2] and angels move and repose on clouds ; the same do monarchs, but on less compact ones, and scarcely firm enough for a dream to pillow on. Visions of reluctant homage from crowned heads, and of enthusiastic love from those who keep them so, have passed away from me, and leave no vacancy. One thought commemorative of my country, and characteristic of my countrymen, is worth them all.

ABBOT. Here are barely,[3] I reckon, more than three-score men ; and, considering the character both of their prince and of their race, I cannot but believe that the scrip across my saddlebow contains a full receipt for the discharge of my sovereign. Certain I am that little is left unto him of the prize he made in [4] the caravan of Egypt.

RICHARD. The [5] gold and silver were distributed among my sol diers ; for the only prizes worthy of me were Saladin and Jerusalem. I have no hesitation in esteeming Saladin not only above all the potentates now living, which of a truth is little, but, from what hath been related to me, above all who have ever reigned ; such is his

adventurer to whom a petty prince or his valet has given a pennyworth of ribbon, looks proudly and disdainfully on anyone who has nothing else in his button-hole than the button.

Few [1] authors are sounder than Plutarch ; and no remark of his more judicious than the following on Juba ; at which however there is not a deputy-commissary or under-secretary who would not laugh.

" His son, named also Juba, was carried in triumph while yet a child : and truly most happy was his imprisonment, by which, barbarian as he was, he came to be numbered among the most learned writers."—W. S. L.

[1] 1st ed. reads : " I cease not to be king who rule," etc.
[2] From " Genii " to " worth them all " added in 2nd ed.
[3] 1st ed. reads : " hardly."
[4] 1st ed. reads : " from."
[5] 1st ed. reads : " The only prizes worthy of Richard were Saladin and Jerusalem. I divided the gold and silver among my soldiers. I have," etc.

[1] 1st ed. reads : "There are few writers more sensible . . . his appears to me more," etc.

9

wisdom, his courage, his courtesy, his fidelity ; and I acknowledge that if I had remained to conquer him, I would have restored to him the whole of his dominions, excepting Palestine. And the crown of Palestine which of the crusaders should wear ? which among them could have worn it one twelvemonth ? I would do nothing in vain ; no, not even for glory. The Christian princes judged of me from their own worthlessness : Saladin judged of me from himself : to them he sent pearls and precious stones, to me figs and dates ; and I resolved from that moment to contend with him and to love him. Look now toward the Holy Alliance. Philip swore upon the Evangelists to abstain from aggression in my absence Collecting [1] an army on the borders of Normandy, he protests that his measures are pacific, invokes heaven against usurpers, and invades the province. He would persuade me, no doubt, that a squadron of horse on the low grounds is a preventive of agues, and a body of archers on the hills a specific for a fever. Ay, abbot, and his bishops lead him forth and light him on : his nobility follows him with alacrity and applause. In the whole extent of France there is neither sword nor crozier unsullied by perjury. Where upon earth was there ever a people so ready to swear and to forswear, to fight and to fly ? Equally enthusiastic in opposite causes, and embracing them without breathing betwixt, their enthusiasm is always in proportion to their number. A Frenchman, like a herring, loses his course when he loses his company, and his very instinct (in truth he has little else) forsakes him. The bravest kings with him are those who cast down conscience the most readily, and those whose appetites are the most grovelling are the best. As in the black-puddings of our country-folk, if blood is wanting, it must be made out by fat.*

ABBOT. Times ought to be very quiet, and nations very prosperous, when rulers are valued like bears and porpoises for their fur and grease. The perfidy of a rival may justly have excited the disdain, but ought never to have turned aside the arms, of Richard. The

---

[1] From " Collecting " to " upholden " added in 2nd ed. 1st ed. reads : " He invades Normandy and sanctions usurpation. Saladin was defeated," etc.

* The ancient fare of our kings differed from that of the commonalty in plenteousness only. If Richard did not dress his own dinner, like Achilles, he knew at least the composition of the few plain dishes then in use. Indeed the *black-pudding* was of such moment that it shook the whole Christian world. Michael Cellularius, patriarch of Constantinople, condemned the Bishop of Rome, Leo IX., for eating unleavened bread in the eucharist, and *black-pudding* at home.—W. S. L.

RICHARD I. AND THE ABBOT OF BOXLEY

cause of truth and righteousness is thine, O king! and when hast thou deserted what thou hast once upholden?

RICHARD. Saladin was defeated and Jerusalem would have fallen; but God will forgive me if, leaving his bones and sepulchre to his own care and protection, I chastise a disloyal rather than a loyal enemy.

ABBOT. I wish my liege could have taken him prisoner, that he might have saved such a soul by infusing into it the true faith under baptism.

RICHARD. Ay, that indeed were well. Tunny-fish[1] under oil, men under baptism, those alone of both creatures are worth a November melon. So said the bishop of Hermopolis one day after dinner; and I wish he could have kept awake and sober, to edify us more at large thereupon.

A[2] word in your ear, my abbot. Saladin lives in a country where prophet comes after prophet, and each treads out the last vestige from the sand. I am afraid it would not hold.

ABBOT. Better as it is then.

RICHARD. There are many in foreign parts who cannot be brought to comprehend how a sprinkle of water should prepare a man's eternal happiness,* or the curtailment of a cuticle his eternal misery.

---

[1] From " Tunny-fish " to " thereupon " added in 2nd ed.
[2] From " A " to " abbot " added in 3rd ed.

* If[1] Richard had lived a few centuries later, he would surely have been less a freethinker than we hear he was. Fra Sebastiano di Giesu[2] related to Pietro della Valle, that a Persian *male-witch* (stregone) taken in the fact of witchcraft, was asked whether he could eat the heart of a Portuguese captain, in the same manner as he had just eaten the heart of a cucumber; that is, merely by looking at it. He replied in the negative; for that the Franks had in the breast something like a corslet, of such hardness that no witchery could penetrate it; which, beyond doubt, says Pietro, can be nothing else than the virtue of baptism, the armour of faith, and the privilege of being sons of the Church. This honest traveller[3] falls, in almost every letter, on some unlucky comparison between the idolatry of his native country and of those he visits. " It appears," says he, " that a great part of the worship paid to their idols, consists in nothing but music and singing, &c., to pass the time gaily and luxuriously." He speaks of the right reverend their fly-flappers as " making a wind and driving off the flies from the idols in the palanquin, *offering that obsequiousness which we use toward the Pope, with fans made from the tails of white peacocks.*[4] And there were not

---

[1] Footnote added in 2nd ed.
[2] 2nd ed. reads: " Giesu, a Portuguese Augustin monk, related," etc.
[3] 2nd ed. reads: " traveller, a most zealous catholic, falls," etc.
[4] 2nd ed. reads: " *peacocks*, when he comes forth in pontificals."

IMAGINARY CONVERSATIONS : ENGLISH

Abbot. Alas, my liege, society is froth above and dregs below, and we have hard work to keep the middle of it sweet and sound, to communicate right reason and to preserve right feelings. In voyages you may see too much and learn too little. The winds and waves throw about you their mutability and their turbulence. When we lose sight of home, we lose something else than that which school-boys weep for.

Richard. By [1] the keenness of your eye, compassionate as it is, I discover, my good abbot, that you have watched and traced me from the beginning of my wanderings. Let me now tell my story—to confession another time. I sailed along the realms of my family : on the right was England, on the left was France : little else could I discover than sterile eminences and extensive shoals. They fled behind me : so pass away generations ; so shift and sink and die away affections. In the wide ocean I was little of a monarch : old men guided me, boys instructed me ; these taught me the names of my towns and harbours, those showed me the extent of my dominions: one cloud, that dissolved in one hour, covered them.

I debark in Sicily, place my hand upon the throne of Tancred, and fix it. Again we sail, and within a day or two behold, as the sun is setting, the solitary majesty of Crete, mother of a religion, it is said, that lived two thousand years. Onward, and many bright specks bubble up along the blue Ægean ; islands, every one of which, if the songs and stories of the pilots are true, is the monument of a greater man than I am. We leave them afar off—and for whom ? For creatures of less import than the sea-mews on their cliffs ; men praying to be heard and fearing to be understood, ambitious of another's power in the midst of penitence, avaricious of another's wealth under vows of poverty, and jealous of another's glory in the service of their God. Is this Christianity ? and is Saladin to be damned if he despises it ?

wanting about the idols many of their *religious*,[1] and many many torches, with the splendour whereof the night was lighted up." Who would not imagine this description to have rather been made by a Hindoo in Rome, than by a Roman in [2] Hindostan ?—W. S. L.

[1] From " By " to " is " added in 2nd ed.

---

[1] 2nd ed. reads: "*religious*, or ministers of the temple, who accompany them, and particularly one who appeared head, or *archimandrite*," etc.

[2] 2nd ed. reads: "in India? The chief, indeed the only, difference is, that in the one country the night is illuminated by processions, in the other the sun."

12

RICHARD I. AND THE ABBOT OF BOXLEY

Before [1] I joined my worthy brotherhood of the faith, I was tossed about among the isles and islets, which in some places are so thickly set, you may almost call them sea-stars.

A sailor's story is worth little without a tempest : I had enough of one to save my credit at the fireside and in the bower.

The despot or emperor of Cyprus * (I forget his title) threw into prison the crew of an English vessel wrecked on his coast ; and, not contented with this inhumanity, forbade the princess of Navarre my spouse, and the queen of Sicily who attended her, to take refuge from the storm in any of his ports. I conquered his dominions, with the loss, on my part, of a dinner, two men, and a bridle. He was brought before me. My emperor had an aversion to iron in every form [2] : therefore I adorned his imperial feet with a silver chain, and invited him to the festivities of my nuptials with Berengere, followed by her coronation as queen of Cyprus. We placed his daughter under the protection of Jane,† knowing her sweet temper and courtesy, and reminding her that a lady of rank rises one step higher by misfortune. She hath exchanged the cares of a crown for the gaiety of a court, and I hope that what she lost as princess she will gain as woman. I intend to place her suitably in marriage, and her dowry shall be what my treasury is at the time.

ABBOT. We have only to consider now what lies before us. Could not my liege have treated with the Duke of Austria ?

RICHARD. Yes, had he been more nearly my equal. I punished his neglect of discipline : it became in his power to satiate his revenge. Henry is mercenary in the same degree, but perhaps less perfidious, certainly less irritated and hostile. No potentate can forgive the superiority of England : none can forget that I treated him as a trooper and dependant, and that the features of my contempt were too broad for any mask in all the rich wardrobe of dissimulation. Henry alone is capable of ensuring my return. I remember the fate of Robert : and if I am not presently in London, I may be in Cardiff.

Those who have abandoned me must ransom me ; I myself will

---

[1] From " Before " to " bower " added in 2nd ed., where the passage begins: " But before."

* Isaac the usurper of Cyprus styled himself emperor.—W. S. L.

[2] 1st ed. reads : " form. I adorned," etc.

† Queen of Sicily.—W. S. L.

13

dictate the conditions, and they shall be such as no emperor of Germany can refuse.*

Ride on with me.

* *Emperor* is the title usually given to the heads of the Germanic league : but in fact there never was an *emperor of Germany*. Adrien Valois, in a letter to Albert Portner, writes thus : " Legi Conringii librum *de finibus Imperii Germanici*, cujus libri titulum jure quis arguat ; nullum enim imperium Germanicum fuit unquam, nullum est hodieque ; nec imperator etiamsi in Germaniâ sedem habeat, Germanorum imperator est, sed, ut ipse se more majorum appellat, rex Germaniæ et Romanorum imperator." Here we see the *rex* is before the *imperator :* if in the patents of Charles V. it is otherwise, the reason is that the title of king is applied to the dominion of several states which his ancestors had acquired more recently. Valois proceeds : " Si tamen Romanorum imperator vocari debet qui urbi Romæ non imperat, et ab episcopo ecclesiæ Romanæ, Romæ, ac senatûs populique Romani sententià, dudum desiit consecrari." This letter is not printed among the works of Valois or his brother, but is of unquestionable authenticity, and may be found entire in the *Amœnitates Literariæ* of Schelhorn, Tom. V. p. 542. Valois was a good scholar, but he errs in his latinity when he objects to the expression *imperium Germanicum*, for that expression would be correct whether Germany were governed by a king, an emperor, an aristocracy, or a democracy. The Roman state was just as much *imperium Romanum* under the consuls and tribunes as under Tiberius or Caligula. The justice of the remark made by Valois is proved by the patents of Charles V., which always began " Carolus V., divinâ favente clementiâ, Romanorum Imperator Augustus, *ac rex Germaniæ*, Hispaniarum, utriusque Siciliæ, Hierusalem, Hungariæ, &c." The late emperor of Austria formally laid down a title which never belonged to him : he and all his ministers were ignorant of this, and it may be doubted whether there was a statesman in Europe who knew it.—W. S. L. [Crump errs in describing this footnote as added in 2nd ed. ; it appears as additional matter at the end of 1st ed.]

III. JOHN OF GAUNT AND JOANNA OF KENT [1]

(Imag. Convers., iv., 1829 ; *Wks.*, i., 1846 ; *Wks.*, v., 1876.)

JOANNA. How is this my cousin,* that you are besieged in your own house, by the citizens of London ? I thought you were their idol.

GAUNT. If their idol, madam, I am one which they may tread on as they list when down ; but which, by my soul and knighthood ! the ten best battle-axes among them shall find it hard work to unshrine.

Pardon me—I have no right perhaps to take or touch this hand—yet, my sister, bricks and stones and arrows are not presents fit for you : let me conduct you some paces hence.

JOANNA. I will speak to those below in the street : quit my hand : they shall obey me.

GAUNT. If you intend to order my death, madam, your guards who have entered my court, and whose spurs and halberts I hear upon the staircase, may overpower my domestics ; and, seeing no such escape as becomes my dignity, I submit to you. Behold my sword at your feet ! Some formalities, I trust, will be used in the proceedings against me. Entitle me, in my attainder, not John of Gaunt, not Duke of Lancaster, not King of Castile ; nor commemorate my father, the most glorious of princes, the vanquisher and pardoner of the most powerful ; nor style me, what those who loved or who flattered me did when I was happier, cousin to the Fair Maid of Kent. Joanna ! those days are over ! But no enemy, no law, no eternity can take away from me, or move further off, my affinity in blood to the conqueror in the field of Cressy, of Poictiers, and Najora. Edward was

---

[1] The incident with which Landor here deals is to be dated shortly before, not after, the death of Edward III.

* Joanna, called the fair maid of Kent, was cousin of the Black Prince, whom she married. John of Gaunt was suspected of aiming at the crown in the beginning of Richard's minority, which, increasing the hatred of the people against him for favouring the sect of Wicliffe, excited them to demolish his house and to demand his impeachment.—W. S. L.

my brother when he was but your cousin ; and the edge of my shield has clinked on his in many a battle. Yes, we were ever near, if not in worth, in danger.[1]

JOANNA. Attainder! God avert it! Duke of Lancaster, what dark thought—alas! that the Regency should have known it! I came hither, sir, for no such purpose as to ensnare or incriminate or alarm you.

These weeds might surely have protected me from the fresh tears you have drawn forth.

GAUNT. Sister, be comforted! this visor too has felt them.

JOANNA. O my Edward! my own so lately! Thy memory— thy beloved image—which never hath abandoned me—makes me bold ; I dare not say generous ; for in saying it I should cease to be so—and who could be called generous by the side of thee! I will rescue from perdition the enemy of my son.

Cousin, you loved your brother : love then what was dearer to him than his life : protect what he, valiant as you have seen him, can not! The father, who foiled so many, hath left no enemies : the innocent child, who can injure no one, finds them!

Why have you unlaced and laid aside your visor? Do not expose your body to those missiles. Hold your shield before yourself, and step aside. I need it not. I am resolved——

GAUNT. On what, my cousin ? Speak, and by the Lord! it shall be done. This breast is your shield ; this arm is mine.

JOANNA. Heavens! who could have hurled those masses of stone from below ? they stunned me. Did they descend all of them together ? or did they split into fragments on hitting the pavement ?

GAUNT. Truly I was not looking that way : they came, I must believe, while you were speaking.

JOANNA. Aside! aside! further back! disregard *me!* Look! that last arrow sticks half its head deep in the wainscot. It shook so violently, I did not see the feather at first.

No, no, Lancaster! I will not permit it. Take your shield up again ; and keep it all before you. Now step aside—I am resolved to prove whether the people will hear me.

GAUNT. Then, madam, by your leave——

JOANNA. Hold! forbear![2] Come hither! hither—not forward.

---

[1] 1st ed. here adds : " She weeps."
[2] From " forbear " to " forward " added in 2nd ed.

JOHN OF GAUNT AND JOANNA OF KENT

GAUNT. Villains! take back to your kitchens those spits and skewers that you forsooth would fain call swords and arrows; and keep your bricks and stones for your graves!

JOANNA. Imprudent man! who can save you? I shall be frightened: I must speak at once.

O good kind people! ye who so greatly loved me, when I am sure I had done nothing to deserve it, have I (unhappy me!) no merit with you now, when I would assuage your anger, protect your fair fame, and send you home contented with yourselves and me? Who is he, worthy citizens, whom ye would drag to slaughter?

True indeed he did revile someone; neither I nor you can say whom; some feaster and rioter, it seems, who had little right (he thought) to carry sword or bow, and who, to show it, hath slunk away. And then another raised his anger; he was indignant that, under his roof, a woman should be exposed to stoning. Which of you would not be as choleric in a like affront? In the house of which among you, should I not be protected as resolutely?

No, no: I never can believe those angry cries. Let none ever tell me again he is the enemy of my son, of his king, your darling child Richard. Are your fears more lively than a poor weak female's? than a mother's? yours, whom he hath so often led to victory, and praised to his father, naming each—he, John of Gaunt, the defender of the helpless, the comforter of the desolate, the rallying signal of the desperately brave!

Retire, Duke of Lancaster! This is no time——

GAUNT. Madam, I obey: but not through terror of that puddle at the house-door, which my handful of dust would dry up. Deign to command me!

JOANNA. In the name of my son then, retire!

GAUNT. Angelic goodness! I must fairly win it.

JOANNA. I think I know his voice that crieth out, "Who will answer for him?" An honest and loyal man's, one who would counsel and save me in any difficulty and danger. With what pleasure and satisfaction, with what perfect joy and confidence, do I answer our right-trusty and well-judging friend!

"Let Lancaster bring his sureties," say you, "and we separate." A moment yet before we separate; if I might delay you so long, to receive your sanction of those sureties ; for in such grave matters it would ill become us to be over-hasty. I could bring fifty, I could bring a hundred, not from among soldiers, not from among courtiers, but selected from yourselves, were it equitable and fair to show such partialities, or decorous in the parent and guardian of a king to offer any other than herself.

Raised by the hand of the Almighty from amidst you, but still one of you, if the mother of a family is a part of it, here I stand, surety for John of Gaunt, Duke of Lancaster, for his loyalty and allegiance.

GAUNT (*running toward Joanna*). Are the rioters then bursting into the chamber through the windows ?

JOANNA. The windows and doors of this solid edifice rattled and shook at the people's acclamation. My word is given for you : this was theirs in return. Lancaster ! what a voice have the people when they speak out ! It shakes me with astonishment, almost with consternation, while it establishes the throne : what must it be when it is lifted up in vengeance !

GAUNT. Wind : vapor——

JOANNA. Which none can wield nor hold. Need I say this to my cousin of Lancaster ?

GAUNT. Rather say, madam, that there is always one star above which can tranquillise and control them.

JOANNA. Go, cousin ! another time more sincerity !

GAUNT. You have this day saved my life from the people : for I now see my danger better, when it is no longer close before me. My Christ ! if ever I forget——

JOANNA. Swear not : every man in England hath sworn what you would swear. But if you abandon my Richard, my brave and beautiful child, may—— Oh ! I could never curse, nor wish an evil : but, if you desert him in the hour of need, you will think of those who have not deserted you, and your own great heart will lie heavy on you, Lancaster !

Am I graver than I ought to be, that you look dejected ? Come then, gentle cousin, lead me to my horse, and accompany me home. Richard will embrace us tenderly. Everyone is dear to every other upon rising out fresh from peril : affectionately then will he look, sweet boy, upon his mother and his uncle ! Never mind how many questions he may ask you, nor how strange ones. His only dis-

18

pleasure, if he has any, will be, that he stood not against the rioters ; or among them.

GAUNT. Older than he have been as fond of mischief, and as fickle in the choice of a party.

I shall tell him that, coming to blows, the assailant is often in the right ; that the assailed is always.

IV. KING HENRY IV. AND SIR ARNOLD SAVAGE

(Imag. Convers., i., 1824 ; i., 1826 ; *Wks.*, i., 1846 ; *Wks.*, iii., 1876.)

SAVAGE. I obey the commands of my liege.

HENRY. 'Tis well : thou appearest more civil and courteous, Sir Arnold Savage, than this morning in another place, when thou declaredst unto me, as Speaker of the Commons, that no subsidy should be granted me until every cause of public grievance were removed.*

SAVAGE. I am now in the house of the greatest man upon earth ; I was then in the house of the greatest nation.

HENRY. Marry ! thou speakest rightly upon both points ; but the latter, I swear unto thee, pleaseth me most. And now, Savage, I do tell thee with like frankness, I had well-nigh sent a score of halberts among your worshipful knights and sleek wool-staplers, for I was sore chafed ; and, if another had dealt with me in such wise, I should have straightway followed my inclination. Thou knowest I am grievously let and hindered in my projected war, by such obstinacy and undutifulness in my people. I raised up the House of Commons four years ago, and placed it in opposition to my barons, with trust and confidence that, by the blessing of Christ and his saints, I might be less hampered in my complete conquest of France. This is monstrous [1] : Parliament speaks too plainly and steps too stoutly for a creature of four years' growth.

SAVAGE. God forbid that any king of England should achieve [2] the conquest of all France. Patience, my liege and lord ! Our Norman ancestors, the most warlike people on whose banners the morning sun ever lighted, have wrested the sceptre from her swaddling kings, and, pushing them back on their cushions and cupboards,

---

* The words reported by Hakewell, *De modo tenendi Parliamentum.*—W. S. L.
[This footnote in 1st ed. reads : " Such are the words reported by Hakewill," etc. In 2nd ed. : " Such . . . Hakewell in his treatise," etc.]

[1] 1st and 2nd eds. read : " monsterous."
[2] 1st and 2nd eds. read : " atchieve."

20

have been contented with the seizure of their best and largest province. The possession of more serfs would have tempted them to sit down in idleness, and no piece of unbroken turf would have been left for the playground of their children in arms. William the Conqueror, the most puissant of knights and the wisest of statesmen, thought fit to set open a new career, lest the pride of his chivalry[1] should be troublesome to him at home. He led them forth against the brave and good Harold, whose armies had bled profusely in their war against the Scot. Pity that such blood as the Saxon should ever have been spilt ! * but hence are the title-deeds to our lands and tenements, the perpetuity of our power and dominion.

HENRY. To preserve them from jeopardy, I must have silver in store ; I must have horses and armour, and wherewith to satisfy the cravings of the soldier, always sharp, and sharpest of all after fighting.

SAVAGE. My liege must also have other things, which escaped his recollection.

HENRY. Store of hides, and of the creatures that were within them ; store of bacon ; store of oats and barley, of rye and good wheaten corn ; hemp, shipping, masts, anchors ; pine-tree and its pitch from the Norwegian, yew-tree from Corse and Dalmat. Divers other commodities must be procured from the ruler of the Adriatic, from him who never was infant nor stripling, whom God took by the right-hand and taught to walk by himself the first hour. Moreover I must have instruments of mine own device, weighty, and exceeding costly ; such as machinery for beating down walls. Nothing of these have escaped my knowledge or memory, but the recital of some befits a butler or sutler or armourer, better than a king.

SAVAGE. And yet methinks, sir, there are others which you might have mentioned and have not, the recital of which would befit a king, rather than sutler, butler, or armourer : they are indeed the best and most necessary things in the world to batter down your enemy's walls with.

HENRY. What may they be ? you must find them.

SAVAGE. Sir, you have found them, and must keep them : they are the hearts of your subjects. Your horse will not gallop far with-

---

[1] 1st and 2nd eds. read : " chevalry."

* The Danes under Harold were not numerous, and there were few vestiges of the Britons out of Wales and Cornwall.—W. S. L.

out them, though you empty into his manger all the garners of Surrey. Wars are requisite, to diminish the power of your Barons, by keeping them long and widely separate from the main body of retainers, and under the ken of a stern and steady prince, watching their movements, curbing their discourses, and inuring them to regular and sharp discipline. In general they are the worthless exalted by the weak, and dangerous from wealth ill acquired and worse expended. The whole people is a good king's household : quiet and orderly when well treated, and ever in readiness to defend him against the malice of the disappointed, the perfidy of the ungrateful, and the usurpation of the familiar. Act in such guise, most glorious Henry, that the king may say *my* people, and the people may say *our* king : I then will promise you more, passing any computation, than I refused you this morning ; the enjoyment of a blessing, to which the conquest of France in comparison is as a broken flagstaff—self-approbation [1] in government and security in power. A Norman by descent, and an Englishman by birth and inheritance, the humiliation of France is requisite to my sense even of quiet enjoyment. Nevertheless I can not delude my understanding, on which is impressed this truth, namely, that the condition of a people which hath made many conquests, doth ultimately become worse than that of the conquered. For, the conquered have no longer to endure the sufferings of weakness or the struggles of strength ; and some advantages are usually holden forth to keep them peaceable and contented : but under a conquering prince the people are shadows, which lessen and lessen as he mounts in glory, until at last they become, if I may reasonably say it and unreprovedly, a thing of nothing, a shapeless form.

It [2] is my office and my duty to provide that this evil, in the present day, do not befall us ; and that our late descendants, with the same incitements to bravery, the same materials and means of greatness, may deserve as well of your family, my liege, as we have deserved of you.

HENRY. Faith ! I could find it in my heart, Sir Arnold, to clip thine eagle's claws and perch thee somewhere in the peerage.

SAVAGE. Measureless is the distance between my liege and me : but I occupy the second rank among men now living, forasmuch as, under the guidance of Almighty God, the most discreet and

---

[1] From " self-approbation " to " power " added in 2nd ed.
[2] From " It " to " you " added in 2nd ed.

HENRY IV. AND SIR ARNOLD SAVAGE

courageous have appointed me, unworthy as I am, to be the great comprehensive symbol of the English people.

Writers differ on the first appointment of Speaker in the House of Commons, for want rather of reflection than of inquiry. The Saxons had frequently such chiefs ; not always, nor regularly. In the reign of William Rufus there was a great council of parliament at Rockingham, as may be seen in the history of Eadmerus : his words are *totius regni adunatio*. He reports that a certain *knight* came forth and stood before the *people* and spoke in the name and in the behalf of all. Peter de Montfort, in the reign of Henry III., spoke *vice totius communitatis, and consented* to the banishment of Ademar de Valence, bishop of Winchester. A Sir John Bushey was the first presented by the Commons to the King in full parliament. Elsynge calls him " a special minion " to Richard II. It appears that he, like all his predecessors, was chosen for one particular speech, purpose, or sitting.

Sir Arnold Savage, according to Elsynge, " was the first who appears *upon any record* " to have been appointed to the dignity as now constituted. He [1] was elected a second time four years afterward, a rare honour in earlier days ; and during this presidency he headed the Commons, and delivered their Resolutions in the plain words recorded by Hakewell.

The business on which the dialogue is founded, may be described by an extract from Rapin, who speaks of *remonstrance* only.

" Le roi, ayant representé à ce parlement le besoin qu'il avait d'un secours extraordinaire, les Communes allèrent en corps lui présenter une Adresse, dans laquelle elles lui remontraient que, sans fouler son peuple, il pouvoit subvenir à ses besoins. Elles exposaient que le clergé possédait la troisième partie des biens du royaume, et que, ne rendant au roi aucun service personnel, il était juste qu'il contribuât de ses richesses aux besoins pressans de l'Etat. L'archevêque de Canterbury disait que leur demande n'avait pour fondement que l'irreligion et l'avarice."

The reformers, we see, were atheists in those days, as in ours : to strip off what is superfluous was to expose the body politic to decay.

In [2] decorating the people's House of Parliament, it is resolved to admit no

---

[1] From " He " to " Hakewell " added in 2nd ed.

[2] From " In " to " characteristic " added in 3rd ed. to replace the following paragraphs in the 1st and 2nd eds. :—

" Henry IV. was among the most politic of our princes. He and his successor may be compared with Philip and Alexander ; but the two great Macedonian princes had not such difficulties to surmount as the two great English. Epaminondas alone, of all the Greeks, atchieved a victory so arduous as that of Agincourt. That of Poictiers was greater. To subdue the Athenians, or the Asiatics, and to subdue the French are widely different things. Henry V. broke down their valour, and subverted the fundamental laws of their monarchy, as is proved by the sixth article in the treaty of Troyes.

" ' Après la mort du roi Charles, la couronne de France, avec toutes ces dépendances, appartiendra au roi d'Angleterre, et à ses héritiers.' . . . A female then might eventually inherit it.

memorial of the man without whom neither house nor parliament would exist. Poetry and fable are thought more characteristic.

"The monkish historians, and, more than these, Shakespear, have given a glorious character of Henry IV. The fact is, Henry permitted any irregularity at home, and suffered any affront from his rival kings, rather than hazard the permanency of his power. He rose by the people; he stood by the clergy. He suffered even the Isle of Wight to be invaded by the French, without a declaration of war against them.

"We should be slow in our censure of princes. Kingship is a profession which has produced both the most illustrious and the most contemptible of the human race. That sovran is worthy of no slight respect, who rises in moral dignity to the level of his subjects; so manifold and so great are the impediments."

V. HENRY VIII. AND ANNE BOLEYN

(*Imag. Convers.*, ii., 1824 ; ii., 1826 ; *Wks.*, i., 1846 ; *Wks.*, v., 1876.)

HENRY. Dost thou know me, Nanny, in this yeoman's dress ? 'S blood [1] ! does it require so long and vacant a stare to recollect a husband after a week or two ? No tragedy-tricks with me ! a scream, a sob, or thy kerchief a trifle the wetter, were enough. Why, verily the little fool faints in earnest. These whey faces, like their kinsfolk the ghosts, give us no warning. (*Sprinkling water over her.*[2]) Hast had water enough upon thee ? take that then—art thyself again ?

ANNE. Father of mercies ! do I meet again my husband, as was my last prayer on earth ! do I behold my beloved lord—in peace —and pardoned, my partner in eternal bliss ! It was his voice. I can not see him—why can not I ? O why do these pangs interrupt the transports of the blessed !

HENRY. Thou openest thy arms : faith ! I came for that : Nanny, thou art a sweet slut * : thou groanest, wench : art in labour ? Faith ! among the mistakes of the night, I am ready to think almost that thou hast been drinking, and that I have not.

---

[1] " Blood " in 1st ed.   [2] Italicized words absent in 1st ed.

* Henry was not unlearned, nor indifferent to the costlier externals of a gentleman ; but in manners and language he was hardly on a level with our ostlers of the present day. He was fond of bear-baitings and other such amuse-ments in the midst of the rabble, and would wrestle with Francis I. His reign is one continued proof, flaring and wearisome as a Lapland summer day, that even the English form of government, under a sensual king with money at his disposal, may serve only to legitimatize injustice. The Constitution was still insisted on, in all its original strength and purity, by those who had abolished many of its fundamental laws, and had placed the remainder at the discretion of the king. It never has had a more zealous advocate than Empson. This true patriot of legitimacy requested on his trial, that, " if he and Dudley were punished, it might not be divulged to other nations, lest they should infer that the final dissolution of the English government was approaching." The [1] government was whatever the King ordered ; and he a ferocious and

---

[1] 1st ed. reads: "On the government and the King only one opinion now subsists : but perhaps there are some who, from malignity or scanty knowledge, doubt the innocence of Anne Boleyn. In fact she was too innocent for her station. The frank," etc.

ANNE. God preserve your Highness : grant me your forgiveness for one slight offence. My eyes were heavy ; I fell asleep while I was reading ; I did not know of your presence at first, and when I did I could not speak. I strove for utterance ; I wanted no respect for my liege and husband.

HENRY. My pretty warm nestling, thou wilt then lie ! Thou wert reading and aloud too, with thy saintly cup of water by thee, and—what ! thou art still girlishly fond of those dried cherries !

ANNE. I had no other fruit to offer your Highness the first time I saw you, and you were then pleased to invent for me some reason why they should be acceptable. I did not dry these : may I present them, such as they are ? We shall have fresh next month.

HENRY. Thou art always driving away from the discourse. One moment it suits thee to know me, another not.

ANNE. Remember, it is hardly three months since I miscarried * ; I am weak and liable to swoons.

HENRY. Thou hast however thy bridal cheeks, with lustre upon them when there is none elsewhere, and obstinate lips resisting all impression : but now thou talkest about miscarrying, who is the father of that boy ?

terrific thing, swinging on high between two windy superstitions, and caught and propelled alternately by Fanaticism and Lust. In Anne Boleyn, the frank and unsuspicious gaiety of her temper, the restless playfulness of high spirits, which we often saw formerly in the families of country gentlemen, first captivated the affections and afterward raised the jealousy of Henry.[1] Lightness of spirit, which had made all about her happy the whole course of her life, made her so the last day of it. She was beheaded on the 19th of May, and Henry on the morrow married Jane Seymour.—W. S. L.

* She miscarried of a son January the twenty-ninth, 1536 : the King concluded from this event that his marriage was disagreeable to God. He had abundance of conclusions for believing that his last marriage was disagreeable to God, whenever he wanted a fresh one, and was ready in due time to give up this too with the same resignation ; but he never had any *conclusions* of doing a thing disagreeable to God when a divorce or decapitation was in question.[2]—W. S. L.

---

[1] 1st ed. here continues : "There is no instance in any public trial (not even where the defendent [sic] was acquitted) of accusations so improbable and ill-supported. Those who entertain no doubt whatever of her purity, acknowledge her indiscretion : but if indiscretion is far removed from all indecency, from all injury to others, why censure it ? What they call indiscretion in an unfortunate queen they would call affability in a fortunate one. Lightness," etc.

[2] 1st ed. continues : "Cruelty which, if not the only sin, is certainly the greatest, has been overlooked as one altogether by the zealots of religion."

HENRY VIII. AND ANNE BOLEYN

ANNE. The [1] father is yours and mine ; he who hath taken him to his own home, before (like me) he could struggle or cry for it.

HENRY. Pagan, or worse, to talk so ! He did not come into the world alive : there was no baptism.

ANNE. I thought only of our loss : my senses are confounded. I did not give him my milk, and yet I loved him tenderly ; for I often fancied, had he lived, how contented and joyful he would have made you and England.

HENRY. No subterfuges and escapes. I warrant, thou canst not say whether at my entrance thou wert waking or wandering.

ANNE. Faintness and drowsiness came upon me suddenly.

HENRY. Well, since thou really and truly sleepedst, what didst dream of ?

ANNE. I begin to doubt whether I did indeed sleep.

HENRY. Ha ! false one—never two sentences of truth together —but come, what didst think about, asleep or awake ?

ANNE. I thought that God had pardoned me my offences, and had received me unto him.

HENRY. And nothing more ?

ANNE. That my prayers had been heard and my wishes were accomplishing : the angels alone can enjoy more beatitude than this.

HENRY. Vexatious little devil ! she says nothing now about me, merely from perverseness. Hast thou never thought about me, nor about thy falsehood and adultery ?

ANNE. If I had committed any kind of falsehood, in regard to you or not, I should never have rested until I had thrown myself at your feet and obtained your pardon : but if ever I had been guilty of that other crime, I know not whether I should have dared to implore it, even of God's mercy.

HENRY. Thou hast heretofore cast some soft glances upon Smeaton ; hast thou not ?

ANNE. He taught me to play on the virginals, as you know, when I was little, and thereby to please your Highness.

HENRY. And Brereton and Norris, what have they taught thee ?

ANNE. They are your servants, and trusty ones.

HENRY. Has not Weston told thee plainly that he loved thee ?

ANNE. Yes ; and——

HENRY. What didst thou ?

---

[1] 1st ed. reads : " Yours and mine."

ANNE. I defied him.

HENRY. Is that all ?

ANNE. I could have done no more if he had told me that he hated me. Then indeed I should have incurred more justly the reproaches of your Highness : I should have smiled.

HENRY. We have proofs abundant : the fellows [1] shall one and all confront thee.—Ay, clap thy hands and kiss my sleeve, harlot !

ANNE. O that so great a favour is vouchsafed me ! my honor is secure ; my husband will be happy again ; he will see my innocence.

HENRY. Give me now an account of the monies thou hast received from me within these nine months : I want them not back : they are letters of gold in record of thy guilt. Thou hast had no fewer than fifteen thousand pounds in that period, without even thy asking ; what hast done with it, wanton ?

ANNE. I have regularly placed it out to interest.

HENRY. Where ? I demand of thee.

ANNE. Among the needy and ailing. My lord archbishop has the account of it, sealed by him weekly * : I also had a copy myself : those who took away my papers may easily find it, for there are few others, and they lie open.

HENRY. Think on my munificence to thee ; recollect who made thee. Dost sigh for what thou hast lost ?

ANNE. I do indeed.

HENRY. I never thought thee ambitious ; but thy vices creep out one by one.

ANNE. I do not regret that I have been a queen and am no longer one ; nor that my innocence is called in question by those who never knew me : but I lament that the good people who loved me so cordially, hate and curse me ; that those who pointed me out to their daughters for imitation, check them when they speak about me ; and that he whom next to God I have served with most devotion, is my accuser.

---

[1] 1st and 2nd eds. read " they " instead of " the fellows."

* The Duke of Norfolk obtained an order that the Archbishop of Canterbury should retire to his palace of Lambeth on the Queen's trial. Burnet, very sharp-sighted on irregularities in ladies, says that she had distributed, in the last nine months of her life, between fourteen and fifteen thousand pounds among the poor ; a sum equal in value to nearly five times the amount at present. It tends to prove how little she could have reserved for vanities or favourites.— W. S. L.

HENRY VIII. AND ANNE BOLEYN

HENRY.[1] Wast thou conning over something in that dingy book for thy defence ? Come, tell me, what wast thou reading ?

ANNE. This ancient chronicle. I was looking for someone in my own condition, and must have missed the page. Surely in so many hundred years, there shall have been other young maidens, first too happy for exaltation, and after too exalted for happiness : not perchance doomed to die upon a scaffold, by those they ever honoured and served faithfully : that indeed I did not look for nor think of : but my heart was bounding for anyone I could love and pity. She would be unto me as a sister dead and gone, but hearing me, seeing me, consoling me, and being consoled. O my husband, it is so heavenly a thing——

HENRY. To whine and whimper, no doubt, is vastly heavenly.

ANNE. I said not so : but those, if there be any such, who never weep, have nothing in them of heavenly or of earthly. The plants, the trees, the very rocks and unsunned clouds, show us at least the semblances of weeping : and there is not an aspect of the globe we live on, nor of the waters and skies around it, without a reference and a similitude to our joys or sorrows.

HENRY. I do not remember that notion anywhere. Take care no enemy rake out of it something of materialism. Guard well thy empty hot brain : it may hatch more evil. As for those odd words, I myself would fain see no great harm in them, knowing that grief and frenzy strike out many things, which would else lie still, and neither spirt nor sparkle. I also know that thou hast never read any thing but Bible and history, the two worst books in the world for young people, and the most certain to lead astray both prince and subject. For which reason I have interdicted and entirely put down the one, and will (by the blessing of the Virgin and of holy Paul) commit the other to a rigid censor. If it behoves us kings to enact what our people shall eat and drink, of which the most unruly and rebellious spirit can entertain no doubt, greatly more doth it behove us to examine what they read and think. The body is moved according to the mind and will : we must take care that the movement be a right one, on pain of God's anger in this life and the next.

ANNE. O my dear husband [2] ! it must be a naughty thing indeed

---

[1] From " HENRY " to " are good themselves," p. 30, added in 2nd ed.

[2] 2nd ed. reads : " husband, God is very good natured, if you let him be so : it must," etc.

29

that makes him angry beyond remission. Did you ever try how pleasant it is to forgive anyone ? There is nothing else wherein we can resemble God perfectly and easily.

HENRY. Resemble God perfectly and easily ! Do vile creatures talk thus of the Creator ?

ANNE. No, Henry, when his creatures talk thus of him, they are no longer vile creatures ! When they know that he is good they love him, and when they love him they are good themselves. O Henry [1] ! my husband and king ! the judgments of our Heavenly Father are righteous : on this surely we must think alike.

HENRY. And what then ? speak out : again I command thee, speak plainly : thy tongue was not so torpid but this moment. Art [2] ready ? must I wait ?

ANNE. If any doubt remains upon your royal mind of your equity in this business ; should it haply seem possible to you that passion or prejudice, in yourself or another, may have warped so strong an understanding, do but supplicate the Almighty to strengthen and enlighten it, and he will hear you.

HENRY. What ! thou wouldst fain change thy quarters, ay ?

ANNE. My spirit is detached and ready, and I shall change them shortly, whatever your highness may determine. Ah ! [3] my native Bickling is a pleasant place. May I go back to it ? Does that kind smile say *yes ?* Do the hounds ever run that way now ? The fruit-trees must be all in full blossom, and the gorse on the hill above quite dazzling. How good it was in you to plant your park at Greenwich after my childish notion, tree for tree, the very same as at Bickling ! Has the hard winter killed them ? or the winds loosened the stakes about them ?

HENRY. Silly child ! as if thou shouldst see them any more.

ANNE. Alas ! what strange things happen ! But they and I are nearly of the same age ; young alike, and without hold upon any thing.

HENRY. Yet thou appearest hale and resolute, and (they tell me) smirkest and smilest to everybody.

ANNE. The withered leaf catches the sun sometimes, little as it

---

[1] 1st ed. reads : " O my lord, my husband and king ! the judgments of God," etc.

[2] From " Art " to " wait " added in 3rd ed.

[3] From " Ah ! " to " upon any thing " added in 3rd ed.

can profit by it ; and I have heard stories of the breeze in other climates,[1] that sets in when daylight is about to close, and how constant it is, and how refreshing. My heart indeed is now sustained strangely : it became the more sensibly so from that time forward, when power and grandeur and all things terrestrial were sunk from sight. Every act of kindness in those about me gives me satisfaction and pleasure, such as I did not feel formerly. I was worse before God chastened me ; yet I was never an ingrate. What pains have I taken to find out the village-girls who placed their posies in my chamber ere I arose in the morning ! how gladly would I have recompensed the forester who lit up a brake on my birthnight, which else had warmed him half the winter ! But these are times past : I was not queen of England.

HENRY. Nor adulterous, nor heretical.

ANNE. God be praised !

HENRY. Learned saint ! thou knowest nothing of the lighter, but perhaps canst inform me about the graver of them.

ANNE. Which may it be, my liege ?

HENRY. Which may it be, pestilence ! I marvel that the walls of this tower do not crack around thee at such impiety.

ANNE. I would be instructed by the wisest of theologians : such is your Highness.

HENRY. Are the sins of the body, foul as they are, comparable to those of the soul ?

ANNE. When they are united they must be worst.

HENRY. Go on, go on : thou pushest thy own breast against the sword : God hath deprived thee of thy reason for thy punishment. I must hear more ; proceed, I charge thee.

ANNE. An aptitude to believe one thing rather than another, from ignorance or weakness, or from the more persuasive manner of the teacher, or from his purity of life, or from the strong impression of a particular text at a particular time, and various things beside, may influence and decide our opinion ; and the hand of the Almighty, let us hope, will fall gently on human fallibility.

HENRY. Opinion in matters of faith ! rare wisdom ! rare religion ! Troth ! Anne, thou hast well sobered me. I came rather warmly and lovingly ; but these light ringlets, by the holy rood, shall not shade this shoulder much longer. Nay, do not start ; I tap it for the last

---

[1] " in other climates " added in 2nd ed.

time, my sweetest. If the church permitted it, thou shouldst set forth on thy long journey with the eucharist between thy teeth, however loth.

ANNE. Love your Elizabeth, my honoured lord, and God bless you ! She will soon forget to call me : do not chide her : think how young she is.*

Could I, could I kiss her, but once again ! it would comfort my heart—or break it.

* Elizabeth [1] was not quite three years old at her mother's death, being born the seventh of September, 1533.

It does not appear that the Defender of the Faith brought his wife to the scaffold for the good of her soul, nor that she was pregnant at the time, which would have added much to the merit of the action, as there is the probability that the child would have been heretical. Casper Scioppius, who flourished in the same century, says in his *Classicum Belli Sacri* that the children of heretics should not be pardoned, lest, if they grow up, they be implicated in the wickedness of their parents, and perish eternally.

Literature and Religion seem to have been contending two hundred years unintermittingly, which of them should be most efficient in banishing humanity and civility from the world, the very things which it was their business to propagate and preserve, and without which they not only are useless but pernicious. Scioppius stood as bottle-holder to both, in their most desperate attacks. He, who was so munificent to children, in little faggots, little swords, and little halters, gave also a Christmas-box to James I. " *Alexipharmacum regium felli draconum et veneno aspidum, sub Philippi Mornæi de Plessis nuperâ papatûs historiâ abdito, appositum, et serenissimo Domino, Jacobo Magnæ Britanniæ regi,* strenæ Januariæ *loco, muneri missum.*" From the inexhaustible stores of his generosity he made another such present.[2] " *Collyrium Regium, Britanniæ regi, graviter ex oculis laboranti, muneri missum.*" Sir Henry Wootton, who found him in Madrid, to requite him for his Christmas-box and box of eye-salve, ordered him to be whipt without a metaphor : on which Lavanda says, " Quid Hispane calleat Scioppius haud scio ; si quid tamen istius linguæ in ipso fuit, tunc opinor exseruit maxime quando in Hispaniâ Anglice vapulavit." The remedies of Henry were less fallible, and his gifts more royal.—W. S. L.

---

[1] An instance of Landor's reliance on works of reference when he appears to be drawing on recondite sources. Much of this footnote is derived from Pierre Bayle's Dictionary, article *Scioppius*. In the last sentence of the footnote, 1st ed. reads: "more infallible."
[2] 1st and 2nd eds. continue: "to this monarch."

VI. ROGER ASCHAM AND LADY JANE GREY

(*Imag. Convers.*, ii., 1824 ; ii., 1826 ; *Wks.*, i., 1846 ; *Wks.*, v., 1876.)

ASCHAM. Thou art going, my dear young lady, into a most awful state ; thou art passing into matrimony and great wealth. God hath willed it : submit in thankfulness.

Thy affections are rightly placed and well distributed. Love is a secondary passion in those who love most, a primary in those who love least. He who is inspired by it in a high [1] degree, is inspired by honour in a higher [2] : it never reaches its plenitude of growth and perfection but in the most exalted minds. . . . Alas ! alas !

JANE. What aileth my virtuous Ascham ? what is amiss ? why do I tremble ?

ASCHAM. I [3] remember a sort of prophecy, made three years ago : it is a prophecy of thy condition and of my feelings on it. Recollectest thou who wrote, sitting upon the sea-beach the evening after an excursion to the Isle of Wight, these verses ?

> Invisibly bright water ! so like air,
> On looking down I feared thou couldst not bear
> My little bark, of all light barks most light,
> And look'd again, and drew me from the sight,
> And, hanging back, breath'd each fresh gale aghast,
> And held the bench, not to go on so fast.

JANE. I was very childish when I composed them ; and, if I had thought any more about the matter, I should have hoped you had been too generous to keep them in your memory as witnesses against me.

ASCHAM. Nay, they are not much amiss for so young a girl, and there being so few of them, I did not reprove thee. Half an hour, I thought, might have been spent more unprofitably ; and I now shall believe it firmly, if thou wilt but be led by them to meditate a little on the similarity of situation in which thou then wert to what thou art now in.

---

[1] 1st and 2nd eds. read : " great degree."
[2] 1st and 2nd eds. read : " greater."
[3] From " I " to " given," p. 34, added in 2nd ed.

JANE. I will do it, and whatever else you command ; for I am weak by nature and very timorous, unless where a strong sense of duty holdeth and supporteth me. There God acteth, and not his creature.

Those were with me at sea who would have been attentive to me if I had seemed to be afraid, even though worshipful men and women were in the company ; so that something more powerful threw my fear overboard. Yet I never will go again upon the water.

ASCHAM. Exercise that beauteous couple, that mind and body, much and variously, but at home, at home, Jane ! indoors, and about things indoors ; for God is there too. We have rocks and quicksands on the banks of our Thames, O lady, such as ocean never heard of ; and many (who knows how soon !) may be engulfed in the current under their garden-walls.

JANE. Thoroughly do I now understand you. Yes indeed, I have read evil things of courts ; but I think nobody can go out bad who entereth good, if timely and true warning shall have been given.

ASCHAM. I see perils on perils which thou dost not see, albeit [1] thou art wiser than thy poor old master. And it is not because Love hath blinded thee, for that surpasseth his supposed omnipotence ; but it is because thy tender heart, having always leant affectionately upon good, hath felt and known nothing of evil.

I once persuaded thee to reflect much : let me now persuade thee to avoid the habitude of reflection, to lay aside books, and to gaze carefully and stedfastly on what is under and before thee.

JANE. I have well bethought me of my duties : O how extensive they are ! what a goodly and fair inheritance ! But tell me, would you command me never more to read Cicero and Epictetus and Plutarch [2] and Polybius ? The others I do resign [3] : they are good for the arbour and for the gravel-walk : yet leave unto me, I beseech you, my friend and father, leave unto me for my fireside and for my pillow, truth, eloquence, courage, constancy.

ASCHAM. Read them on thy marriage-bed, on thy child-bed, on thy death-bed. Thou spotless undrooping lily, they have fenced thee right well. These are the men for men : these are to fashion

---

[1] 1st and 2nd eds. read : " although."
[2] " Plutarch and " added in 3rd ed.
[3] 1st and 2nd eds. read : " resign unto thee."

ROGER ASCHAM AND LADY JANE GREY

the bright and blessed creatures [1] whom God one day shall smile upon in thy chaste bosom.—Mind thou thy husband.

JANE. I sincerely love the youth who hath espoused me ; I love him with the fondest, the most solicitous affection ; I pray to the Almighty for his goodness and happiness, and do forget at times,— unworthy supplicant !—the prayers I should have offered for myself. Never fear that I will disparage my kind religious teacher, by disobedience to my husband in the most trying duties.

ASCHAM. Gentle is he, gentle and virtuous : but time will harden him ; time must harden even thee, sweet Jane ! Do thou, complacently and indirectly, lead him from ambition.

JANE. He is contented with me and with home.

ASCHAM. Ah Jane ! Jane ! men of high estate grow tired of contentedness.

JANE. He told me he never liked books unless I read them to him : I will read them to him every evening ; I will open new worlds to him, richer than those discovered by the Spaniard ; I will conduct him to treasures,—Oh what treasures !—on which he may sleep in innocence and peace.

ASCHAM. Rather do thou walk with him, ride with him, play with him, be his fairy,[2] his page, his everything that love and poetry have invented : but watch him well ; sport with his fancies ; turn them about like the ringlets round his cheek ; and if ever he meditate on power, go toss up thy baby to his brow, and bring back his thoughts into his heart by the music of thy discourse.

Teach him to live unto God and unto thee ; and he will discover that women, like the plants in woods, derive their softness and tenderness from the shade.

[1] 1st and 2nd eds. read : " creatures, O Jane, whom," etc.
[2] 1st and 2nd eds. read : " faery."

VII. PRINCESS MARY AND PRINCESS ELIZABETH

(Wks., ii., 1846 ; *Wks.,* v., 1876.)

MARY. My dear dear sister ! it is long, very long, since we met.

ELIZABETH. Methinks it was about the time they chopped off our uncle Seymour's head for him. Not that he was *our* uncle though—he was only Edward's.

MARY. The Lord Protector, if not your uncle, was always doatingly fond of you ; and he often declared to me, even within your hearing, he thought you very beautiful.

ELIZABETH. He said as much of you, if that is all ; and he told me why—" *not to vex me* "—as if, instead of vexing me, it would not charm me. I beseech your Highness, is there anything remarkable or singular in thinking me—what he thought me ?

MARY. No indeed ; for so you are. But why call me *Highness ?* drawing back and losing half your stature in the circumference of the curtsey.

ELIZABETH. Because you are now, at this blessed hour, my lawful queen.

MARY. Hush, prythee hush ! The parliament has voted otherwise.

ELIZABETH. They would chouse you.

MARY. What would they do with me ?

ELIZABETH. Trump you.

MARY. I am still at a loss.

ELIZABETH. Bamboozle you.

MARY. Really, my dear sister, you have been so courted by the gallants, that you condescend to adopt their language, in place of graver.

ELIZABETH. Cheat you then—will that do ?

MARY. Comprehensibly.

ELIZABETH. I always speak as the thing spoken of requires. To the point. Would our father have minded the caitiffs ?

MARY. Naming our father, I should have said, *our father now in*

36

bliss ; for surely he must be ; having been a rock of defence against the torrent of irreligion.

ELIZABETH. Well ; in bliss or out, there, here, or anywhere, would he, royal soul ! have minded parliament ? No such fool he. There were laws before there were parliaments ; and there were kings before there were laws. Were I in your Majesty's place (God forbid the thought should ever enter my poor weak head, even in a dream !) I would try the mettle of my subjects : I would mount my horse, and head them.

MARY. Elizabeth ! you were always a better horsewoman than I am : I should be ashamed to get a fall among the soldiers.

ELIZABETH. Pish ! Pish ! it would be among knights and nobles —the worst come to the worst. Lord o' mercy ! do you think they never saw such a thing before ?

MARY. I must hear of no resistance to the powers that be. Beside, I am but a weak woman.

ELIZABETH. I do not see why women should be weak, unless they like.

MARY. Not only the Commons, but likewise the peers, have sworn allegiance.

ELIZABETH. Did you ever in your lifetime, in any chronicle or commentary, read of any parliament that was not as ready to be forsworne as to swear ?

MARY. Alas !

ELIZABETH. If ever you did, the book is a rare one, kept in an out-of-the-way library, in a cedar chest all to itself, with golden locks and amber seals thereto.

MARY. I would not willingly think so ill of men.

ELIZABETH. For my part, I can't abide 'em. All that can be said, is, some are not so bad as others. You smile, and deem the speech a silly and superfluous one. We may live, sister Mary, to see and acknowledge that it is not quite so sure and flat a verity as it now appears to us. I never come near a primrose but I suspect an adder under it ; and the sunnier the day the more misgivings.

MARY. But we are now, by the settlement of the monarchy, farther out of harm's way than ever.

ELIZABETH. If the wench has children to-morrow, as she may have, they will inherit.

MARY. No doubt they would.

ELIZABETH. No doubt? I will doubt: and others shall doubt too. The heirs of my body—yours first—God prosper them! Parliament may be constrained to retrace its steps. One half sees no harm in taking bribes, the other no guilt in taking fright. Corruption is odious and costly: but, when people have yielded to compulsion, conscience is fain to acquiesce. Men say they were forced, and what is done under force is invalid.

MARY. There was nothing like compulsion.

ELIZABETH. Then let there be. Let the few yield to the many, and all to the throne. Now is your time to stir. The furnace is mere smut, and no bellows to blow the embers. Parliament is without a leader. Three or four turnspits are crouching to leap upon the wheel; but, while they are snarling and snapping one at another, what becomes of the roast? Take them by the scuf, and out with 'em. The people will applaud you. They want bread within doors, and honesty without. They have seen enough of partisans and parliaments.

MARY. We can not do without one.

ELIZABETH. Convoke it then: but call it with sound of trumpet. Such a body is unlikely to find a head. There is little encouragement for an honest knight or gentleman to take the station. The Commons slink away with lowered shoulders, and bear hateful compunction against the very names and memory of those braver men, who, in dangerous times and before stern authoritative warlike sovrans, supported their pretensions. Kings, who peradventure would have strangled such ringleaders, well remember and well respect them: their fellows would disown their benefactors and maintainers. Kings abominate their example; clowns would efface the images on their sepulchres. What forbearance on our part can such knaves expect, or what succour from the people?

MARY. What is done is done.

ELIZABETH. Oftentimes it is easier to undo than to do. I should rather be glad than mortified at what has been done yonder. In addition to those churls and chapmen in the lower house, there are also among the peers no few who voted most audaciously.

MARY. The majority of them was of opinion that the Lady Jane should be invested with royal state and dignity.

ELIZABETH. The majority! So much the better—so much the better, say I. I would find certain folk who should make sharp inquest

PRINCESS MARY AND PRINCESS ELIZABETH

into their title-deeds, and spell the indentures syllable by syllable. Certain lands were granted for certain services ; which services have been neglected. I would not in such wise neglect the lands in question, but annex them to my royal domains.

MARY. Sister ! sister ! you forget that the Lady Jane Grey (as was) is now queen of the realm.

ELIZABETH. Forget it indeed ! The vile woman ! I am minded to call her such as vile women are called out of doors.

MARY. Pray abstain ; not only forasmuch as it would be unseemly in those sweet slender delicate lips of yours, but also by reason that she is adorned with every grace and virtue, bating (which indeed outvalues them all) the true religion. Sister ! I hope and believe I in this my speech have given you no offence : for your own eyes, I know, are opened. Indeed, who that is not wilfully blind can err in so straight a road, even if so gentle and so sure a guidance were wanting ? The mind, sister, the mind itself must be crooked which deviates a hair's breadth. Ay, that intelligent nod would alone suffice to set my bosom quite at rest thereupon. Should it not ?

ELIZABETH. It were imprudent in me to declare my real opinion at this juncture. We must step warily when we walk among cocatrices. I am barely a saint ; indeed far from it ; and I am much too young to be a martyr. But that odious monster, who pretends an affection for reformation, and a reverence for learning, is counting the jewels in the crown, while you fancy she is repeating her prayers, or conning her Greek.

Sister Mary ! as God is in heaven, I hold nothing so detestable in a woman as hypocrisy. Add thereunto, as you fairly may, avarice, man-hunting, lasciviousness. The least atom of the least among these vices is heavy enough to weigh down the soul to the bottomless pit.

MARY. Unless divine grace——

ELIZABETH. Don't talk to me. Don't spread the filth fine.

Now could not that empty fool, Dudley, have found some other young person of equal rank with Mistress Jane, and of higher beauty ? Not that any other such, pretty as the boy is, would listen to his idle discourse.

And, pray, who are these Dudleys ? The first of them was made a man of by our grandfather. And what was the man after all ? Nothing better than a huge smelting-pot, with a commodious screw at the colder end of the ladle.

39

I have no patience with the bold harlotry.

MARY. I see you have not, sister !

ELIZABETH. No, nor have the people. They are on tip-toe for rising in all parts of the kingdom.

MARY. What can they do ? God help them !

ELIZABETH. Sister Mary ! good sister Mary ! did you say *God help them ?* I am trembling into a heap. It is well you have uttered such words to safe and kindred ears. If they should ever come whispered at the Privy Council, it might end badly.

I believe my visit hath been of as long continuance as may seem befitting. I must be gone.

MARY. Before your departure, let me correct a few of your opinions in regard to our gentle kinswoman and most gracious queen. She hath nobly enlarged my poor alimony. Look here ! to begin.

ELIZABETH. What ! all golden pieces ? I have not ten groats in the world.

MARY. Be sure she will grant unto you plenteously. She hath condescended to advise me of her intent. Meanwhile I do entreat you will take home with you the purse you are stroking down, thinking about other things.

ELIZABETH. Not I, not I, if it comes from such a creature.

MARY. You accept it from me.

ELIZABETH. Then indeed unreservedly. Passing through your hands the soil has been wiped away. However, as I live, I will carefully wash every piece in it with soap and water. Do you believe they can lose anything of their weight thereby ?

MARY. Nothing material.

ELIZABETH. I may reflect and cogitate upon it. I would not fain offer anybody light money.

Troth ! I fear the purse, although of chamois and double stitched, is insufficient to sustain the weight of the gold, which must be shaken violently on the road as I return. Dear sister Mary ! as you probably are not about to wear that head-tire, could you, commodiously to yourself, lend it me awhile, just to deposit a certain part of the monies therein ? for the velvet is stout, and the Venetian netting close and stiff : I can hardly bend the threads. I shall have more leisure to admire its workmanship at home.

MARY. Elizabeth ! I see you are grown forgiving. In the commencement of our discourse I suggested a slight alteration of manner in speaking of our father. Do you pray for the repose of his soul morning and night ?

ELIZABETH. The doubt is injurious.

MARY. Pardon me ! I feel it. But the voices of children, O Elizabeth ! come to the ear of God above all other voices. The best want intercession. Pray for him, Elizabeth ! pray for him.

ELIZABETH. Why not ? He did indeed, but he was in a passion, order my mother up the three black stairs, and he left her pretty head on the landing : but I bear him no malice for it.

MARY. Malice ! The baneful word hath shot up from hell in many places, but never between child and parent. In the space of that one span, on that single sod from Paradise, the serpent never trailed. Husband and wife were severed by him, then again clashed together : brother slew brother : but parent and child stand where their Creator first placed them, and drink at the only source of pure untroubled love.

ELIZABETH. Beside, you know, being king, he had clearly a right to do it, plea or no plea.

MARY. We will converse no longer on so dolorous a subject.

ELIZABETH. I will converse on it as long as such is my pleasure.

MARY. Being my visitor, you command here.

ELIZABETH. I command nowhere. I am blown about like a leaf : I am yielding as a feather in a cushion, only one among a million. But I tell you, honestly and plainly, I do not approve of it anyhow ! It may have grown into a trick and habit with him : no matter for that : in my view of the business, it is not what a husband ought to do with a wife. And, if she did—but she did not—and I say it.

MARY. It seems indeed severe.

ELIZABETH. Yea, afore God, methinks it smacks a trifle of the tart.

MARY. Our father was God's vicegerent. Probably it is for the good of her soul, poor lady ! Better suffer here than hereafter. We ought to kiss the rod, and be thankful.

ELIZABETH. Kiss the rod, forsooth. I have been constrained erewhile even unto that ; and no such a child neither. But I would rather have kissed it fresh and fair, with all its buds and knots upon it, than after it had bestowed on me, in such a roundabout way, such a deal of its embroidery and lace-work. I thank my father for all that. I hope his soul lies easier than my skin did.

MARY. The wish is kind ; but prayers would much help it. Our father of blessed memory, now (let us hope) among the saints, was somewhat sore in his visitations ; but they tended heaven-ward.

ELIZABETH. Yea, when he cursed and cuffed and kicked us.

MARY. He did kick, poor man !

ELIZABETH. Kick ! Fifty folks, young and old, have seen the marks his kicking left behind.

MARY. We should conceal all such his infirmities. They arose from an irritation in the foot, whereof he died.

ELIZABETH. I only know I could hardly dance or ride for them ; chiefly caught, as I was, fleeing from his wrath. He seldom vouchsafed to visit me : when he did, he pinched my ear so bitterly, I was fain to squeal. And then he said, I should turn out like my mother, calling me by such a name moreover as is heard but about the kennel ; and even there it is never given to the young.

MARY. There was choler in him at certain times and seasons. Those who have much will, have their choler excited when opposite breath blows against it.

ELIZABETH. Let them have will ; let them have choler too, in God's name ; but it is none the better, as gout is, for flying to hand or foot.

MARY. I have seen—now do, pray forgive me——

ELIZABETH. Well, what have you seen ?

MARY. My sweet little sister lift up the most delicate of all delicate white hands, and with their tiny narrow pink nails tear off ruffs and caps, and take sundry unerring aims at eyes and noses.

ELIZABETH. Was that any impediment or hindrance to riding and dancing ? I would always make people do their duty, and always will. Remember (for your memory seems accurate enough) that, whenever I scratched anybody's face, I permitted my hand to be kist by the offender within a day or two.

MARY. Undeniable.

ELIZABETH. I may, peradventure, have been hasty in my childhood : but all great hearts are warm ; all good ones are relenting. If, in combing my hair, the hussy lugged it, I obeyed God's command, and referred to the *lex talionis*. I have not too much of it ; and every soul on earth sees its beauty. A single one would be a public loss. Uncle Seymour—but what boots it ? there are others who can see perhaps as far as uncle Seymour.

MARY. I do remember his saying that he watched its growth as he would a melon's. And how fondly did those little sharp grey eyes of his look and wink when you blushed and chided his flattery.

ELIZABETH. Never let any man dare to flatter me : I am above it. Only the weak and ugly want the refreshment of that perfumed fan. I take but my own ; and touch it who dares.

Really it is pleasant to see in what a pear-form fashion both purse and cawl are hanging. Faith ! they are heavy : I could hardly lift them from the back of the chair.

MARY. Let me call an attendant to carry them for you.

ELIZABETH. Are you mad ? They are unsealed, and ill-tied : anyone could slip his hand in.

And so that—the word was well nigh out of my mouth—gave you all this gold ?

MARY. For shame ! O for shame !

ELIZABETH. I feel shame only for her. It turns my cheeks red —together with some anger upon it. But I can not keep my eyes off that book, if book it may be, on which the purse was lying.

MARY. Somewhat irreverently, God forgive me ! But it was sent at the same time by the same fair creature, with many kind words. It had always been kept in our father's bedroom-closet, and was removed from Edward's by those unhappy men who super-intended his education.

ELIZABETH. She must have thought all those stones are garnets : to me they look like rubies, one and all. Yet, over so large a cover, they cannot all be rubies.

MARY. I believe they are, excepting the glory in the centre, which is composed of chrysolites. Our father was an excellent judge in jewellery, as in everything else, and he spared no expenditure in objects of devotion.

ELIZABETH. What creature could fail in devotion with an object such as that before the eyes ? Let me kiss it—partly for my Saviour's and partly for my father's sake.

MARY. How it comforts me, O Elizabeth, to see you thus press it to your bosom. Its spirit, I am confident, has entered there. Disregard the pebbles : take it home : cherish it evermore. May there be virtue, as some think there is, even in the stones about it ! God bless you, strengthen you, lead you aright, and finally bring you to everlasting glory.

ELIZABETH (*going*). The Popish puss !

43

VIII. LORD BROOKE AND SIR PHILIP SIDNEY

(*Imag. Convers.*, i., 1824 ; i., 1826 ; *Wks.*, i., 1846 ; *Wks.*, iv., 1876.)

BROOKE. I come again unto the woods and unto the wilds of Penshurst, whither my heart and the friend of my heart have long invited me.

SIDNEY. Welcome, welcome ! How [1] delightful it is to see a friend after a length of absence ! How delightful to chide him for that length of absence, to which we owe such delight.

BROOKE. I know not whether our names will be immortal ; I am sure our friendship will. For names sound only upon the surface of the earth, while friendships are the purer, and the more ardent, the nearer they come to the presence of God, the sun not only of righteousness but of love. Ours never has been chipt or dimmed even here, and never shall be.

SIDNEY. Let me take up your metaphor. Friendship is a vase which, when it is flawed by heat or violence or accident, may as well be broken at once ; it can never be trusted after. The more graceful and ornamental it was, the more clearly do we discern the hopelessness of restoring it to its former state. Coarse stones, if they are fractured, may be cemented again ; precious ones, never. And now, Greville, seat yourself under this oak ; since, if you had hungered or thirsted from your journey, you would have renewed the alacrity of your old servants in the hall.

BROOKE. In truth I did ; for no otherwise the good household would have it. The birds met me first, affrighted by the tossing up of caps ; and [2] by these harbingers I knew who were coming. When my palfrey eyed them askance for their clamorousness, and shrank somewhat back, they quarrelled with him almost before they saluted me, and asked him many pert questions. What a pleasant spot, Sidney, have you chosen here for meditation ! a solitude is the

---

[1] From " How " to " precious ones, never " added in 3rd ed.
[2] 1st and 2nd eds. read : " and I knew by these," etc.

44

audience-chamber of God. Few days [1] in our year are like this : there is a fresh pleasure in every fresh posture of the limbs, in every turn the eye takes.

> Youth ! credulous of happiness, throw down
> Upon this turf thy wallet, stored and swoln
> With morrow-morns, bird-eggs, and bladders burst,
> That tires thee with its wagging to and fro :
> Thou too wouldst breathe more freely for it, Age !
> Who lackest heart to laugh at life's deceit.

It sometimes requires a stout push, and sometimes a sudden resistance, in the wisest men, not to become for a moment the most foolish. What have I done ? I have fairly challenged you, so much my master.

SIDNEY. You have warned me : I must cool a little and watch my opportunity. So now, Greville, return you to your invitations, and I will clear the ground for the company ; for Youth,[2] for Age, and whatever comes between, with kindred and dependencies. Verily we need no [3] taunts like those in your verses : here we have few vices, and consequently few repinings. I take especial care that my young labourers and farmers shall never be idle, and I supply them with bows and arrows, with bowls and ninepins, for their Sunday evening,* lest they [4] drink and quarrel. In church they are taught to love God ; after church they are practised to love their neighbour ; for business on work-days keeps them apart and scattered, and on market-days they are prone to a rivalry bordering on malice, as competitors for custom. Goodness does not more certainly make men happy than happiness makes them good. We must distinguish

---

[1] 1st and 2nd eds. read : " days, very few, in," etc.

[2] 1st ed. reads : " Youth, Age, . . . with all their kindred," etc.

[3] 1st ed. reads : " few taunts or expostulations," etc.

* Censurable as this practice may appear, it belonged to the age of Sidney. Amusements were permitted the English on the seventh day, nor were they restricted until the puritans gained the ascendancy. Even labour on certain occasions was not only allowed but enjoined. By an order of Edward VI. the farmer was encouraged to harvest upon the Sunday, and in the same article it is called a great offence to God to be scrupulous and superstitious in foregoing such operations. Aylmer, bishop of London, used to play at bowls after the service ; and, according to Strype, when the good prelate was censured for it, he replied that the Sabbath was made for man, and not man for the Sabbath.[1]—W. S. L.

[4] 1st and 2nd eds. read : " they should wench, drink," etc.

---

[1] In 2nd ed., where this note first appears, it begins : "Amusements," and reads at end : "occupations," the final sentence being absent.

between felicity and prosperity : for prosperity leads often to ambition, and ambition to disappointment : the course is then over ; the wheel turns round but once ; while the reaction of goodness and happiness is perpetual.

BROOKE. You reason justly and you act rightly. Piety, warm, soft, and passive as the ether round the throne of Grace, is made callous and inactive by kneeling too much : her vitality faints under rigorous and wearisome observances. A forced match between a man and his religion sours his temper, and leaves a barren bed.

SIDNEY. Desire of lucre, the worst and most general country vice, arises here from the necessity of looking to small gains ; it is however but the tartar that encrusts economy.[1]

BROOKE. I fear Avarice less from himself than from his associates, who fall upon a man the fiercest in old-age. Avarice (allow me to walk three paces further with Allegory) is more unlovely than mischievous, although one may say of him that he at last

> Grudges the gamesome river-fish its food,
> And shuts his heart against his own life's blood.

SIDNEY. We find but little of his handywork among the yeomanry, nor indeed much among those immediately above. The thriving squires are pricked and pinched by their eagerness to rival in expenditure those of somewhat better estate ; for, as vanity is selfishness, the vain are usually avaricious, and they who throw away most, exact most. Penurious men are oftener just than spendthrifts.

BROOKE. O that anything so monstrous should exist in this profusion and prodigality of blessings ! The herbs, elastic with health, seem to partake of sensitive and animated life, and to feel under my hand the benediction I would bestow on them. What a hum of satisfaction in God's creatures ! How is it, Sidney, the smallest do seem the happiest ?

SIDNEY. Compensation for their weaknesses and their fears ; compensation for the shortness of their existence. Their spirits mount upon the sunbeam above the eagle ; and they have more

[1] 1st ed. reads (after " economy ") : " Avarice | Grudges . . . blood. BROOKE. Oh that . . . blessings. The herbs are crisp and elastic with health ; they are warm under my hand, as if their veins were filled with such a fluid as ours. What a hum," etc.

enjoyment in their one summer than the elephant in his century.

BROOKE. Are not also the little and lowly in our species the most happy ?

SIDNEY. I would not willingly try nor overcuriously examine it. We, Greville, are happy in these parks and forests : we were happy in my close winter-walk of box [1] and laurustine. In our earlier days did we not emboss our bosoms with the daffodils,[2] and shake them almost unto shedding with our transport [3] ! Ay, my friend, there is a greater difference, both in the stages of life and in the seasons of the year, than in the conditions of men : yet the healthy pass through the seasons, from the clement to the inclement, not only unreluctantly but rejoicingly, knowing that the worst will soon finish, and the best begin anew ; and we are desirous of pushing forward into every stage of life, excepting that alone which ought reasonably to allure us most, as opening to us the *Via Sacra*, along which we move in triumph to our eternal country. We [4] labor to get through the moments of our life, as we would to get through a crowd. Such is our impatience, such our hatred of procrastination, in everything but the amendment of our practices and the adornment of our nature, one would imagine we were dragging Time along by force, and not he us. We may in some measure frame our minds for the reception of happiness, for more or for less ; we [5] should however well consider to what port we are steering in search of it, and that even in the richest [6] its quantity is but too exhaustible. It [7] is easier to alter the modes and qualities of it, than to increase its stores. There is a sickliness in the firmest of us, which induceth us to change our side, though reposing ever so softly ; yet, wittingly or unwittingly, we turn again soon into our old position. Afterward,[8] when we have fixed, as we imagine, on the object most desirable, we start extravagantly ; and, blinded by the rapidity of our course toward the treasure we would seize and dwell with, we find another hand upon the lock—the hand of one standing in shade—'tis Death !

---

[1] 1st ed. reads : " box and lauristinus and mezereon."
[2] 2nd ed. reads : " crocuses."   [3] 1st ed. reads : " transports."
[4] From " We " to " us " added in 2nd ed.
[5] 1st ed. reads : " but we should well consider," etc.
[6] 1st ed. reads : " richest we shall find but a circumscribed and very exhaustible quantity."   [7] From " It " to " stores " added in 2nd ed.
[8] From " Afterward " to " Death " added in 2nd ed.

IMAGINARY CONVERSATIONS : ENGLISH

BROOKE.[1] There is often a sensibility in poets which precipitates 'em thither.

> The winged head of Genius snakes surround,
> As erewhile poor Medusa's.

We however have defences against the shafts of the vulgar, and such as no position could give.

SIDNEY. God hath granted unto both of us hearts easily contented, hearts fitted for every station, because fitted for every duty. What appears the dullest may contribute most to our genius : what is most gloomy may soften the seeds and relax the fibres of gaiety.[2] We enjoy the solemnity of the spreading oak above us : perhaps we owe to it in part the mood of our minds at this instant : perhaps an inanimate thing supplies me, while I am speaking, with whatever I possess of animation. Do you imagine that any contest of shepherds can afford them the same pleasure as I receive from the description of it ; or that even in their loves, however innocent and faithful, they are so free from anxiety as I am while I celebrate them ? The exertion of intellectual power, of fancy and imagination, keeps from us greatly more than their wretchedness, and affords us greatly more than their enjoyment. We are motes in the midst of generations : we have our sunbeams to circuit and climb. Look at the summits of the trees around us, how they move, and the loftiest the most : nothing is at rest within the compass of our view, except the grey moss on the park-pales. Let it eat away the dead oak, but let it not be compared with the living one.

Poets are in general[3] prone to melancholy ; yet the most plaintive ditty hath imparted a fuller joy, and of longer duration, to its composer, than the conquest of Persia to the Macedonian. A bottle of wine bringeth as much pleasure as the acquisition of a kingdom, and not unlike it in kind : the senses in both cases are confused and perverted.

BROOKE. Merciful heaven ! and for the fruition of an hour's drunkenness, from which they must awaken with heaviness, pain, and terror, men consume a whole crop of their kind at one harvest-home. Shame upon those light ones who carol at the feast of blood !

---

[1] From " BROOKE " to " give " added in 3rd ed. In 1st ed. " God hath granted," etc., is part of Sidney's uninterrupted speech.

[2] 1st ed. has between this and the next sentence : " Sometimes we are insensible to its kindlier influence, sometimes not."

[3] 1st ed. reads : " nearly all."

LORD BROOKE AND SIR PHILIP SIDNEY

and worse upon those graver ones who nail upon their escutcheon the name of great. Ambition is but Avarice on stilts and masked. God sometimes sends a famine, sometimes a pestilence, and sometimes a hero, for the chastisement of mankind ; none of them surely for our admiration. Only some cause like unto that which is now scattering the mental fog of the Netherlands, and is preparing them for the fruits of freedom, can justify us in drawing the sword abroad.

SIDNEY. And only the accomplishment of our purpose can permit us again to sheathe it : for, the aggrandisement of our neighbour is nought of detriment to us ; on the contrary, if we are honest and industrious, his wealth is ours. We have nothing to dread while our laws are equitable and our impositions light : but children fly from mothers who strip and scourge them.

BROOKE.[1]

> Across the hearse where homebred Law lies dead
> Strides Despotism, and seems a bloated boy,
> Who, while some coarse clown drives him, thinks he drives,
> Shouting, with blear bluff face, *give way, give way !*

We are come to an age when we ought to read and speak plainly what our discretion tells us is fit : we are not to be set in a corner for mockery and derision, with our hands hanging down motionless, and our pockets turned inside-out.

SIDNEY. Let us congratulate our country on her freedom from debt, and on the economy and disinterestedness of her administrators ; men altogether of eminent worth, afraid of nothing but of deviating from the broad and beaten path of illustrious ancestors, and propagating her glory in far-distant countries, not by the loquacity of mountebanks or the audacity of buffoons, nor by covering a tarnished sword-knot with a trim shoulder-knot, but by the mission of right learned, grave, and eloquent ambassadors. Triumphantly and disdainfully may you point to others.

> While the young blossom starts to light,
> And heaven looks down serenely bright
>   On Nature's graceful form ;
> While hills and vales and woods are gay,
> And village voices all breathe May,
>   Who dreads the future storm ?

---

[1] From " BROOKE " to " *way* " added in 2nd ed. In 1st ed. " We are . . . inside-out " follows on " scourge them " as part of Sidney's speech.

Where princes smile and senates bend,
What mortal e'er foresaw his end,
    Or fear'd the frown of God ?
Yet has the tempest swept them off,
And the oppressed with bitter scoff
    Their silent marble trod.

To swell their pride, to quench their ire,
Did venerable Laws expire
    And sterner forms arise ;
Faith in their presence veiled her head,
Patience and Charity were dead,
    And Hope beyond the skies.

But away, away with politics : let not this city-stench infect our fresh country-air.

BROOKE. To happiness then, and unhappiness too, since we can discourse upon it without emotion. I [1] know not, Philip, how it is, but certainly I have never been more tired with any reading than with dissertations upon happiness, which seems not only to elude inquiry, but to cast unmerciful loads of clay and sand and husks and stubble along the high road of the inquirer. Theologians and moralists, and even sound philosophers, talk mostly in a drawling and dreaming way about it. He who said that virtue alone is happiness, would have spoken more truly in saying that virtue alone is misery, if *alone* means *singly*; for, beyond a doubt, the virtuous man meets with more opposites and opponents than any other, meets with more whose interests and views thwart his, and whose animosities are excited against him, not only by the phantom of interest, but by envy. Virtue alone cannot rebuff them ; nor can the virtuous man, if only virtuous, live under them, I will not say contentedly and happily, I will say, at all. Self-esteem, we hear, is the gift of virtue, the golden bough at which the gates of Elysium fly open : but, alas! it is oftener, I am afraid, the portion of the strong-minded, and even of the vain, than of the virtuous. By the constant exertion of our best energies, we can keep down many of the thorns along the path of life ; yet some will thwart us, whether we carry our book with us or walk without it, whether we cast our eyes on earth or on heaven. He who hath given the best definition of most things, hath given but an imperfect one here, informing us that a happy life is one

[1] From " I " to " SIDNEY. It must be acknowledged," p. 52, added in 2nd ed.

50

without impediment to virtue.* A happy life is not made up of negatives. Exemption from one thing is not possession of another. Had I been among his hearers, and could have uttered my sentiments in the presence of so mighty a master, I would have told him that the definition is still unfound, like the thing.

A sound mind and sound body, which many think all-sufficient, are but receptacles for it. Happiness, like air and water, the other two great requisites of life, is composite. One kind of it suits one man, another kind another. The elevated mind takes in and breathes out again that which would be uncongenial to the baser, and the baser draws life and enjoyment from that which would be putridity to the loftier. Wise or unwise, who doubts for a moment that contentment is the cause of happiness? Yet the inverse is true : we are contented because we are happy, and not happy because we are contented. Well-regulated minds may be satisfied with a small portion of happiness ; none can be happy with a small portion of content. In fact, hardly anything which we receive for truth, is really and entirely so, let it appear as plain as it may, and let its appeal be not only to the understanding, but to the senses ; for our words do not follow them exactly ; and it is by words we receive truth and express it.

I do not wonder that in the cloud of opinions and of passions (for where there are many of the one, there are usually some of the other) the clearer view of this subject should be intercepted : rather is it to be marvelled at, that no plain reasoning creature should in his privacy have argued thus :

" I am without the things which do not render those who possess them happier than I am : but I have those the absence of which would render me unhappy ; and therefore the having of them should, if my heart is a sound one and my reason unperverted, render me content and blest ! I have a house and garden of my own ; I have competence ; I have children. Take away any of these, and I should be sorrowful, I know not how long: give me any of those which are sought for with more avidity, and I doubt whether I should be happier twenty-four hours. He who has very much of his own, always has a project in readiness for somewhat of another's : he who has very little, has not even the ground on which to lay it.

* Aristoteles says in his *Ethics*, and repeats it in his *Polity*, εὐδαίμονα βίον εἶναι τὸν κατ' ἀρετὴν ἀνεμπόδιστον.—W. S. L.

Thus one sharp angle of wickedness and disquietude is broken off from him."

SIDNEY. Since we have entered into no contest or competition, which of us shall sing or sermonize the other fast asleep, and since we rather throw out than collect ideas on the subject of our conversation, do not accuse me of levity, I am certain you will not of irreligion, if I venture to say that comforts and advantages, in this life, appear at first sight to be distributed by some airy, fantastic Beings, such as figure in the stories of the East. These generally choose a humpback slave or inconsiderate girl to protect and countenance : in like manner do we observe the ill-informed mind and instable character most immediately under the smiles of Fortune and the guidance of Prosperity ; who, as the case is with lovers, are ardent and attached in proportion as they alight upon indifference and inconstancy.

BROOKE. Yes, Happiness doats on her works, and is prodigal to her favourite. As one drop of water hath an attraction for another, so do felicities run into felicities. This course is marked by the vulgar with nearly the same expression as I have employed upon it : men say habitually *a run of luck*. And I wish that misfortunes bore no resemblance to it in their march and tendency ; but these also swarm and cluster and hang one from another, until at last some hard day deadens all sense in them, and terminates their existence.

SIDNEY. It must be acknowledged,[1] our unhappiness appears to be more often sought by us, and pursued more steadily, than our happiness. What courtier on the one side, what man of genius on the other, has not complained of unworthiness preferred to worth ? Who prefers it ? his friend ? no : himself? no surely. Why then grieve at folly or injustice in those who have no concern in him, and in whom he has no concern ? We are indignant at the sufferings of those who bear bravely and undeservedly ; but a single cry from them breaks the charm that bound them to us.

The English character stands high above complaining. I have indeed heard the soldier of our enemy scream at receiving a wound ; I never heard ours. Shall the uneducated be worthy of setting an example to the lettered ? If we see, as we have seen, young persons of some promise, yet in comparison to us as the colt is to the courser, raised to trust and eminence by a powerful advocate, is it not enough

[1] End of passage added in 2nd ed.

to feel ourselves the stronger men, without exposing our limbs to the passenger, and begging him in proof to handle our muscles ? Those who distribute offices, are sometimes glad to have the excuse of merit ; but never give them for it. Only one subject of sorrow, none of complaint, in respect to court, is just and reasonable ; namely, to be rejected or overlooked when our exertions or experience might benefit our country. Forbidden to unite our glory with hers, let us cherish it at home the more fondly for its disappointment, and give her reason to say afterward, she could have wished the union.[1] He who complains deserves what he complains of.

Religions, languages, races of men, rise up, flourish, decay ; and just in the order I assign to them. O my friend ! is it nothing to think that this hand of mine, over which an insect is creeping, and upon which another more loathsome one ere long will pasture, may hold forth to my fellow men, by resolution of heart in me and perseverance, those things which shall outlive the least perishable in the whole dominion of mortality ? Creatures, of whom the best and weightiest part are the feathers in their caps, and of whom the lightest are their words and actions, curl their whiskers and their lips in scorn upon similar meditations.

Let us indulge in them ; they [2] are neither weak nor idle, having been suckled by Wisdom and taught to walk by Virtue. We [3] have never thrown away the keepsakes that Nature has given us, nor bartered them for toys easily broken in the public paths of life.

BROOKE. Argue then no longer about courts and discontents : I would rather hear a few more verses ; for a small draught increases the thirst of the thirsty.

SIDNEY. To write [4] as the ancients have written, without borrowing a thought or expression from them, is the most difficult thing we can achieve in poetry. I attempt no composition which I foresee will occupy more than an hour or two, so that I can hardly claim any rank among the poets ; yet having once collected, in my curiosity, all the *Invocations to Sleep*, ancient and modern, I fancied it possible to compose one very differently ; which, if you consider the simplicity

---

[1] In 1st ed. the Conversation ends here. From "He" to "of," the next sentence, added in 3rd ed.

[2] 2nd ed. reads : "They are not weak ; suckled by Wisdom, taught to walk by Virtue."

[3] From "We" to "life" added in 3rd ed.

[4] See note at end of this Conversation.

of the subject and the number of those who have treated it, may appear no easy matter.

> Sleep ! who contractest the waste realms of Night,
>   None like the wretched can extol thy powers :
> We think of thee when thou art far away,
> We hold thee dearer than the light of day,
>   And most when Love forsakes us wish thee ours :
>   O hither bend thy flight !
>
> Silent and welcome as the blessed shade
>   Alcestis to the dark Thessalian hall,
> When Hercules and Death and Hell obey'd
>   Her husband's desolate despondent call.
>
> What fiend would persecute thee, gentle Sleep,
>   Or beckon thee aside from man's distress ?
> Needless it were to warn thee of the stings
> That pierce my pillow, now those waxen wings
>   Which bore me to the sun of happiness,
>   Have dropt into the deep.

BROOKE. If I cannot compliment you, as I lately complimented a poet on the same subject, by saying, *May all the gods and goddesses be as propitious to your Invocation*, let me at least congratulate you that everything here is fiction.

SIDNEY. There [1] are sensible men who would call me to an account for attempting to keep up with the ancients, and then running down-hill among the moderns, and more especially for expatiating in the regions of Romance.   The fastidious and rigid call it bad taste : and I am afraid they have Truth for their prompter.   But this, I begin to suspect, is rather from my deficiency of power and judgment, than because the thing in itself is wrong.   Chivalry in the beginning was often intemperate and inhumane : afterward the term became syn-onymous with valorous courtesy.   Writers, and the Public after them, now turn it into ridicule.   But there is surely an incentive to noble actions in the deference we bear toward our ladies ; and to carry it in my bosom is worth to me all the applauses I could ever receive from my prince.   If the beloved keep us from them farther than arm's length for years together, much indeed we regret that our happiness is deferred, but more that theirs is.   For pride, and what

[1] From " There " to " reception " added in 3rd ed.

54

is better than pride, our pure conscience tells us, that God would bestow on us the glory of creating it ; of all terrestrial glory far the greatest.

BROOKE. To those whose person and manners, and exalted genius, render them always and everywhere acceptable, it is pleasing to argue in this fashion.

SIDNEY. Greville ! Greville ! it is better to suffer than to lose the power of suffering. The perception of beauty, grace, and virtue, is not granted to all alike. There are more who are contented in an ignoble union on the flat beaten earth before us, than there are who, equally disregarding both unfavourable and favourable clamours, make for themselves room to stand on an elevated and sharp-pointed summit, and thence to watch the motions and scintillations, and occasional overcloudings, of some bright distant star. Is it nothing to have been taught, apart from the vulgar, those graceful submissions which afford us a legitimate pride when we render them to the worthy ? Is there no privilege in electing our own sovereign ? no pleasure in bending heart and soul before her ? I will never believe that age itself can arrest so vivid an emotion, or that his deathbed is hard or uneasy, who can bring before it even the empty image he has long (though in vain) adored. That life has not been spent idly which has been mainly spent in conciliating the generous affections, by such studies and pursuits as best furnish the mind for their reception.[1] How many, who have abandoned for public life the studies of philosophy and poetry, may be compared to brooks and rivers, which in the beginning of their course have assuaged our thirst, and have invited us to tranquillity by their bright resemblance of it, and which afterward partake the nature of that vast body whereinto they run, its dreariness, its bitterness, its foam, its storms, its everlasting noise and commotion ! I have known several such ; and when I have innocently smiled at them, their countenances seemed to say, " I wish I could despise you : but alas ! I am a runaway slave, and from the best of mistresses to the worst of masters ; I serve at a tavern where every hour is dinner-time, and pick a bone upon a silver dish." And what is acquired by the more fortunate among them ? they may put on a robe and use a designation which I have no right to : my cook and footman may do the same : one has a white apron, the other has red hose ; I should be quite as much laughed at if I

[1] End of passage added in 3rd ed.

assumed them. A sense of inferior ability is painful : this I feel most at home : I could not do nearly so well what my domestics do ; what the others do I could do better. My blushes are not at the superiority I have given myself, but at the comparison I must go through to give it.[1]

Two poets cannot walk or sit together easily while they have any poetry about them : they must turn it out upon the table or the grass or the rock or the road-side. I shall call on you presently ; take all I have in the meanwhile.

> Afar behind is gusty March ![2]
> Again beneath a wider arch
>   The birds that fear'd grim winter, fly :
> O'er every pathway trip along
> Light feet, more light with frolic song,
>   And eyes glance back, they know not why.
>
> Say, who is that of leaf so rank,
> Pushing the violet down the bank
>   With hearted spearhead glossy-green ?
> And why that changeface mural box
> Points at the myrtle, whom he mocks,
>   Regardless what her cheer hath been ?
>
> The fennel waves her tender plume ;
> Mezereons cloth'd with thick perfume,
>   And almonds, urge[3] the lagging leaf :
> Ha ! and so long then have I stood
> And not observ'd thee, modest bud,
>   Wherefrom will rise their lawful chief !
>
> O never say it, if perchance
> Thou crown the cup or join the dance,
>   Neither in anger nor in sport ;
> For Pleasure then would pass me by,
> The Graces look ungraciously,
>   Love frown, and drive me from his court.

BROOKE. Considering the chances and changes of humanity, I wish I were as certain that Pleasure will never pass you by, as I am that the Graces will never look on you ungraciously.

---

[1] In 2nd ed. the Conversation ends here.
[2] 2nd ed., terminal note, reads : " Again thou comest, breezy March ! "
[3] 2nd ed., terminal note, reads : " wait."

56

LORD BROOKE AND SIR PHILIP SIDNEY

SIDNEY. So little am I ashamed of the hours I spend in poetry, even a consciousness that the poetry itself is bad never leads me to think the occupation is. Foliage, herbage, pebbles, may put in motion the finer parts of the mind ; and although the first things it throws off be verses, and indifferent ones, we are not to despise the cultivator of them, but to consider him as possessing the garden of innocence, at which the great body of mankind looks only through the gate.

In the corner formed by the court-wall, sheltered and sunny, I found, earlier in the season than usual, a little rose-bud, which perhaps owed its existence to my cutting the plant in summer, when it began to intrude on the path, and had wetted the legs of the ladies with the rain it held. None but trifling poetry could be made out of this, yet other than trifling pleasure was.

BROOKE. Philip, I can give you only spoiled flowers for unspoiled and unopened ones : will you accept them ?

SIDNEY. Gladly.

BROOKE. On what occasion and for whom my verses were composed, you may at once discover. Deem it enough for me to premise in elucidation, that women have no favour or mercy for the silence their charms impose on us. Little are they aware of the devotion we are offering to them, in that state whereinto the true lover is ever prone to fall, and which appears to them inattention, indifference, or moroseness. We must chirp before them eternally, or they will not moisten our beaks in our cages. They like praise best, we thanksgiving.

SIDNEY. Unfold the paper. What are you smiling at ?

BROOKE. The names of the speakers. I call one " *Poet*," the other " *Lady*." How questionably the former ! how truly the latter ! But judge.

> POET. Thus do you sit and break the flow'rs
> That might have lived a few short hours,
> And lived for you ! Love, who o'erpowers
>   My youth and me,
> Shows me the petals idly shed,
> Shows me my hopes as early dead,
> In vain, in vain admonishèd
>   By all I see.

LADY. And thus you while the noon away,
Watching me strip my flowers of gay
Apparel, just put on for May,
    And soon laid by !
Can not you teach me one or two
Fine phrases ? if you can, pray do,
Since *you* are grown too wise to woo,
    To listen I.
 POET. Lady, I come not here to teach,
But learn, the moods of gentle speech ;
Alas ! too far beyond my reach
    Are happier strains.
Many frail leaves shall yet lie pull'd,
Many frail hopes in death-bed lull'd,
Or ere this outcast heart be school'd
    By all its pains.

SIDNEY. Let me hope that here is only

 A volant shadow, just enough to break
 The sleeping sunbeam of soft idleness.

BROOKE. When a woman hath ceased to be quite the same to us, it matters little how different she becomes.

SIDNEY. Hush ! I will hear from you no sentiment but your own, and this can never be yours. Variations there are of temperature in the first season ; and the truest heart has not always the same pulsations. If we had nothing to pardon or be pardoned, we might appear to be more perfect than we are, but we should in fact be less so. Self-love is ungenerous and unforgiving ; love grieves and forgives. Whatever there may be lying hid under those leaves and blossoms shall rest there until our evening walk ; we having always chosen the calmest hours of the most beautiful days for our discourses on love and religion. Something of emotion, I cannot doubt, arose in your breast as you were writing these simple lines ; yet I am certain it was sweet and solacing. Imagination should always be the confidant, for she is always the calmer, of Passion, where Wisdom and Virtue have an equally free admittance.

Let us now dismiss until evening comes (which is much the best time for them) all these disquisitions, and let us talk about absent friends.

BROOKE. We must sit up late, if I am to tell you of all yours.

LORD BROOKE AND SIR PHILIP SIDNEY

SIDNEY. While the weather is so temperate and genial, and while I can be out-of-doors, I care not how late I tarry among

> Night airs that make tree-shadows walk, and sheep
> Washed white in the cold moonshine on gray cliffs.

Our last excess of this nature was nearer the sea, where, when our conversation paused awhile, in the stillness of mid-night we heard the distant wave break heavily. Their sound, you remarked, was such as you could imagine the sound of a giant might be, who, coming back from travel unto some smooth and still and solitary place, with all his armor and all his spoils about him, casts himself slumberously down to rest.

Lord Brooke is less known than the personage with whom he converses, and upon whose friendship he had the virtue and good-sense to found his chief distinction. On his monument at Warwick, written by himself, we read that he was servant of Queen Elizabeth, counsellor of King James, and friend of Sir Philip Sidney. His style is stiff, but his sentiments are sound and manly. The same house produced another true patriot, slain in the civil wars by a shot from Lichfield minster. Clarendon, without any ground for his assertion, says there is reason to believe he would have abandoned his party and principles. The family is extant : a member of it was created Earl of Warwick by George II. for services as Lord of the Bedchamber.[1]

---

[1] In 1st ed. this note begins : " The lord Brooke introduced here." After " manly " 1st ed. reads : " his reflections deep." From " Clarendon " to " principles " was added in 2nd ed. In 1st ed., after " minster," the note reads on : " This conversation was longer. As the speakers were passionately fond of poetry, more was introduced : among the sections cancelled was the following, in which perhaps the verses may, to some readers, not be unacceptable. ' BROOKE. To happiness then and unhappiness, since we can discourse upon it without emotion : but first I would rather hear a few more verses ; for a small draught,' " etc., to the end of Sidney's speech, " comparison I must go through to give it. "

In 2nd ed. there is appended to the Conversation a note : " The following lines were once intended for the preceding dialogue, and they appear to a critical friend of mine so adapted to the time and the persons, that, upon his judgment, I subjoin them." Then follows : " Again thou comest, breezy March," etc.

IX. QUEEN ELIZABETH AND CECIL

(*Imag. Convers.*, i., 1824 ; i., 1826 ; *Wks.*, i., 1846 ; *Wks.*, v., 1876.)

ELIZABETH. I advise thee again, churlish Cecil, how that our Edmund Spenser, whom thou callest most uncourteously, a whining whelp, hath good and solid reason for his complaint. God's blood ! shall the lady that tieth my garter and shuffles [1] the smock over my head, or the lord that steadieth [2] my chair's back while I eat, or the other that looketh to my buck-hounds lest they be mangy, be holden by me in higher esteem and estate, than he who hath placed me among the bravest of past times, and will as safely and surely set me down among the loveliest in the future ?

CECIL. Your Highness must remember he carouseth fully for such deserts—fifty pounds a-year of unclipt monies, and a butt of canary wine [3]; not [4] to mention three thousand acres in Ireland, worth fairly another fifty and another butt, in seasonable and quiet years.

ELIZABETH. The monies are not enow to sustain a pair of grooms and a pair of palfreys, and more wine hath been drunken in my presence at a feast. The monies are given to such men, that they may not incline nor be obligated to any vile or lowly occupation ; and the canary, that they may entertain such promising Wits as court their company and converse ; and that in such manner there may be alway in our land a succession of these heirs unto Fame. He hath written, not indeed with his wonted fancifulness, nor in learned and majestical language, but in homely and rustic wise, some verses which have moved me ; and haply the more so, inasmuch as they demonstrate to me that his genius hath been dampened by his adversities. Read them.

[1] 1st ed. reads : " shuffleth."
[2] 1st and 2nd eds. read : " steddieth."
[3] In 1st and 2nd eds. Landor gives the following footnote :—
" Calculating the prices of provisions and the increase of taxes, the poet-laureate in the time of Elizabeth had about four times as much as at present (1816) ; so that Cecil spoke reasonably, Elizabeth royally."
[4] From " not " to " years " added in 3rd ed.

QUEEN ELIZABETH AND CECIL

CECIL.

> How much is lost when neither heart nor eye
> Rosewinged Desire or fabling Hope deceives ;
> When boyhood with quick throb hath ceased to spy
> The dubious apple in the yellow leaves ;
>
> When, rising from the turf where youth reposed,
> We find but deserts in the far-sought shore ;
> When the huge book of Faery-land lies closed,
> And those strong brazen clasps will yield no more.

ELIZABETH. The said Edmund hath also furnished unto the weaver at Arras, John Blanquieres, on my account, a description for some of his cunningest wenches to work at, supplied by mine own self indeed as far as the subject-matter goes, but set forth by him with figures and fancies, and daintily enough bedecked. I could have wished he had thereunto joined a fair comparison between Dian—no matter—he might perhaps have fared the better for it—but poets' wits, God help them ! when did they ever sit close about them ! Read the poesy, not over-rich, and concluding very awkwardly and meanly.

CECIL.

> Where forms the lotus, with its level leaves
> And solid blossoms, many floating isles,
> What heavenly radiance swift descending cleaves
> The darksome wave ! unwonted beauty smiles
>
> On its pure bosom, on each bright-eyed flower,
> On every nymph, and twenty sate around.
> Lo ! 'twas Diana—from the sultry hour
> Hither she fled, nor fear'd she sight or sound.
>
> Unhappy youth, whom thirst and quiver-reeds
> Drew to these haunts, whom awe forbade to fly !
> Three faithful dogs before him rais'd their heads,
> And watched and wonder'd at that fixed eye.
>
> Forth sprang his favourite [1]—with her arrow-hand,
> Too late the goddess hid what hand may hide,
> Of every nymph and every reed complain'd,
> And dashed upon the bank the waters wide.

---

[1] 1st and 2nd eds. read : " favorite."

On the prone head and sandal'd feet they flew—
    Lo ! slender hoofs and branching horns appear !
The last marr'd voice not e'en the favourite knew,
    But bay'd and fasten'd on the upbraiding deer.

Far be, chaste goddess, far from me and mine
    The stream that tempts thee in the summer noon !
Alas that vengeance dwells with charms divine——

ELIZABETH. Psha ! give me the paper : I forewarned thee how it ended—pitifully, pitifully.

CECIL. I cannot think otherwise than that the undertaker of the aforecited poesy hath choused your Highness ; for I have seen painted, I know not where, but I think no farther off than Putney, the identically same Dian, with full as many nymphs, as he calls them, and more dogs. So small a matter as a page of poesy shall never stir my choler nor twitch my purse-string.

ELIZABETH. I have read in Plinius and Mela of a runlet near Dodona, which kindled by approximation an unlighted torch, and extinguished a lighted one. Now, Cecil, I desire no such a jetty to be celebrated as the decoration of my court : in simpler words, which your gravity may more easily understand, I would not from the fountain of Honour give lustre to the dull and ignorant, deadening and leaving in [1] its tomb the lamp of literature and genius. I ardently wish my reign to be remembered : if my actions were different from what they are, I should as ardently wish it to be forgotten. Those are the worst of suicides, who voluntarily and propensely [2] stab or suffocate their fame, when God hath commanded them to stand on high for an example. [3] We call him parricide who destroys the author of his existence : tell me, what shall we call him who casts forth to the dogs and birds of prey its most faithful propagator and most firm support ? Mark [4] me, I do not speak of that existence which the proudest must close in a ditch, the narrowest too of ditches and the soonest filled and fouled, and whereunto a pinch of ratsbane or a poppyhead may bend him ; but of that which reposes on our own good deeds, carefully picked up, skilfully put together, and decorously laid out for us by another's kind understanding : I speak of an

---

[1] 1st and 2nd eds. read : " leaving in ' cold obstruction ' the lamp," etc.
[2] 1st ed. reads : " prepensely."
[3] 1st and 2nd eds. read : " ensample."
[4] From " Mark " to " for " added in 2nd ed.

existence such as no father is author of, or provides for. The parent gives us few days and sorrowful ; the poet many and glorious : the one (supposing him discreet and kindly) best reproves our faults ; the other best remunerates our virtues.

A page of poesy is a little matter : be it so : but of a truth I do tell thee, Cecil, it shall master full many a bold heart that the Spaniard cannot trouble ; it shall win to it full many a proud and flighty one that even chivalry and manly comeliness cannot touch. I may shake titles and dignities by the dozen from my breakfast-board ; but I may not save those upon whose heads I shake them from rottenness and oblivion. This year they and their sovran dwell together, next year they and their beagle. Both have names, but names perishable. The keeper of my privy-seal is an earl : what then ! the keeper of my poultry-yard is a Cæsar. In honest truth, a name given to a man is no better than a skin given to him : what is not natively his own falls off and comes to nothing.

I desire in future to hear no contempt of penmen, unless a depraved use of the pen shall have so cramped them, as to incapacitate them for the sword and for the council-chamber. If Alexander was the great, what was Aristoteles who made him so ? and taught him every art and science he knew, except three ; those of drinking, of blaspheming, and of murdering his bosom-friends. Come along : I will bring thee back again nearer home. Thou mightest toss and tumble in thy bed many nights, and never eke out the substance of a stanza : but Edmund, if perchance I should call upon him for his counsel, would give me as wholesome and prudent as any of you. We should indemnify such men for the injustice we do unto them in not calling them about us, and for the mortification they must suffer at seeing their inferiors set before them. Edmund is grave and gentle : he complains of Fortune, not of Elizabeth, of courts, not of Cecil. I am resolved, so help me God, he shall have no further cause for his repining. Go, convey unto him those twelve silver spoons, with the apostles [1] on them, gloriously gilded ; and deliver into his hand these twelve large golden pieces, sufficing for the yearly maintenance of another horse and groom. Beside which, set open before him with due reverence this Bible, wherein he may read the mercies of God toward those who waited in patience for his blessing ; and this pair

[1] 1st and 2nd eds. read : " apostols."

of crimson [1] silk hose, which thou knowest I have worn [2] only thirteen months, taking heed that the heel-piece be put into good and sufficient restoration,[3] at my sole charges, by the Italian woman nigh [4] the pollard elm at Charing-cross.

[1] 1st and 2nd eds. read : " cremesin silken hosen."
[2] 1st and 2nd eds. read : " worne."
[3] 1st and 2nd eds. read : " restauration."
[4] From " nigh " to " elm " added in 3rd ed.

X. QUEEN ELIZABETH, CECIL, DUKE OF ANJOU, AND DE LA MOTTE FÉNELON

(*Wks.*, ii., 1846 ; *Wks.*, v., 1876.)

ELIZABETH. You are only nineteen, M. D'Anjou : I, as all the world knows, am bordering on thirty.

LA MOTTE (*aside*). Thirty-nine, that is. (Pretty bordering.)

ELIZABETH (*continuing*). If in fifteen or twenty years, sooner or later, I should haply lose a part of those personal charms which, for the benefit of my people, God's providence hath so bountifully bestowed on me, and which your partial eye hath multiplied ; if they should wane, and their power over your gentle heart become fainter—die I must ; die of grief ; the grievousest of grief ; the loss of your affection.

ANJOU. Impossible ! Such charms perish ! wane ! decline ! in fifteen or twenty years !

LA MOTTE (*aside*). They have all been gone the best part of the time.

ANJOU Angelic vision ! I am unworthy of them ; Earth may be so too. Death alone can deprive her of their radiance ; but the angels can be happy without them ; and mankind hath not so sinned a second time as to deserve a deluge, a universal deluge of tears for which no ark hath been provided.

ELIZABETH (*to Cecil*). He speaks well, rationally, religiously : but, Cecil ! the inches are wanting.

ANJOU. A few years are as unlikely to produce a change on that countenance of a seraph, as eternity is to produce it in my passion.

ELIZABETH. I can not but smile at you, my sweet cousin ! But surely you mock me. Do my features (which, alas ! like my heart, were ever too flexible) seem to you so settled ?

ANJOU. Not otherwise than as the stars above are settled in the firmament.

ELIZABETH. Believe it or not believe it, I have been more beautiful.

LA MOTTE (*aside*). No heretic will ever be burnt for disputing the verity of that article.

ANJOU. More beautiful still ?

ELIZABETH. Ay truly, two years ago.

ANJOU. Truth is powerful ; but modesty is powerfuller. Here indeed Truth flies before her. For this uncourteous speech, thus extorted from me, on my knees do I crave your pardon, O gracious queen ! O empress of my heart !

ELIZABETH. I increase in glory by that application.[1]

ANJOU. I have always heard that the lofty of both sexes love the less in stature, and that the beautiful are partial to the plain.

ELIZABETH. Am I plain ? false traitor ! I could almost find it in my heart to beat you, for changing your tone so suddenly.

ANJOU. That gracious glance could heal even wounds inflicted by the rack, and turn agonies into ecstacies. I spake (alas too truly !) of myself. Whatever are the graces which the world sees in my person, I am shorter than several in the courts of France and England. Indeed I never saw so many personable men before, as I have seen about your Majesty.

ELIZABETH (*aside*). He has caught some of his brother Henry's jealousy : maybe he hath spied at Dudley : maybe he hath heard of the admiral and—the rest.

Sir ! my cousin ! they are well enough : that is, they are well enough for grooms, and servitors about the house.

ANJOU. Your Majesty is now looking at those unfortunate holes and seams left all over my face by the small-pox.

ELIZABETH. Dimples ! dimples ! hiding-places of Love.

ANJOU. La Motte ! did you not assure me that there is a surgeon in London who can remove them all ?

LA MOTTE. And most truly. I have conversed with him myself, and have seen many whose faces he hath put into repair. You would believe that the greater part had never had a speck upon them.

ELIZABETH. Touch your face ? would you let him ? would you suffer him to alter one feature, one component of feature, in that countenance ?

ANJOU. My mother has insisted that it might be improved.

ELIZABETH. My dear sister the Queen Catarina is the wisest of

[1] 1st ed. reads : " appellation."

queens and of women. A mother so perspicacious might espy a
defect, when another of equal perspicacity (if any such existed) could
find none.

(*To Cecil.*) What a monkey! How hideous! and how vain!
worst of all!

CECIL. His Highness hath much penetration.

ELIZABETH. But the inches! Cecil! the inches!

ANJOU. I perceive your Majesty has been comparing my stature
with my lord Burleigh's. I wish indeed I resembled his lordship in
figure and dignity. I would gladly be half an inch taller.

ELIZABETH. Men never are contented. You are between five and
six feet high.

(*Aside.*) Eleven inches from six though.

ANJOU. If my highth is unobjectionable, my heart is quite at ease :
for it has been certified to me that the surgeon can render my face
as smooth as——

ELIZABETH (*aside*). The outside of an oyster-shell.

ANJOU. And should he fail, should he peradventure, my beard in
another year will overgrow the marks.

ELIZABETH (*to Cecil*). Such creatures are usually born with beards
from chin to eyebrow, and from eyebrow to nose.

(*To Anjou.*) Beards so comprehensive add more to majesty than
to comeliness.

(*To Cecil.*) 'Fore Gad! Cecil, I would not have him for a husband, were he ten inches taller, and ten wider across the shoulders.
To gratify my beloved people, on whom all my thoughts are bent, I
must look narrowly to the succession, seeing that from my body must
descend the issue of their future kings. We want the inches, Cecil!
we verily do want the inches. My father was a portly man, Cecil!
and my grandfather, albeit spare, was wirily elastic. For reasons of
state, I would never have my sister Mary's widower. The nation
might possibly have been disappointed in the succession, and I should
have wasted away among the bleeding hearts of my people. Say
something to the man, and let him go. Were there the inches—
but we must not press upon that point.

CECIL. May it please your Majesty, ten or a dozen in highth
and breadth would cover a multitude of sins, and almost atone for
the mass.

ELIZABETH. At him upon that!

ANJOU. I do perceive there are difficulties ; but I humbly trust that none of them are insurmountable.

ELIZABETH. Excuse my maidenly sighs, sweet cousin !

LA MOTTE (*aside*). No sighs of that description have escaped her since she was fourteen. The first and last of them caught the sails of the High Admiral, and cast him on the breakers.

ANJOU. Those tender breathings, most gracious lady, seem to arise from my breast, and to murmur on your lips ; those beauteous lips which may soften or shorten the thread of my destiny.

ELIZABETH. Faith and troth, Cecil, this rogue duke possesses a vast treasury of jewelled language. The boy is well educated and hath much discernment. It would cost no ordinary poet half a day's labour, and the better part of his ten nails, to have devised what our cousin hath spoken off-hand.

(*To Anjou.*) Sir, my cousin ! of all the princes who have wooed me, none so well knows the avenues to my heart as you do. I beseech you, urge me no further in this moment of my weakness. The woman who avoweth her love loseth her lover. Forbear ! O forbear ! have patience ! leave my wits to settle ! Time, too clearly I perceive it, will only rivet my chains.

LA MOTTE (*to Anjou*). He hath taken his leisure in forging them, and hath left them brittle at last.

ANJOU (*to La Motte*). Forty-nine years ! Women of that age have bent down their spectacles over the cradles of their great-grand-children. In God's name, La Motte ! how much older do they ever grow ?

ELIZABETH. What did I overhear of children ? The Lord vouch-safe us whatever number of girls it may please his Divine Providence ! I would implore of it, in addition, only just two boys ; one for France, and one for England.

LA MOTTE. We can not be quite happy with fewer than four girls, may it please your Majesty.

ELIZABETH. It pleaseth me well : and I see no difficulty in inserting so discreet a prayer in our Litany. But why four ? why four precisely ?

LA MOTTE. May it please your Majesty ! in order to represent their mother and the Graces. In the first I have presumed to mention, the cardinal virtues have already their representative.

CECIL. M. de la Motte Fénelon ! her Majesty has been graciously

68

pleased to impose on me her royal command, that I should express her Majesty's deep sorrow (since she herself is incapable in this presence of expressing any such sentiment) at the strange misadventure, the sad untoward demise, of so many Protestant lords and gentlemen, in his most Christian Majesty's good city of Paris, on the feast of St. Bartholomew last past. And her most gracious Majesty, in the tenderness of her royal heart, urged by the cries and clamours of her loving subjects, would remonstrate, however blandly, thereupon. In order to pacify her people, who are dearer to her than life, and in order that no delay whatever may be interposed to your forthcoming nuptials, her Majesty would fain insure your Highness's compliance with the established religion of the realm ; and is ready to accept any valid security, that your and her royal progeny (the first-born and second-born son especially) be educated in the same. The daughters, in course, follow the footsteps of the mother.

Anjou. My children can receive no better instruction than from their most religious and accomplished mother. I am tolerant of all religions ; and to give a proof of it, I am going to fight for the Protestants in the Low-Countries.

Elizabeth (*to Cecil*). Do not let him go : he will obtain great influence over them, and curtail our traffic and taxes.

(*To Anjou.*) O Anjou ! Anjou ! O my beloved Francis ! do you, must you, can you, leave us ? My sobs choke me. Is war, is even glory, preferable to love ? Alas ! alas ! you can not answer me : you know not what love is. O imperfection of speech ! In the presence of Anjou to separate war and glory ! But when will you return ?

Anjou. Before the end of next month at farthest.

Elizabeth. What years, what ages, roll within that period ! My heart is already on the ocean with you, swelling more tumultuously. The danger I most dread is from the elements ; no other enemy is great enough to hurt you. Only look from the window ! The waves are beating and roaring against our town of Sandwich, ready to engulf it.

Anjou. Sweet lady ! the sun is shining on the eighth of February as brightly as it ever shone on May before. But shines it not at this moment on May ?

Elizabeth. Flatterer ! deceiver ! I am shipwrecked and lost already. Adieu ! adieu !—must I only say—*my cousin !*

Anjou. She is gone—God be praised ! why did not you tell me,

Fénelon! what a hyæna the creature is? Her smile cured me at once of love-qualms.

LA MOTTE. She is not so amiss. Really she was well-looking no longer than some twenty years ago. But every woman has been several women if she has lived long. The English at this hour call her handsome.

ANJOU. The English may be good historians; they are bad grammarians; they confound the preterite and the present. Beside, to call her otherwise, would cost the best among them his head. How many days ago is it that she chopped off the hand of the most eloquent and honest man in her universities, for disapproving of her intended marriage with me? and yet he praised her and spoke affectionately. What prince, whether in modern times or ancient, ever inflicted so many and such atrocious pains and penalties, or ever expected such enormous sums in proportion to the ability of the people? But in England the pack is well whipt in, and always follows the first hound at full cry, muzzle to hoof. The English have belief for everything but religion : there they would run wild ; only a few good Catholics whimper and sit quiet. Englishmen verily believe the queen loves them tenderly, while they see one after another led with the halter round their necks up the ladder, some wanting their ears, some their noses, and some their hands. Talk to me of St. Bartholomew's day! The dead upon that day died whole.

What stomachs have these islanders! The Lord High Admiral well deserved his commission ; but he was braver on land than at sea.

LA MOTTE. The English drink valiantly, and do not see clearly small defects in beauty by bedtime. They are hale, and deem it unmeet and unmanly to be squeamish.

ANJOU. So it appears, by what my brother told me, and by what (as we know) went against the grain with him. But he was heir-apparent. If Dudley had been a gentleman by descent, Charles perhaps might not have so taken to heart his precedency.

LA MOTTE. She has points about her.

ANJOU. Ay truly ; too many. Were her nose but awry, she might see to read through it. Then (mercy upon us !) those long narrow ferret's teeth, intersecting a face of such proportions, that it is like a pared cucumber set on end. And then those foxy eyelashes and eyebrows ! And those wild-fire eyes, equal in volubility to her tongue and her affections, and leering like a panther's when it yawns. Gramercy ! the fellow who pretends he can fill up the trenches and pitfalls in my face, may try his hand at hers ; I never will. Sacré ! the skinny old goshawk, all talon and plumage. By St. Martin ! I would not have her—no, not even to nail against my stable-door. I do not wonder that Dudley requires a couple of wives to take the taste of this wormwood out of his mouth. My wonder is, that he should have been at the trouble to murder the same number of handsome ones to make room for her. I myself would have done a good deal, perhaps as much, or nearly so, to get a kingdom ! but my charger could never overleap this bar. No, La Motte ! I must be contented with the Netherlands.

XI. LORD BACON AND RICHARD HOOKER.[1]

(*Imag. Convers.*, ii., 1824 ; ii., 1826 ; *Wks.*, i., 1846 ; *Wks.*, iv., 1876.)

BACON. Hearing much of your worthiness and wisdom, Master Richard Hooker, I have besought your comfort and consolation in this my too heavy affliction : for we often do stand in need of hearing what we know full well, and our own balsams must be poured into our breasts by another's hand.   As [2] the air at our doors is sometimes more expeditious in removing pain and heaviness from the body than the most far-fetched remedies would be, so the voice alone of a neighbourly and friendly visitant may be more effectual in assuaging our sorrows, than whatever is most forcible in rhetoric and most recondite in wisdom.   On these occasions we cannot put ourselves in a posture to receive the latter, and still less are we at leisure to look into the corners of our store-room, and to uncurl the leaves of our references.   As for Memory, who, you may tell me, would save us the trouble, she is footsore enough in all conscience with me, without going further back.   Withdrawn as you live from court and courtly men, and having ears occupied by better reports than such as are flying about me, yet haply so hard a case as mine, befalling a man heretofore not averse from the studies in which you take delight, may have touched you with some concern.

HOOKER. I do think, my Lord of Verulam, that, unhappy as you appear, God in sooth has foregone to chasten you, and that the day which in his wisdom he appointed for your trial, was the very day on which the King's Majesty gave unto your ward and custody the great seal of his English realm.   And yet perhaps it may be, let me utter it without offence, that your features and stature were from that day forward no longer what they were before.   Such an effect do power and rank and office produce even on prudent and religious men.

[1] Among Landor's most daring defiances of chronology. Hooker died twenty-one years before Bacon's downfall.

[2] From " As " to " back " added in 2nd ed.

LORD BACON AND RICHARD HOOKER

A hound's whelp howleth if you pluck him up above where he stood : man, in much greater peril from falling, doth rejoice. You, my Lord, as befitted you, are smitten and contrite, and do appear in deep wretchedness and tribulation to your servants and those about you ; but I know that there is always a balm which lies uppermost in these afflictions, and that no heart rightly softened can be very sore.

BACON. And yet, Master Richard, it is surely no small matter to lose the respect of those who looked up to us for countenance ; and the favour of a right learned king ; and O Master Hooker ! such a power of money ! But money is mere dross. I should always hold it so, if it possessed not two qualities ; that of making men treat us reverently, and that of enabling us to help the needy.

HOOKER. The respect, I think, of those who respect us for what a fool can give and a rogue can take away, may easily be dispensed with ; but it is indeed a high prerogative to help the needy ; and when it pleases the Almighty to deprive us of it, let us believe that he foreknoweth our inclination to negligence in the charge entrusted to us, and that in his mercy he hath removed from us a most fearful responsibility.

BACON. I know a number of poor gentlemen to whom I could have rendered aid.

HOOKER. Have you examined and sifted their worthiness ?

BACON. Well and deeply.

HOOKER. Then you must have known them long before your adversity, and while the means of succouring them were in your hands.

BACON. You have circumvented and entrapped me, Master Hooker. Faith ! I am mortified : you the schoolman, I the schoolboy !

HOOKER. Say not so, my Lord. Your years [1] indeed are fewer than mine, by seven or thereabout, but your knowledge is far higher, your experience richer. Our wits are not always in blossom upon us. When the roses are overcharged and languid, up springs a spike of rue. Mortified on such an occasion ! God forefend it ! But again to the business.—I should be never over-penitent for my neglect of needy gentlemen who have neglected themselves much

---

[1] 1st ed. reads : " Your years and wisdom are abundantly more than mine, your experience richer."

73

worse. They have chosen their profession with its chances and contingencies. If they had protected their country by their courage or adorned it by their studies, they would have merited, and, under a king of such learning and such equity, would have received in some sort their reward. I look upon them as so many old cabinets of ivory and tortoise-shell, scratched, flawed, splintered, rotten, defective both within and without, hard to unlock, insecure to lock up again, unfit to use.

BACON. Methinks it beginneth to rain, Master Richard. What if we comfort our bodies with a small cup of wine, against the ill-temper of the air. Wherefore, in God's name, are you affrightened ?

HOOKER. Not so, my Lord ; not so.

BACON. What then affects you ?

HOOKER. Why, indeed, since your Lordship interrogates me—I looked, idly and imprudently, into that rich buffet ; and I saw, unless the haze of the weather has come into the parlour, or my sight is the worse for last night's reading, no fewer than six silver pints. Surely six tables for company are laid only at coronations.

BACON. There are many men so squeamish that forsooth they would keep a cup to themselves, and never communicate it to their nearest[1] and best friend ; a fashion which seems to me offensive in an honest house, where no disease of ill repute ought to be feared. We have lately, Master Richard, adopted strange fashions ; we have run into the wildest luxuries. The Lord Leicester, I heard it from my father—God forefend it should ever be recorded in our history— when he entertained Queen Elizabeth at Kenilworth Castle, laid before her Majesty a fork of pure silver. I the more easily credit it, as Master Thomas Coriatt doth vouch for having seen the same monstrous sign of voluptuousness at Venice. We are surely the especial favourites of Providence, when such wantonness hath not melted us quite away. After this portent, it would otherwise have appeared incredible that we should have broken the Spanish Armada.

Pledge me : hither comes our wine.

[To the Servant.[2]

Dolt ! villain ! is not this the beverage I reserve for myself ?

[1] 1st ed. reads : " neighbour or best friend."   [2] Not in 1st ed.

LORD BACON AND RICHARD HOOKER

The blockhead must imagine that Malmsey runs in a stream under the ocean, like the Alpheus. Bear with me, good Master Hooker, but verily I have little of this wine, and I keep it as a medicine for my many and growing infirmities. You are healthy [1] at present : God in his infinite mercy long maintain you so ! Weaker drink is more wholesome for you. The lighter ones of France are best accommodated by Nature to our constitutions, and therefore she has placed them so within our reach, that we have only to stretch out our necks, in a manner, and drink them from the vat. But this Malmsey, this Malmsey, flies from centre to circumference, and makes youthful blood boil.

Hooker. Of a truth, my knowledge in such matters is but spare. My Lord of Canterbury once ordered part of a goblet, containing some strong Spanish wine, to be taken to me from his table, when I dined by sufferance with his chaplains, and, although a most discreet prudent man, as befitteth his high station, was not so chary of my health as your Lordship. Wine is little to be trifled with, physic less. The Cretans, the brewers of this Malvasy, have many aromatic and [2] powerful herbs among them. On their mountains, and notably on Ida, grows that dittany which works such marvels, and which perhaps may give activity to this hot medicinal drink of theirs. I would not touch it, knowingly : an unregarded leaf, dropped into it above the ordinary, might add such puissance to the concoction, as almost to break the buckles in my shoes : since we have good and valid authority, that the wounded hart, on eating thereof, casts the arrow out of his haunch or entrails, although it stuck a palm deep.

Bacon. When I read of such things I doubt them. Religion and politics belong to God and to God's vicegerent the King : we must not touch upon them unadvisedly : but if I could procure a plant of dittany on easy terms, I would persuade my apothecary and my gamekeeper to make some experiments.

Hooker. I dare not distrust what grave writers have declared, in matters beyond my knowledge.

Bacon. Good Master Hooker, I have read many of your reasonings ; and they are admirably well sustained : added to which, your genius has given such a strong current to your language as can come

[1] 1st ed. reads : " You are younger ; weaker drink," etc.
[2] 1st ed. reads : " and very powerful."

only from a mighty elevation and a most abundant plenteousness. Yet forgive me, in God's name, my worthy Master, if you descried in me some expression of wonder at your simplicity. We are all weak and vulnerable somewhere : common men in the higher parts ; heroes, as was feigned of Achilles, in the lower. You would define to a hair's breadth, the qualities, states, and dependencies, of Principalities, Dominations, and Powers ; you would be unerring about the Apostles and the Churches ; and 'tis marvellous [1] how you wander about a potherb.

HOOKER. I know my poor weak intellects, most noble Lord, and how scantily they have profited by my hard painstaking. Comprehending few things, and those imperfectly, I say only what others have said before, wise men and holy ; and if, by passing through my heart into the wide world around me, it pleaseth God that this little treasure shall have lost nothing of its weight and pureness, my exultation is then the exultation of humility. Wisdom consisteth not in knowing many things, nor even in knowing them thoroughly ; but in choosing and in following what conduces the most certainly to our lasting happiness and true glory. And this wisdom, my Lord of Verulam, cometh from above.

BACON. I have observed among the well-informed and the ill-informed nearly the same quantity of infirmities and follies : those who are rather the wiser keep them separate, and those who are wisest of all keep them better out of sight. Now examine the sayings and writings of the prime philosophers ; and you will often find them, Master Richard, to be untruths made to resemble truths. The business with them is to approximate as nearly as possible, and not to touch it : the goal of the charioteer is *evitata fervidis rotis*, as some poet [2] saith. But we who care nothing for chants and cadences, and have no time to catch at applauses, push forward over stones and sands straitway to our object. I have persuaded men, and shall persuade them for ages, that I possess a wide range of thought unexplored by others, and first thrown open by me, with many fair inclosures of choice and abstruse knowledge. I have incited and instructed them to examine all subjects of useful and rational inquiry : few that occurred to me have I myself left untouched or untried : one however hath almost escaped me, and surely one worth the trouble.

---

[1] 1st ed. reads : " wonderful."   [2] Horace, *Carm.*, I. i. 5.

LORD BACON AND RICHARD HOOKER

HOOKER. Pray, my Lord, if I am guilty of no indiscretion, what may it be ?

BACON. Francis Bacon.

Lest it be thought that authority is wanting for the strong expression of Hooker on the effects of dittany, the reader is referred to the curious treatise of Plutarch [1] on the reasoning faculties of animals, in which (near the end) he asks, " Who instructed deer wounded by the Cretan arrow to seek for dittany ? on the tasting of which herb the bolts fall immediately from their bodies." [2]

---

[1] Pliny.

[2] 1st ed. reads on : " I do not remember to have read in other authors that the effect is quite so instantaneous ; and I have not leisure for an index-hunt— a good half-hour's work."

XII. KING JAMES I. AND ISAAC CASAUBON [1] *

(*Imag. Convers.*, i., 1824 ; i., 1826 ; *Wks.*, i., 1846 ; *Wks.*, iii., 1876.)

JAMES. Good M. Casaubon, I am vexed and perturbed in spirit, to find that my moderation and my zeal, which never has departed from it, should be opposed and thwarted by the pontificals.

CASAUBON. Touch [2] gently, Sire, the hinder quarters of a vicious horse, and he will lay down his ears and kick : smite him resolutely and stoutly, and, behold ! he draws his legs in, and sidles toward you.

JAMES. As I am a king and a Christian, I have a mind to act vigorously and with my whole courage. Methinks it would not be misplaced. What are these doughty bishops of Rome, forsooth, that they should lay hands thus rudely upon God's anointed ? I shudder at their violence, though I see it athwart times gone by. Raymond the Sixth, Count of Toulouse—God forefend that anything mischievous should lie upon the number—I being, as you know, the sixth monarch of my name in Scotland—what think you, Casaubon ?

CASAUBON. I see no reason why your Majesty should apprehend any.

JAMES. Raymond then, a descendant of Charlemagne, was dragged to the church of Saint Ægidius, naked to the waist and with

---

[1] So much altered in 2nd and 3rd eds. that certain variants have been relegated to an Appendix to the final volume of *Imag. Convers.* in this ed.

* Casaubon wrote a treatise *De Libertate Ecclesiasticâ*, of which 264 pp. were printed, when Henry IV., on the agreement of the Venetians with the pope, forbade the continuation, and attempted to suppress the commencement. Some copies escaped ; and Goldast inserted the 264 pp. in the first volume of his *Monarchia Imperii*.

Pompous as James was, he was less unbending than many constitutional kings have been. The royal practice of unnatural stiffness did not prevail in Europe until the minor potentates thought it becoming to imitate Louis XIV., and took that part of his character which was the easiest to copy. Unbendingness, in the moral as in the vegetable world, is an indication as frequently of unsoundness as of strength. Indeed wise men, kings as well as others, have been free from it. Stiff necks are diseased ones.—W. S. L.

[2] From " Touch " to " even " (first sentence of Casaubon's speech beginning " Not only counts ") added in 3rd ed.

KING JAMES I. AND ISAAC CASAUBON

a halter round his neck, to be flogged by a monk while the pope's legate was at dinner. His son, although a catholic, yet being the begotten of a reputed heretic, was stripped, not of his shirt, like the father, but of all his domains and hereditaments. He fought, however, so valiantly (which I would likewise do were I not unaccountably afraid of a naked sword) that the pope could only extort from him the county of Venaissin, the richest of his lands indeed, with seventy-three castles, on the other side of the Rhone, and 13,800 marks in silver.

CASAUBON. Crimes, of which the heresy of princes is the richest, fertilize Saint Peter's patrimony. The celebrated Queen Giovanna, of Naples, a descendant from the brother of Saint Louis, accused of privity to the murder of her husband——

JAMES. I do not believe a word of it ; a fabrication, a forgery ! Proceed forthwith to the pope's part in the business : there lies the guilt : say on.

CASAUBON. The beautiful young queen had need of his protection. Although the people of Provence had obliged her to swear upon the Gospels that she would alienate none of her dominions, his Holiness, a few months afterward, compelled her to sell him Avignon.

JAMES. Ay, and never paid her. I know not which is the more execrable ; that a vicar of Christ should be guilty of simony, and of exacting the commission of a perjury, or that a people should require an oath from a prince.

CASAUBON. The people, Sire, have sometimes been suspicious ; and overwatchfulness hath made them feverish : but pontiffs in all ages have mounted and ridden hard both restive rulers and well-broken ones.

JAMES. Afore God ! my back shall never bend under them. If they run restive with me, they shall bleed in both flanks ere the last leg quit the stirrup.

CASAUBON. Not only counts, lords paramount, as your Majesty hath recited, but even kings[1] have been stripped bare, and emperors unbreeched, by the popes, who followed them up into their very dreams, threatening them as disobedient children, rod in hand. The[2] Emperor Maximilian swore to defend the freedom of religion as declared in the Confession of Augsburg. Terrified by the pope's

---

[1] From " kings " to " hand " added in 2nd ed.
[2] From " The " to " spit at," p. 80, added in 3rd ed.

denunciations, he rescinded the diploma; and he protested, in excuse of such conduct, that he saw Pius shaking a scourge over his shoulder in his sleep. Pius the Fifth, too, commanded Charles the Ninth, of France, to revoke the Edict of Orléans on religious toleration. The holy father was introduced into the farce by the *Most Apostolic* and *Most Christian* Majesties. They prevailed on his Holiness that he should oblige them to loosen and lay aside their sacred obligations. On timorous and treacherous men like these, depended, and still depend, the prosperity and improvement of the human race. Charles and Maximilian, the reverse of Achilles, abhorred the gates of hell far more than falsehood.

JAMES. No promises, oaths, or treaties, are sacred any longer than these Holinesses and Beatitudes will permit. Even Cæsars are super-cæsared by their tenants of the Vatican. Nothing is too high or too low for the vultures of the Seven Hills. Not only churches and kingdoms are their quarry, but they swoop into colleges and kitchens, and order what our manciples shall bring into the buttery. One would think they might at least be as complacent as owls are to owlets, and cats to kittens. No such thing : nor do they keep under their own hedges, but prowl far a-field. They pull a tag from the fur of a lawyer if it looks a little too rough, or doth not sit to their liking. Thus, in 1220, unless I mistake the year, Honorius, by his *Interdict*, took away from the University of Paris the power of conferring degrees in civil law. So we see not only the consolations of religion are snatched at once from the innocent as well as from the guilty, whenever a pope cries for a penny and cannot get it ; but even the rights of the injured are left without defence. The worst is, that anointed kings are treated so unceremoniously. Gregory the Seventh excommunicated the Emperor Henry the Fourth, and refused him absolution until he had sitten at his gate three days, and barefoot. Soon afterward he repents of this clemency, deposes him, and raises a duke of Suabia to the throne. His successor would put anybody upon mine, excepting the rightful master. But I advise him never to grapple with such a wrestler as I am, until he hath well oiled himself, or I may peradventure make him blow his fingers and caper. I came forward with the olive-branch in my hand, little thinking it a plant for a toad in his rage to spit at.

CASAUBON. Your Majesty could entertain but feeble hopes of accommodation where avarice and pride are the directors of every

KING JAMES I. AND ISAAC CASAUBON

counsel. The advantage, however, which I pointed out to your Majesty, is obtained, inasmuch as you have hung your proofs upon the highest peg in the chambers of the Vatican : and these manifest to the world below the sincerity of your heart, and the solidity of your arguments.

JAMES. And [1] yet they call me *sectary* !

CASAUBON. Those who dissent from the domineering party have always been thus stigmatized. When the pope called Luther, and afterward your Majesty, by such an appellation, a small particle of learning might have shown him that the title better suited himself. According to Cato, in his Treatise on Husbandry, " *Sectarius* porcus est qui gregem præcedens ducit."

JAMES. I am truly and completely a catholic. How can ever the name be refused me without a manifest and gross injustice ? acknowledging, as I do, the Three Creeds, the Œcumenical Councils, and every doctrine taught as necessary to salvation, in the four first centuries of Christianity. And being so in all sincerity, I could have wished that whatever leads to fellowship and concord were tolerated and encouraged. It is not the interest of kings to carry the forest-laws into churches. On this principle and persuasion I admitted many papists to offices about my person, not expecting that they would prepare for me such a blazing fire so early in the season : yet, such is my spirit of peace and conciliation, though I would rather keep them out of my cellar and my kitchen, I should not however be loth to go with them, if their priests would allow me, to the communion-table.

The Gospel says, *this is my body ;* it does not say *how.* I am far from angry with the mass-maker for knowing more about it than I do, or than my Master chose to tell my betters, his apostles and disciples, or for insisting on transubstantiation, the name of which was not in existence for some hundred years after he left the earth. Let every Christian take the sacrament : let families,[2] friends, dependants, neighbours, take it together : let each apply to it his own idea of its import and its essence. At a commemoration dinner, one would wish something which he does not see upon the table, another is desirous that the dish which stands before him were away ; yet surely

---

[1] From " And " to " sincerity " added in 3rd ed. Compare with the final note on Washington and Franklin, *Imag. Convers.*, ii , 1826.

[2] 1st ed. reads : " let all neighbours," etc.

both may find that wherein their tastes agree ; and nothing, of what is present or of what is absent, can alter their sentiments as to the harmony of the meeting or the object of the entertainment. Such feelings, let me ascend from the little to the great, from the ordinary to the solemn, will the Christian's be at the sacrament of the eucharist. The memory of that day when it first was celebrated, makes me anxious to open my arms toward all, and to treat the enemies of my throne with the charity of the Gospel.

We gratify our humours in sovereignty, in Christianity our affections ; in this always our best, in that often our worst. You know not, M. Casaubon, how pleasant a thing it is to converse naturally, because you have always done so ; but we kings feel it sensibly, those at least among us to whom God hath vouchsafed a plain understanding. It is like unto a removal from the curtained and closed chamber of sickness, where every footfall is suspended and measured, every voice constrained and lowered, into our native air again, amid the songs and piping of our shepherds, and the wilder and more exuber-ant harmony of our woodlands. To you the whole intellectual world lies open : we must speak in epigrams or in oracles. The book however which I hold in my hand, teaches me that the practice should be laid aside, and that we ought not to be ashamed of acknowledging a sort of relation, at home, with those whom in the house of God we call our brethren. If I fall rather short of this, I do not pretend to tell a man how he should sing, or how he should pronounce his language, or upon which side he should lie in bed,* much less would I admonish him in what manner he should think on subjects which concern not me. Everybody [1] knows that I am a great deal more liberal and merciful than the lady who occupied the throne before me : yet surely my cousin Elizabeth ought to have been more tolerant of those who believed too much ; she who believed that gallants could be in love with her at seventy. I would exclude none from the benefit of law, none from the enjoyment of dignity : I would establish the catholic peers in that House, from which their friends Garnet and Catesby [2] would, to serve their own purposes, have exploded them. What think you ?

* Yet never did king interfere so minutely in the private concerns of his subjects. Here, as men are apt to do, he claims exemption from the very failing to which he was most liable.—W. S. L. [Added in 3rd ed.]

[1] From " Everybody " to " seventy " added in 3rd ed.

[2] 1st ed. has a footnote, for which see Appendix.

82

KING JAMES I. AND ISAAC CASAUBON

CASAUBON. I see not how your Majesty can receive as your counsellors, or indeed as any part of those who are to govern, judge, or administrate, men who profess that another has by right a greater power in this realm, not only than your Majesty, but than all the three estates conjointly. They are bound to assist in placing the instruction of your people out of your hands : they are bound to murder you if you resist the authority of the pope, or even if they are informed by him that such an action is of advantage to the Church : indeed anyone may murder you, let him only be persuaded by two or three factious but learned men that it is conducive to the interests of His *Holiness*.

JAMES. It [1] is impossible that the common sense of mankind shall permit such a pest as popery to exist much longer ; but there will be smoke and stench for some time after the explosion. So long as this nuisance is reeking on the earth, religion will be a prostitute, civilization a starveling, and freedom a dishonest outcast and maimed beggar. This grieveth me : for it is only in kings' palaces that freedom can be properly educated and worthily entertained.

CASAUBON. But, Sire ! what security for the palace when the parliament-house is blown up ? Garnet being asked whether he held it lawful to extinguish the innocent with the guilty, answered in the affirmative, if as much advantage were derivable from it as would compensate for the loss of the unoffending. Murder then may be committed, and even without advantage. The Jesuit, the catholic in perfection, requires only a balance of good, and reckons the murder itself as an indifferent and inoffensive method of obtaining it.

JAMES. The same doctor, in another place, delivered it as his opinion that the exploit was not only lawful, but would even be a most glorious one indeed, if it eventually turned out well for mother-church. She hath been sharpening her teeth for us until some of the grinders begin to ache, and the rest are loosening. This puts her into worse and worse humour, and makes her look uglier than usual.

What think you now ? am I not liberal enough in all conscience, when I declare my readiness to admit her children about me, if they will only come without cutlery and crackers ?

CASAUBON. If their conscience is not at their own disposal, can we

---

[1] From " It " to " virtues " (in James's speech beginning " Christ forgive me ! ") added in 3rd ed. Parts of this and succeeding passages are derived from a footnote in 1st and 2nd eds., for which see Appendix.

reasonably hope that their consent will be ? The question, which your Majesty hath cited, was not an idle nor a speculative one : it brushed the way to the murder of two monarchs of France, Henry the Third and Fourth. The name itself of the former was inserted in a thesis for *illustration;* whether it were lawful to slay, for instance, Henry the Third, after he had begun to be called a tyrant by a few seditious but learned men. Such are the expressions.

JAMES. Lamentable ! that the governments of Europe should have permitted such questions to be agitated by the clergy, to whom they least appertain. Exterminate the appointed and anointed of the Lord ! It becomes us to seize, to imprison, and to punish capitally, any religionist, pope or other, who disseminates or countenances such bloody rebellion at once against king and God.

CASAUBON. The first attempt to murder the Prince of Orange was committed by one who carried in the same pocket with his pistol a string of prayers to the Virgin Mary and the angel Gabriel, and a catechism of the Jesuits.

JAMES. The death of the Prince of Orange was commanded by a lawful king ; and, although he might employ worthier instruments, he being anointed, and thereby judge supreme in his own cause, had an unquestionable right to inflict the penalty. He had disobedient subjects to deal with, instigated by the devil of democracy ; and the Prince of Orange was a ringleader of republicans, rank and riotous in his love of power ; which love I hold unlawful and ungodly in any under the throne.

CASAUBON. Sire ! What I ventured to commemorate was mainly in demonstration that not only Jesuits and Dominicans were assassins, but, under the influence of the same religion, even kings themselves.

JAMES. Nay, nay, nay, M. Isaac ! A king may peradventure slay unadvisedly, rashly, wrathfully ; but a king can never be an assassin, even though he should smite unto the death with his own right hand ; forasmuch as the Lord hath given him the sceptre in Israel. King Philip, of whom you made reference, did encompass and bring about the decease of his son Charles, and likewise of his brother (not uterine but spurious) John of Austria, as many sound scholars and rational thinkers do surmise : yet reverential awe hath alway stood between him and that untoward appellation of assassin. Therefore, were it only for the sake of rhetoric and euphony, I do,

KING JAMES I. AND ISAAC CASAUBON

think I would cast about for some palatabler word. It beseems and behoves the learned, most of all, to hold their caps before their faces where any foulness is ; and not to see it ; but, if they have seen it, to put the same before their mouths, and never to let such expressions. break out full-syllabled. As for the pope indeed, I do not acknowledge in him either prince or priest ; wherefore you may take him and Jacques Clément by the throat again, and deal with them condignly.

CASAUBON. Clément, being interrogated on the reasons why he undertook the perpetration of his atrocious crime, said plainly that he did it because the king was preparing to aid and succour the Protestants in Germany ; and that, intending thereby a thing offensive to God, he was worthy of death ; he added, *the pope is God, and God is pope.*

JAMES. Christ forgive me ! but I am almost fain to cry out, Happy the people whose Gods were leeks ! Religion never taught them that perfidy and murder are virtues. I apprehend that my intentions must be deferred. O Lord ! preserve my life for thy glory ! preserve it for the union of Christians ! Casaubon, it is verily, though we enter thereby into bliss, an ugly thing to die. The malignity of popery may soften : I should be sorry to inflict new pains and penalties.

CASAUBON. I would not inflict any : I would authorize no inabilities or privations for a difference in mere articles of faith : for instance, it would be tyranny or madness to declare a man incapable of beating the enemy because he believes in transubstantiation : but I would exclude from all power, all trust, all office, whoever should assert that any man has legitimate power of any kind within this realm, unless it repose in, or originate from, the king or parliament, or both united.[1] According to confessors, no treason of a priest against a king is criminal. Emmanuel Sa, in his guide to them, says, " The rebellion of a priest against a king is not treason, because ' non est principi subjectus ' " : and again : " Tyrannice gubernans justum acquisitum dominium non potest spoliari sine publico judicio : latâ vero sententiâ potest quisque fieri executor."

JAMES. Horrible ! Christ says, *My kingdom is not of this world :* the pope says, *My kingdom is.* Pius V. excited to rebellion the subjects of Elizabeth ; Clement VIII. (it is ludicrous to hear the titles of these ruffians) ordered all the Roman Catholics, " quantum in

[1] For 1st ed. reading see Appendix.

85

ipsis esset, ut post Elizabethæ obitum rex eligeretur, omni sanguinis propinquitate spretâ." For this purpose it was requisite that the consciences of men should be modified ; and hence arose *mental reservation*, to which all the abominations of other religions, even of popery itself, are trifles. Christ says, " Let your discourse be yea, yea ; nay, nay " : the Jesuit says, supported by the pope, " The speech by equivocation being saved from a lie, the same speech may be without perjury, confirmed by oath, or by any other way, though it were by receiving the sacrament, if just necessity so require." Cannot a lie be circuitous ? Whatever is said in order to make a man believe an untruth, is a lie ; yet a Jesuit has no hesitation to swear it upon the eucharist ; and princes have no hesitation to let Jesuits be the instructors of youth ! Falsely have they been called the supporters of thrones : they never support them but when they can govern from them, by means of deluded or affrighted princes. The papacy is the guardian of governments as a bawd is the guardian of girls : for profit. Antonius Capellus, a Franciscan friar, says that kings are unworthy of presiding over the church of their dominions, in any way whatever ; and that God in the books of Moses declares his dislike of them. Blasphemy ! Eudæmono-Johannes,[1] a monk of Crete, a true Jesuit, extols the son of the Emperor Henry IV. for insulting the dead body of his father, who had been disobedient to the See of Rome. The opinions of these men are not private ; they are sanctioned *facultate superiorum*, by the doctors of theology, and by the chancery of the papal court. The spirit of their church has always been and always will be the same, whenever it can exercise its authority ; arrogant, intolerant, persecuting, unforgiving. Its poison has been sublimated, and its froth and fumes have been condensed, by the Jesuits.

CASAUBON. It is singular and anomalous in the political world, that subjects should claim a right of appeal to foreign princes ; and it is absurd to argue that the appeal is made not to the prince but to the priest, when the person is invested with both characters, and acts in both. It[2] was determined in the *council of the Lateran*, by seventy bishops, in presence of the ambassadors of all the Christian princes, that the Holy See held a jurisdiction *in every place* ; that its authority extended over all ; that it was empowered to decide

---

[1] John Andrew Eudæmon.
[2] From " It " to " perjury " added in 3rd ed.

the causes of princes, to deprive them of their government, and to confer it on others at their own option. On this principle, in the exercise of this authority, Pope Zacharias gave the crown of France to Charles Martel,[1] ejecting Chilperic, and commanding a whole nation to commit a perjury.

JAMES.[2] What should I think if the fellows of Trinity college in Cambridge, or of Christchurch in Oxford, rose from table, and shut themselves in their common-room for the day, and sent me word the next morning that they had appointed a head of the church, enclosing his circular, wherein he ordereth my obedience ? Verily, from pure good will, I should diet and scourge the knaves into their sounder senses, clapping up their head-piece, with his tiara on, in my fool's-hospital, and giving him the precedency in it he had claimed outside. And yet, M. Casaubon, the fellows of either college are better scholars and honester men, I trow, than your pediculous friars and parti-coloured bald-coot priests, into whose frowsy bodies, incrusted with libidinousness and blood, enters that legion-spirit which overshadows and shakes the world. I have exorcised my three kingdoms ; and by the Lord ! if such spirit encroacheth, I will set those at him who shall leave him no easier a horn than Achelöusis, and no more tail than I have.

CASAUBON. It were an easy matter to prove that deacons, called subsequently cardinal-deacons, have no right to elect a pope ; that they themselves were not a corporate body many centuries ago, much less an elective one, but rather so many gourds sprung up in one dark night, with nobody then to heed, and nobody now to pluck them.

JAMES. Nay, but they have though.

CASAUBON. Bishops, priests, and deacons, were instituted by the apostles ; and what proves that after their time, we had no earthly and visible head of the church, is this : on the decease of the twelve, the provincial priests elected them, not without the suffrages of the people.

JAMES. We may hold back this latter part, M. Casaubon ! Never let people know it. All religions have their secrets and conveniences. Saint Cyprian [3] in several places, and particularly in his epistle to Felix the presbyter, doth indeed testify to the custom you have cited.

---

[1] Read : " Pippen the Short, son of Charles Martel."
[2] From " JAMES " to " conveniences " added in 3rd ed.
[3] From " Saint Cyprian " to " Antherus " added in 2nd ed., altered in 3rd ed.

A bishop thus elected was initiated into his ministry by the other bishops in the nearer dioceses ; and it was decreed in the council of Nicæa, that no fewer than three of them should attend on this occasion. Bonifacius the Third left the election to the priests and people, but usurped to himself the right of confirming it. Afterward the emperor's will and pleasure were consulted ; Louis, the son of Charlemagne, was the first who waived the ceremony. Cardinals were instituted by Pope Marcellus, to bury and baptize. That there was no regular nor certain method of electing popes themselves, is manifest by the Council holden at Rome in 610, which established one : but the establishment hath been sapped and subverted.

CASAUBON. The violation mentioned by your Majesty of this ordinance, and of that order made in the council of Nicæa, are not the only ones. It was there determined that a bishop removed from a diocese could never be placed in another : which determination was unfixed by Pope Antherus.

JAMES.[1] Well, well : let them overturn and overturn to their hearts' content, so that what they overturn do not fall against our shins. My bishops see no harm in removals, which they designate by the auspicious name of *trans-lation.* It were more prudent on my part, and more to the purpose, to touch upon the popes again.

CASAUBON. Your Majesty needs not be reminded that, according to papal infallibility, every potentate in Europe is base-born.

JAMES. How ? do you mean spurious, or merely that he can be traced by genealogists to a low origin ?

CASAUBON. I mean a bastard, or the descendant of one : which, as affecting his right to the crown, is the same thing. Innocent III. prohibited marriages within the seventh degree of affinity : by which prohibition there not only is no crowned head, but no nobleman in Europe, who is not a bastard or the descendant of one. What an immense field, what a forest, what a new world for absolution ! what a mine of gold throughout the whole extent, all lying on the surface !

JAMES. Yet those divines who prohibited marriages within the seventh degree, put a niece into bed with her uncle, or an aunt into a nephew's, and tucked them up and wished them pleasant dreams. Show me the same fraudulence in any other religion, the same

---

[1] From " JAMES " to " expert " (in the speech of James beginning " The only intelligible ") added in 3rd ed.

KING JAMES I. AND ISAAC CASAUBON

venality and impudence in the priesthood, and you shall have my crown for your pains, Master Isaac, and the head that is under it to boot.

CASAUBON. Sire, it is easier to find flaws in the ring of Infallibility. At the Council of Chalcedon it was resolved that the sees of Constantinople and Rome should possess equal authority. One century later a Council was convoked by the Emperor Justinian at Constantinople, where the patriarch presided, and no bishop of the Latin church attended ; none of them understanding Greek any more than they do now. In 680 another Council was assembled there under Constantine the Bearded, who himself presided at it, placing on his right the patriarchs of Constantinople and Antioch, on his left the deputies of Jerusalem and Rome. It was there that Pope Honorius was condemned. In 879 Pope John the Eighth declared that all are Judases who assert the Holy Ghost to proceed from the Father and the Son.

JAMES. Another short vacation for Infallibility !

CASAUBON. In 1215 a General Council was holden in Saint John Lateran, by Pope Innocent the Third, forbidding the establishment of religious orders.

JAMES. The greater part of them, methinks, have been founded since.

CASAUBON. It was not until this Council that the doctrine of Transubstantiation was established.

JAMES. The only intelligible sense of it is what Christ's vicar gave, when he took away the substance of the Count of Toulouse and transferred it to himself. Lo! here is a practical kind of transubstantiation, in which his successors have had perpetual practice and are admirably expert. These [1] gentles care neither for bishops their equals, nor for synods their superiors. A pope, like the Glaucus of antiquity, has taken his leap, and from a fisherman is become a God. He may advise and enlighten ; he may also command and fulminate : a favourite designation of one among the supernatural powers which he arrogates to himself from the Divinity.

CASAUBON. By a less exertion, he might transfuse in a perennial stream his wisdom and his holiness into a succession of bishops : hence appeals to Rome would be unnecessary. Power is always the

---

[1] From " These " to " God " added in 2nd ed., where the passage from " These " to " for the dead " is spoken by James.

more immoderate and the more jealous when it rises out of usurpation ; but those who contend for liberty of any kind should in no instance be its abettors. If the popes had been conscientious or decently honest men, if they could have abstained from laughing in their sleeves when they called themselves the successors of Saint Peter, if they could have been contented with his quiet mediocrity of fortune, his dignified and righteous exercise of authority, their influence upon sound consciences would have been greater and more permanent : and neither would rape and incest and the abominations of Lampsacus and Crete have been committed in their closets, under the images of the saints and under the lamp of the Virgin ; nor would forbearance from evil and activity in good be postponed to frogs and flounders, to horse-hair, hemp, and ashes, or prayers to the dead for the dead. Pope [1] John XXII. established a Tariff for sins : and if Leo X. published in like manner a Brief containing one, it did not, as many imagine, bring about the Reformation, which, in the midst of general depravity, it was likelier to prevent.

JAMES. But it was a stinkpot in the hands alike of the pious and of the ambitious, swung about in opposition to the thuribule, and a piece of furniture from the same chamber.

CASAUBON. Enormity was not taken into the account. Impurities and incests, the least likely to be committed, paid least.* That which desolated the house of Œdipus, and filled Greece with horror and dismay, was compounded for at the rate of six shillings ; while that incontinence, which peradventure might be committed by two persons who happened to have the same sponsor at baptism, cost them sixteen. For this is incest too, according to the *Decretals :* according to the authority of men whose interest is threefold : first, to increase the number of sins ; secondly, to split them artificially, and to plant them like the cuttings of vines in long and well-laboured and well-manured trenches ; and thirdly, to facilitate the means of atonement.

JAMES. I would not say openly, for evil might come therefrom, that popes might as rationally deduce their origin from Julius Cæsar as from Simon Peter ; yet I will declare and protest that the religion

---

[1] From " Pope " to " Europe and beyond " added in 3rd ed.

* The list entitled *Taxæ Pœnitentiariæ*, the genuineness of which publication has been denied, was edited at Paris by Toussain Denis, 1520, and at Venice in the *Oceanus Juris.*—W. S. L.

they attempt to impose on us resembles more Julius's than Peter's ; and that the means they employ to get into office are the same as his ; which, after he had ruined his estate by debauchery, would, if he had failed to bribe his electors, have left him without a penny in his pouch. Let me rather mind my own matters : I have nothing to do with crimes out of my kingdom. But *mine* these audacious robbers will not let me call it, if they can hinder me ; these infesters of the king's high-road, through England, through Europe, and beyond.

CASAUBON. Infallibility [1] was never claimed by the bishops of Rome, nor ever thought of, until they were sufficiently powerful for the assertion of any falsehood and any usurpation. Pope Honorius, in later times, gave his sanction to the Ecthesis of Sergius, which was accepted by a synod convoked under him : it was declared heretical by his successors. Where was then Infallibility ?

A [2] question far more important to kings and nations lies before us. The Cardinal Bellarmin, unable to confute the slightest of your remonstrances, came forward in his master's name, threw down the key of Peter and took up the sword, cutting short the question between you, and asserting that the King of England is also in temporals the pope's feudatory and subject. After this, according to the constitution, your Majesty may declare rebels all adherents of the pope in any way whatever, all who hold direct or indirect communication with him, all who receive or give intelligence for the furtherance of his machinations and designs.

JAMES.[3] The pope has many true and just causes for hostility against us : the truest and justest is this : the Reformation has shown that bishops are appointed by the secular power, though selected by the spiritual, at least in form. Now, he may be frightened at the apparition of some mighty prince in armour, who, although surrounded by the clouds and fogs of his native superstition, calls upon his own bishops to nominate one, and gives his sanction to their nomination. On this principle Rome may receive her bishop at his hands.

One thing is plain and demonstrable from the Scripture, and admits no doubt nor equivocation, nor can it be interpreted with

---

[1] From " Infallibility " to " Infallibility ? " added in 2nd ed., when the passage is spoken by James.

[2] From " A " to " us " added in 3rd ed.

[3] From " JAMES " to " exploded " (end of speech of James beginning " I do not like ") added in 2nd ed.

more or less force; which is, that the guides of Christians must abstain altogether from political concerns.

CASAUBON. May not that, Sire, affect the bishops as lords in parliament?

JAMES. They sit there only to give their counsel on such discipline as may be propounded for the clergy. Hence they are called lords spiritual; two very good words, although rather strange together.

If anyone of mine in his pruriency should cast his wild eye askance, and ruffle his mane and neigh and snort to overleap this boundary, I would thrust the Bible into his mouth forthwith, and thereby curb his extravagance. For, M. Isaac, we do possess this advantage : our bishops acknowledge in spirituals the sole authority of that sacred book : whereas your papist, when you push him, slinks off from it as he lists, now to one doctor, now to another, now to saint, now to father, now to confessor; and, as these retire from him and will have nothing to say to him or for him, he has recourse to tradition, which is anywhere or nowhere. If you follow him up into this whispering-gallery, and press him closer, he flies at your throat, and swears (by God's help) he will throttle you.

CASAUBON. The English have reflected at all times more intensely on religion than any other people in the universe, and began the earliest to examine its innovations and abuses. The *Trialogue* of Wicklif * is the first important work published in this country, and few more important have been published since.

JAMES. I do not like Wicklif : he would make men equal : let me hear no more of him. Bishop Reginald Peacock went exactly far enough. He resisted the authority of the pope, and refuted the doctrine of transubstantiation, with several other papalities, and particularly those paganisms which Vigilantius, in ancient times, buffeted and exploded.

CASAUBON.[1] The Council of Trent hath defined and settled all the questions at issue in the Roman Catholic creed; so that popes can pretend to inculcate nothing new for the future. Matters of discipline are likewise fixed. The appointment to ecclesiastical dignities, of every degree, may be safely entrusted to the native hierarchy in each kingdom. Your Majesty has a right to demand from your

---

* This book was first printed without date, and written about the year 1360. Peacock flourished a century later.—W. S. L.

[1] From " CASAUBON " to " goatskin of the Arab. CASAUBON " added in 3rd ed.

KING JAMES I. AND ISAAC CASAUBON

Roman Catholic subjects, that no papal bull, no order, brief, decree, or mandate of any kind, hereafter be received in your dominions.

Throughout the Christian world the popes have stipulated with usurpers for almost every accession of authority and power. Bonifacius III. obtained from the Emperor Phocas, who had assassinated his master and benefactor Mauritius, an imperial Rescript, ordering that he should be styled *Œcumenicus,* which the papists interpret Universal Bishop. Mauritius had resolved to confer the title on the Patriarch of Constantinople ; but Gregory, at that time Bishop of Rome, opposed it, " using Christian freedom," says Eusebius, " and declaring that he could not assent to it ; for that no bishop ought to arrogate to himself the style and dignity of Universal Bishop." * In the East the church received with scorn and anger the intelligence of this usurpation : and the spirit of discord, which never breathed so violently and uninterruptedly in any other religion, and which never has intermitted a moment in the sixteen centuries since peace and goodwill were first proclaimed to mankind, induced an Arab to collect a few of his countrymen, disbanded and defrauded by Heraclius, and to preach among them plainer doctrines. Provinces, kingdoms, empires, gazed, trembled, and bowed before him : Religions, old and young, seceded and slank away : not a camel crossed the desert with a grain of incense. While Arians and Catholics were fighting for Christ against the command of Christ, the most populous and civilised part of the world revolted from both standards.

JAMES. To establish things as now constituted, it was necessary to reverse the prophecy of Isaiah, and instead of making the rough smooth, to make the smooth rough.

CASAUBON. Hence we find perpetually the terms, pernicious errors, impious doctrines, execrable heresies, and rarely a word about the perniciousness, impiety, and execrableness, of cruelty, malice, fraudulence, lust, avarice, and ambition. Hence the people are not permitted to read in their houses the precepts of our Saviour, but are ordered to believe the legend of Saint Handkerchief or Saint Eleven-thousand ; to embrace the faith of a hot-headed enthusiast who tells us he believes a thing because it is impossible, and to place confidence in a lying old dotard who asserts that he filed his teeth in order to speak Hebrew.

* Orta est contentio, &c. Carrionis Chron : L. 4, p. 272. Venetiis, 1540.— W. S. L.

93

JAMES. It must be confessed, his followers have sharpened theirs for worse purposes. Mahomet, of whom you were speaking, borrowed the best of his doctrines from the Christians, and the Christians the worst of theirs from him. Pope John VIII. declared that they who died fighting against the infidels should obtain the entire pardon of their sins. So, whoever wished to commit a rape or murder, had only to make haste and to run from one holy city to the other. As the predecessors of Pope John clipped something from the older religions, so Pope John crooked his finger and filched these spicy and intoxicating comforts from the goatskin of the Arab.

CASAUBON. Among the various religions that have been established in the world, the papal is the only one which, as though it wished to ridicule and parody the Athanasian creed, insists that a kingdom shall have two *chief* magistrates,* that nevertheless one of these shall be *superior* to the other, and that he of right is so who has never seen the country, never will see it, never had parentage or progeny or land or tenement in it ; that a kingdom neither conquered nor hereditary, neither bequeathed nor surrendered by itself, must admit an alien arbitrator whenever it pleases him to raise a question, and that this alien arbitrator shall always give an irreversible verdict in his own favour ; lastly, that a kingdom, to the detriment of its defence, of its agriculture, of its commerce, of its population, of its independence, shall raise a body of men for the service of this intruder, unlimited in number, enormous in expenditure, which he alone shall discipline, he alone shall organise, he alone shall direct and control. Mahomet left a family, and was far from deficient in impudence, but he wanted the assurance to claim for his own successors what the pretended ones of St. Peter claim for theirs : here however we have somewhat worse than common absurdity, or than common arrogance, to contend with.

* Casaubon must be supposed to mean two magistrates each of whom pretended to power independently of the other. For in Sparta were two kings ; and in Japan was a kind of pope, reported to possess an equal authority with the emperor. Where any such magistrate exists, a short time is requisite for his growth into inordinate power : where there is a hierarchy there will be usurpation. The Japanese pope, or dairo, is reduced to order, and his chief privileges are, the keeping of twelve wives, with as many concubines as are necessary for the prosperity of the state and the interests of religion. The number of these, no doubt, would be diminished if no serious danger were to be apprehended from the example of innovation.—W. S. L. [Not in 1st ed.]

KING JAMES I. AND ISAAC CASAUBON

JAMES.[1] A harlot was not contented with debauching your servants, with getting drunk at your expense, and with picking your pocket of some loose money every time you approached her : she became impatient for your strong-box and title-deeds, and invoked the blessed Virgin to witness that, unless she had them, you should never, as she hoped for salvation, leave the room alive. She now is angry that you have turned her off; is [2] ready to bring attestations by the thousands, that she is fairer and cleaner and safer than any other : reminds you, as peculiar to herself, that you may enjoy her as well asleep as awake, as well by proxy as in person ; complains of your levity and violence, boasts of her sweet temper, affection and fidelity ; pouts, pants, and swells, and swears that neither you nor yours shall enter her house again.[3] I see not therefore what we can do better than to cut her laces and put her decently to bed, slipping out of the door with as little noise as possible.

CASAUBON. Rather should we act so in every case, than exchange a pledge with the perfidious, or reason with the unreasonable.

JAMES. Nicodemus asked our Saviour *how can these things be?* and his divine instructor heard and answered him with complacency : put the same question to his vicar, issuing from some mountain monastery or some suburban lane, and the fellow will illuminate you with a cartload of faggots.

The [4] French displayed long before the English a resolution to defend the prerogatives of royalty against the usurpations of the Popedom. Vigilantius,[5] afore cited, a Frenchman by birth, although a bishop in Spain, condemned the celibacy of priests, the adoration of relics, and the lighting of lamps and candles by day in churches. Pierre Bruis, neither less intelligent nor less holy, took up and maintained his doctrines, which had languished six centuries, and taught them for twenty years at Toulouse. He was burned alive : for the Roman shepherds have not only their shears but their tar-pot. Henri le Moine followed his doctrine, and preached the words of his master with such good effect, that half the nation came back again from Rome to Christ. At the same season flourished Valdo, as you remember, and translated the Bible into French. His followers,

[1] " JAMES " added in 3rd ed.
[2] From " is " to " person " added in 2nd ed.
[3] For reading of 1st ed. see Appendix.
[4] From " The " to " Popedom " added in 2nd ed.
[5] From " Vigilantius " to " plumage " added in 3rd ed.

95

called by his name and by that of Albigenses, carried this precious treasure through more than the third and fourth generation, and yielded it up only with their lives to the God who gave it. Indulgences were in vain held forth to this poor and lonely remnant of the apostolic church. Nicolas Oremus, plucking up courage by example, wrote to prove that the Papacy is Antichrist, and translated anew the Holy Scriptures into French, by order of King Charles V. Under the next of that name the secretary Maître Alain wrote his *Somnium Vividarium* ; for which I hope, rather than for any other work, my kinswoman Margaret, wife of the Dauphin, gave him a kiss upon the mouth while (it is said) he lay asleep.

The greatest blow of all was received in 1395, when the Sorbonne decreed that the two contending popes might box it out by themselves, and that the people of France should have nothing to do with either. In pursuance of which resolution the kingdom was exempt from papal jurisdiction three whole years. In soberer times, when the popes were neither in the cockpit nor upon the perch, we have proofs before us that the French knew how to clip their combs, shorten their tails, and cleanse their plumage. To [1] pretermit the vigour and firmness of Philippe le Bel, who burnt the Bull of Bonifacius VIII. in the streets of Paris by the hands of the hangman, and, having seized *his Holiness* at Anagni, would have treated him with as little ceremony, had he not been rescued, Giovanni Buonacorsi of Lucca published, under the reign of Louis XII., a proposition that the pope was above the king in temporals. The parliament of Paris condemned him to be stripped of his canonical dress, to put on one of green and yellow, to carry a candle of the same colour, to confess before the image of the Virgin Mary that this proposition was contrary to the Roman Catholic religion, and to ask pardon of the king, of justice, and of the people : of the people, because he had put their souls in danger : else the parliament of Paris was always most discreet in its consignment of liberty ; not leaving any in places where it might do harm, and placing it abundantly in the king's treasury, to be distributed at his royal will and pleasure. The doctors of that country, and none but doctors and princes are fit to handle the subject, are unanimous that law and liberty, like offices and honours, can emanate only from the throne. I throw out this in friendship and generosity, M. Casaubon, feeling that you, born and educated as you were at

[1] From " To " to " to suppress them " added in 2nd ed.

KING JAMES I. AND ISAAC CASAUBON

Geneva, might think erroneously upon a point which the nicest hand can not separate from religion, and loving you with all my heart, and most anxious for your welfare and salvation.

CASAUBON. Sire, I will think thereupon.

JAMES. Friend Casaubon, do you speak in the royal sense of the word or in the popular ? We kings, when we say to parliament or other folk that we will think upon anything, mean always that we will dismiss it from our thoughts.

CASAUBON. That would not be easy to do with the words of your Majesty.

JAMES. We have already seen and examined the anarchal doctrines of the popish priesthood, and can never be surprised at any atrocity committed by a sect, the only one since the creation of the world, by which fratricide has been protected. Juan Diaz, in the memory of some now living,[*] was murdered in Nuremberg at the instigation of his brother Alfonso, for having adopted the doctrine of the apostles in preference to the glosses of the popes. His murderers were imprisoned in the jail of Inspruck : the Emperor Charles V. stopped the proceedings, under the pretext that he himself would take cognisance of them at the approaching diet. I know not whether the facts have been divulgated.

CASAUBON. The whole history of the assassination has been published in Latin, under the name of Claudius Senarclæus. I possess one of the few copies that have escaped the searches made in order to suppress them. Medals [1] were coined by order of Gregory XIII. to commemorate Saint Bartholomew's day : on one side is the pope, on the other is the slaughter. He commanded it also to be painted in the Vatican, where the painting still exists. In popes no atrocity is marvellous or remarkable ; but how painful is it to find a scholar like Muretus exulting in a massacre ! Horatius Tursellinus, another eminent scholar, is another proof among thousands that literature, the tamer and subduer of barbarism, can not penetrate a heart immersed in this searing superstition.

JAMES. Tursellinus is not so rapturous as Muretus, but he counts the number of the victims with a sedate and calm pleasure.

CASAUBON. Spondanus, in his *Auctarium ad Annales Baronii*, represents a similar scene on a smaller scale, exhibited two centuries

[*] 1545.—W. S. L.
[1] From " Medals " to " occident " added in 3rd ed.

ago in the Valtellina, under the auspices of the Duke of Feria, governor of the Milanese for the Spanish king. " Catholici, mense Julio, omnes Calvinistas, tam incolas quàm exteros, occidunt."

JAMES. Is it not wonderful that [1] an ignorant, vicious, and ferocious priest, covered with filth and vermin, being hailed as another God by some dozens of the same caste, instantly treats kings as his inferiors and subjects, and is obeyed in a country like this, high-minded, free, and enlightened ? Is there anything more irrational or more humiliating in the worship of the Delai-Lama ? Far otherwise : he is innocent, gentle, and beneficent ; no murderer, no instigator to assassinations, no approver of massacres,* no plunderer, no extortioner, no vender of pardons, no dealer in dispensations, no forestaller and regrater of manna from heaven or of palms from paradise, no ringdropper of sacraments, no scourer of incests, no forger, no betrayer.†

[1] For reading of 1st ed. see Appendix.

* The following words are part of an oration addressed by him to Gregory, in the name of Charles IX., on the celebration of this festival.

" O noctem illam memorabilem, et in fastis eximiæ alicujus notæ adjectione signandam, quæ *paucorum seditiosorum* interitu regem a præsenti cædis periculo, regnum a perpetuâ civilium bellorum formidine, liberavit ! Quâ quidem nocte stellas equidem ipsas luxisse solito nitidiùs arbitror, et flumen Sequanam majores undas volvisse, quo citiùs illa impurorum hominum cadavera evolveret et exoneraret in mare ! O felicissimam mulierum Catharinam regis matrem ! &c."

Such are the expressions of Muretus, as the most agreeable he could deliver to the successor of him who proclaimed on earth peace, good will toward men. This language of Charity had been corrected by Infallibility, and altered to *pax hominibus . . . bonæ voluntatis :* terms on which a massacre is a commentary.

His words on the same occasion are these : " Gregorius XIII. deinde pontifex summus patrum studiis electus ; *cujus pontificatús initia lætiora lætus de Parisiensi Hugonotorum cæde nuncius fecit.* Per occasionem nuptiarum regis Navarri, Calviniani proceres jussu Franci regis oppressi ad LX. millia Parisiis cæsa traduntur." Treachery in the mask of Festivity, Murder in that of Religion, are thus congratulated and applauded.—W. S. L.

† Almost the only good, or rather almost the only cessation of evil, permitted by catholic princes, is the abolition of the Jesuits, which must however be considered as merely the dismissal of old servants grown insolent. Princes still maintained and supported the Inquisition. During the period of these two institutions, more mischief has been done to mankind by their religion, than by all the other religions that have existed in the world. The Jesuits taught youth, but only to a certain and very circumscribed extent, and their principal dogma was the legitimacy of falsehood : hence knowledge and virtue have suffered worse from them than from the most profligate and ignorant of the other confraternities.

Catholicism is the cause, we are informed, why sculpture and painting were revived : it is more certainly the cause why they have made no progress, and

KING JAMES I. AND ISAAC CASAUBON

O Casaubon ! I blush to reflect that dissimulation is necessary to the maintenance of peace. A rotten rag covers worse rottenness : remove it, and half the world is tainted with infidelity. In England, in Holland, in any country where laws are equitable and morals pure, how often would these *Eminences* and *Holinesses* have clasped the whipping-post, and with how much more fervency than they clasp the cross ! Bellarmin must have been convinced : he must have struggled against his conscience : heated with that conflict, he advances the more outrageously against me.

CASAUBON. Bellarmin throws all your arguments into the fire, and assumes a fiercer attitude, not from any resentment at being convinced, for convinced he was long before, but on the principle that, when we are tired of parrying, we thrust. Your Majesty has now a declared competitor for the throne : but parliament will provide, if the statute of Queen Elizabeth is insufficient, the means necessary to maintain your possession. On the compliance of your Roman Catholic subjects with such conservatory statutes, nothing can be so unjust or so needless, as to exclude from the rights of citizenship, or from the dignities of state, a body of men who believe not differently from your Majesty, but more.

Popery [1] is an amalgam of every religion and every institution by which mankind in all countries under heaven had been subjugated. Not only the Egyptian and Syrian, the Brahmin and Persian, the Phrygian and Greek, but even the Druidical, was found useful in its structure ; and thereupon were erected the fulminating batteries of Excommunication. This, which satisfied and satiated the ferocity of the most ferocious race among men, satisfied not the papal priesthood. They conducted their Inquisition far beyond it, extinguishing, as they went, all other lights than such as served for illusion. In Spain they

---

why they have been employed on ignoble objects ; on scourgers and hangmen, on beggarly enthusiasts and base impostors. Look at the two masterpieces of the pencil; the Transfiguration of Raphael and the St. Jerome of Correggio : can anything be more incongruous, anything more contrary to truth and history ? We may be persuaded that the little town of Sicyon produced a greater number of masterpieces than all the modern world. The sculptors of Sicyon are celebrated, the painters not : but sculpture was never brought to perfection anywhere until drawing was ; and we are instructed by the defect in our own school, how much rarer and more difficult is this part. In landscape only, where superstition has no influence, are the moderns to be thought on a level with the ancients. Claude and Titian, Cuyp and Hobbima, were probably not excelled.—W. S. L.

[1] From " Popery " to " suppleness " added in 2nd ed.

succeeded perfectly ; nearly so in Italy ; in France the machine stuck and miscarried. The vivacity and courage of the French, and their felicity in ridicule and mimicry, kept them up from suffocation and submersion. The strong moral principle of the English, their serious. temper, their habit of long reflection, their unreserved confidence one in another, their dauntless practice of delivering their opinions, their liberality in accepting and exchanging them, and, upon these, the attempering countenance of your Majesty, will deprive the papal poison of its circulation and activity. Threats are yet murmured : but if your Majesty will cease to notice them, they will die away. There is no echo but from repercussion ; no repercussion but from some place higher than the voice. The scourge of reason and humanity, left upon the ground awhile, will break in the hand of the first who strikes hard therewith : it has already lost much of its weight and suppleness.

Casaubon here finished his discourse, and James made no farther observation. Such was his simplicity, he really had imagined that reason and truth, urged so forcibly by him, would alter the system and conciliate the goodwill of the papal court, and that it would resign a wide dominion for a weighty argument. He stroked his beard, licked softly the extremities of his whiskers, ejaculated, sighed, and sate down quietly. He was, notwithstanding, in a frame of mind capable of receiving with satisfaction whatever could derogate from the dignity of the Roman Catholic rites, when Archibald Pringle, one of his pages, entered the apartment.

" Archy," said his Majesty, who was fond of such abbreviations, " I remember to have chidden you for a wicked little story you told me last winter, touching a Japanese at Rouen. Come now, if you can divest it of irreverence, I would fain hear it repeated. I think it a subject for the disquisition of my bishops, whether the pagan sinned or not, or whether, if he sinned, his faith was of a nature to atone for it."

Such were really, if not the first thoughts, those however which now arose in the king's mind. The page thus began his narration.

A young Japanese was brought over to Rouen on the day of Pentecost. He had expressed in the voyage a deep regret at the death of the chaplain, who might have instructed him in the mysteries, and who, the only time he conversed with him, recommended to him zealously the worship of the living God. He was constant in his desire to be edified, and immediately on his debarkation was conducted to the cathedral. He observed the elevation of the Host with imperturbable devotion, and an utter indifference to the flattering whispers of the fairest among the faithful ; such as, " O the sweet jonquil-coloured skin ! O the pretty piercing black eyes ! O the charming long twisted tail ! and how finely those flowers and birds and butterflies are painted upon his trousers ! and look at that leopard in the centre ! it seems alive."

When the service was over, and the archbishop was mounting his carriage-step, he ran after him, and, with eyes half-closed, bit him gently by the calf of the leg. Vociferations were raised by the attendants, the soldiers, and the congregation, ill accordant with sanctity, and wronging the moral character and pious disposition of the Japanese. These however the good prelate quieted, by waving his hand and smiling with affability. The neophyte was asked what induced him to bite the archbishop by the leg : he answered that he wished to pay the living god the same reverence and adoration as the living god had paid the dead one.

" See now," cried James, "the result of proclaiming that the pope is god upon earth. It led this poor heathen, who amid such splendour and prostrations might well mistake an archbishop for a pope, to the verge of an abyss, dark, precipitous, and profound, as any that superstition hath opened in his own deplorable country."

XIII. OLIVER CROMWELL [1] AND WALTER NOBLE * [2]

(*Imag. Convers.*, i., 1824 ; i., 1826 ; *Wks.*, ii., 1846 ; iii., 1876.)

CROMWELL. What brings thee back from Staffordshire, friend Walter ?

NOBLE. I hope, General Cromwell, to persuade you that the death of Charles will be considered by all Europe as a most atrocious action.

CROMWELL. Thou hast already persuaded me : what then ?

NOBLE. Surely then you will prevent it, for your authority is great. Even those who upon their consciences found him guilty, would remit [3] the penalty of blood, some from policy, some from mercy. I have conversed with Hutchinson, with Ludlow,† your friend and mine, with Henry Nevile, and Walter Long : you will oblige these worthy friends, and unite in your favour the suffrages of the truest and trustiest men living. There are many others, with whom I am in no habits of intercourse, who are known to entertain the same sentiments ; and these also are among the country gentlemen, to whom our parliament owes the better part of its reputation.

---

[1] 1st and 2nd eds. read " Cromwel " throughout.

* He [1] represented the city of Lichfield : he lived familiarly with the best patriots of the age, remonstrated with Cromwell and retired from public life on the punishment of Charles. The memorial of my ancestor's virtues I hold in trust for the benefit of our descendants.—W. S. L.

[2] Forster's *Life*, p. 243, contains the following :—

" Oliver Cromwell and that Michael (misnamed by him Walter) Noble . . . some of whose blood ran in Landor's own veins ; his grandfather, Robert Landor of Rugeley, having (in 1732) married the sole daughter and heiress of Noble's grandson Walter, of Chorley Hall, Longdon, through whom Landor's father inherited a good estate."

[3] 1st and 2nd eds. read : " remitt."

† Ludlow, a most humane and temperate man, signed the death-warrant of Charles, for violating the constitution he had sworn to defend, for depriving the subject of property, liberty, limbs, and life, unlawfully. In equity he could do no otherwise ; and to equity was the only appeal, since the laws of the land had been erased by the king himself.—W. S. L.

---

[1] The footnotes on Noble and Ludlow were added by Landor in 3rd ed. From "He" to "descendants" taken from Preface, vol. i., 1st ed.

OLIVER CROMWELL AND WALTER NOBLE

CROMWELL. You country gentlemen bring with you into the People's House a freshness and sweet savour, which our citizens lack mightily. I would fain merit your esteem, heedless of those pursy fellows from hulks and warehouses, with one ear lappeted by the pen behind it, and the other an heir-loom, as Charles would have had it, in Laud's star-chamber. Oh! they are proud and bloody men. My heart melts; but, alas! my authority is null: I am the servant of the Commonwealth: I will not, dare not, betray it. If Charles Stuart had threatened my death only, in the letter we ripped out of the saddle, I would have reproved him manfully and turned him adrift: but others are concerned, lives more precious than mine, worn [1] as it is with fastings, prayers, long services, and preyed upon by a pouncing disease. The Lord hath led him into the toils laid for the innocent. Foolish man! he never could eschew evil counsel.

NOBLE. In comparison with you, he is but as a pinnacle to a buttress. I acknowledge his weaknesses, and cannot wink upon his crimes: but that which you visit as the heaviest of them, perhaps was not so, although the most disastrous to both parties; the bearing of arms against his people. He fought for what he considered his hereditary property: we do the same: should we be hanged for losing a lawsuit?

CROMWELL. No, unless it is the second.[2] Thou talkest finely and foolishly, Wat, for a man of thy calm discernment. If a rogue holds a pistol to my breast, do I ask him who he is? do I care whether his doublet be of catskin or of dogskin? Fie upon such wicked sophisms! Marvellous, how the devil works upon good men's minds. Friend [3]! friend! hast thou lost thy recollection? On the third of June, 1628, an usher stood at the door of our Commons-house, to hinder any member from leaving it, under pain of being sent to the Tower. On the fifth of the same month, the Speaker said he had received the King's order to interrupt any who should utter a word against his ministers. In the following year we might have justly hanged him for the crime of forgery, seeing that on the twenty-first of January he commanded his printer, Norton, to falsify the text of his own *Declaration*, in which he had acknowledged our rights, and had been paid handsomely for the acknowledgment. I sorely fear the

---

[1] 1st ed. reads: " worne."
[2] 1st and 2nd eds. read: " the second . . . thou talkest," etc.
[3] From " Friend " to " exempted " added in 3rd ed.

month of January is marked in the Calendar by the finger of the Almighty, for the heavy chastisement of this misdeed. We must take heed unto our ways, and never again be led into the wicked temptation of trusting the false and the reprobate. Equity might demand from the traitor more than his worthless and pernicious life. Equity might retaliate on him what Eliot and other most innocent and most virtuous men have suffered; pestilential imprisonment, lingering, painful, incurable disease, fetters and thumbscrews, racks and mutilations. Should the guiltless have suffered these things rather than the guilty? the defender of his home and property rather than the robber who broke into them? If the extinction of a spark prevents worse things than the conflagration of twenty cities, if it prevents the expansion of principles endemically noxious through incalculable ages, such as slavish endurance and all unmanly propensities, I would never take by the collar him who resolutely setteth his foot thereon. Whether a grain of dust be blown away in the morning, in the noon, or in the evening, what matter? But it imports very seriously whether it be blown in the eyes and darken the sight of a nation. This is the difference between him who dies in the solitude of his chamber, and him whom halberts, by God's ordinance, may surround upon the scaffold.

NOBLE. From so cruel an infliction let me hope our unfortunate king may be exempted. He [1] was always more to be dreaded by his friends than by his enemies, and now by neither.

CROMWELL. God forbid that Englishman should be feared by Englishman! but to be daunted by the weakest, to bend before the worst—I tell thee, Walter Noble, if Moses and the prophets commanded me to this villany, I would draw back and mount my horse.

NOBLE. I wish that our history, already too dark with blood, should contain, as far as we are concerned in it, some unpolluted pages.

CROMWELL. 'Twere better, much better. Never shall I be called, I promise thee, an unnecessary shedder of blood. Remember, my good prudent friend, of what materials our sectaries are composed: what hostility against all eminence, what rancour against all glory. Not [2] only kingly power offends them, but every other; and they talk

---

[1] 1st ed. reads : " Charles," etc.
[2] From " Not " to " world " added in 2nd ed. 1st ed. reads : " glory. How the knaves dictate . . . bleeding for them ! with what fatherly scourges," etc.

104

of *putting to the sword*, as if it were the quietest, gentlest, and most ordinary thing in the world. The knaves even dictate from their stools and benches to men in armour, bruised and bleeding for them ; and with schooldames' scourges in their fists do they give counsel to those who protect them from the cart and halter. In the name of the Lord, I must [1] spit outright (or worse) upon these crackling bouncing firebrands, before I can make them tractable.

NOBLE. I lament their blindness ; but follies wear out the faster by being hard run upon. This fermenting sourness will presently turn vapid, and people will cast it out. I am not surprised that you are discontented and angry at what thwarts your better nature. But come, Cromwell, overlook them, despise them, and erect to yourself a glorious name by sparing a mortal enemy.

CROMWELL. A glorious name, by God's blessing, I will erect, and all our fellow-labourers shall rejoice at it : but I see better than they do the blow descending on them, and my arm better than theirs can ward it off. Noble, thy heart overflows with kindness for Charles Stuart : if he were at liberty to-morrow by thy intercession, he would sign thy death-warrant the day after, for serving the Commonwealth. A generation of vipers ! there is nothing upright or grateful in them : never was there a drop of even Scotch blood in their veins. Indeed we have a clue to their bedchamber still hanging on the door, and I suspect that an Italian fiddler or French valet has more than once crossed the current.

NOBLE. That may be: nor indeed is it credible that any royal or courtly family has gone on for three generations without a spur from interloper. Look at France ! some stout Parisian saint performed the last miracle there.*

CROMWELL. Now thou talkest gravely and sensibly : I could hear thee discourse thus for hours together.

NOBLE. Hear me, Cromwell, with equal patience on matters more important. We all have our sufferings : why increase one another's wantonly ? Be the blood Scotch or English, French or Italian, a drummer's or a buffoon's, it carries a soul upon its stream, and every soul has many places to touch at, and much business to perform,

---

[1] 1st and 2nd eds. read : " must piss upon these firebrands."

* The birth of Louis XIV. is somewhat like a miracle to true believers, while among sceptics the principal doubt is not whether the child was supposititious, but whether he was so after his birth or before.—W. S. L.

before it reaches its ultimate destination. Abolish the power of Charles ; extinguish not his virtues. Whatever is worthy to be loved for anything is worthy to be preserved. A wise and dispassionate legislator, if any such should arise among men, will not condemn to death him who has done, or is likely to do, more service than injury to society. Blocks and gibbets are the nearest objects to ours, and their business is never with virtues or with hopes. Justice upon earth has forgotten half her lesson, and repeats the other half badly. God commanded her to reward and to punish. She would tell you that punishment is the reward of the wicked, and that the rewards of the good belong to him, whose delight is their distribution in another place. She is neither blind, as some have represented her, nor clear-sighted : she is one-eyed, and looks fixedly and fondly with her one eye upon edge-tools and halters. The best actions are never re-compensed, and the worst are seldom chastised. The virtuous man passes by without a *good morrow* from us, and the malefactor may walk at large where he will, provided he walk far enough from en-croachment on our passions and their playthings. Let us, Cromwell, in God's name, turn the laws to their right intention : let us render it the interest of all to love them and keep them holy. They are at present, both in form and essence, the greatest curse that society labours under ; the scorn of the wicked, the consternation of the good, the refuge of those who violate, and the ruin of those who appeal to them.

CROMWELL. You have paid, I see, chancery fees, Walter.

NOBLE. I should then have paid not only what is exorbitant, but what is altogether undue. Paying a lawyer, in any court, we pay over again what we have paid before. If government has neglected to provide that our duties be taught us, and our lives, properties, and station in society, be secured, what right has it to one farthing from us ? for what else have our forefathers and ourselves been taxed ? for what else are magistrates of any kind appointed ? There is an awfulness in symmetry which chastens even the wildest, and there is a terror in distortion at which they strike and fly. It is thus in regard to law. We should be slow in the censure of princes, and slower in the chastisement. Kingship is a profession which has produced few among the most illustrious, many among the most despicable, of the human race. As in our days they are educated and treated, he is deserving of no slight commendation who rises in moral worth to the level of his lowest subject ; so manifold and so great are the impediments.

Reverting to the peculiar case of Charles, in my opinion you are ill justified by morality or policy in punishing him capitally. The representatives of the people ought to superintend the education of their princes ; where they have omitted it, the mischief and the responsibility rest with them. As kings are the administrators of the commonwealth, they must submit their whole household to the national inspection : on which principle, the preceptors of their children should be appointed by parliament : and the pupils, until they have attained their majority, should be examined twice annually on the extent and on the direction of their studies, in the presence of seven men at least, chosen out of the Commons-house by ballot. Nothing of the kind having been done, and the principles of this unfortunate king having been distorted by a wrong education, and retained in their obliquity by evil counsellors, I would now, on the reclamation both of generosity and of justice, try clemency. If it fails, his adherents will be confounded at his perfidy, and, expecting a like return for their services, will abandon him.

CROMWELL. Whatever his education was, thinkest thou he was not wise enough to know his wickedness, his usurpation and tyranny, when he resolved to rule without a parliament ? to levy taxes, to force consciences, to imprison, to slay, at his own arbitrement and pleasure ? Some time before the most violent of his outrages, had he not received a grant of money from us on conditions which he violated ? He then seized forcibly what belonged to the public : and, because we remonstrated against this fraud and theft, did he not prosecute us as rebels ? Whereas, when a king acts against the laws or without them, there can be but one rebel in the kingdom. Accomplices there may be ; and such we may treat with mildness, if they do not wring and wrest it away from us and turn it against us, pushing down those who raised them. When the leading stag of such a herd is intractably wild, and obstinately vicious to his keepers, he ought to be hamstrung and thrown across the paling, wherever he is overtaken. What ! pat his hide forsooth ! hug his neck, garland his horns, pipe to him, try gentleness, try clemency ! Walter, Walter ! we laugh at speculators.

NOBLE. Many indeed are ready enough to laugh at speculators, because many profit, or expect to profit, by established and widening abuses. Speculations toward evil lose their name by adoption : speculations toward good are for ever speculations, and he who hath proposed them is a chimerical and silly creature. Among the matters under this denomination I never find a cruel project, I never find an oppressive or unjust one : how happens it ?

CROMWELL. Proportions should exist in all things. Sovereigns are paid higher than others for their office ; they should therefore be punished more severely for abusing it, even if the consequences of this abuse were in nothing more grievous or extensive. We cannot clap them in the stocks conveniently, nor whip them at the market-place. Where there is a crown there must be an axe : I would keep it there only.

NOBLE. Lop off the rotten, press out the poisonous, preserve the rest ; let it suffice to have given this memorable example of national power and justice.

CROMWELL. Justice is perfect ; an attribute of God : we must not trifle with it.

NOBLE. Should we be less merciful to our fellow-creatures than to our domestic animals ? Before we deliver them to be killed, we weigh their services against their inconveniences. On the foundation of policy, when we have no better, let us erect the trophies of humanity : let us consider that, educated in the same manner and situated in the same position, we ourselves might have acted as reprovably. Abolish that for ever which must else for ever generate abuses ; and attribute the faults of the man to the office, not the faults of the office to the man.

CROMWELL. I [1] have no bowels for hypocrisy and I abominate and detest kingship.

NOBLE. I abominate and detest hangmanship ; but in certain stages of society both are necessary. Let them go together ; we want neither now.

CROMWELL. Men,[2] like nails, lose their usefulness when they lose their direction and begin to bend : such nails are then thrown into the dust or into the furnace. I must do my duty ; I must accomplish what is commanded me ; I must not be turned aside. I am loth to be cast into the furnace or the dust ; but God's will be done !

---

[1] From " I " to " hypocrisy and " added in 3rd ed.
[2] From " Men " to " done " added in 3rd ed.

OLIVER CROMWELL AND WALTER NOBLE

Prythee, Wat, since thou readest, as I see, the books of philosophers, didst thou ever hear of Digby's remedies by sympathy?

NOBLE. Yes, formerly.

CROMWELL. Well, now, I protest, I do believe there is something in them. To cure my headache, I must breathe a vein in the neck of Charles.

NOBLE. Oliver, Oliver! others are wittiest over wine, thou over blood : cold-hearted, cruel man.*

CROMWELL. Why, dost thou verily think me so, Walter? Perhaps thou art right in the main : but He alone who fashioned me in my mother's womb, and who sees things deeper than we do, knows that.[1]

* Cromwell was not cruel. Had he been less sparing of the worst blood in the three kingdoms, the best would never have been spilled upon the scaffold ; and England would have been exempt from the ignominy of Sidney's death, Milton's proscription, the sale of the nation to the second Charles, and the transfer of both to Louis.—W. S. L.

[The above footnote was added in 3rd ed.]

[1] The following further variations of text are to be noted :—

(1) P. 106, l. 2. 1st ed. reads : "virtues ; he may be a good father who was a bad king. Whatever," etc.

(2) P. 106, l. 7. From "Justice" to "law" added in 2nd ed.

(3) P. 106, l. 35. From "We" to "impediments" added in 3rd ed.

(4) P. 107, l. 3. From "Reverting" to "abandon him" added in 3rd ed.

(5) P. 107, l. 21. From "CROMWELL" to "clemency" added in 3rd ed.

(6) P. 108, l. 4. From "Among" to "it" added in 2nd ed.

XIV. BARROW AND NEWTON

(*Imag. Convers.*, v., 1829 ; *Wks.*, i., 1846 ; *Wks.*, iv., 1876.)

NEWTON. I come, sir, before you with fear and trembling, at the thoughts of my examination tomorrow. If the masters are too hard upon me, I shall never take my degree. How I passed as bachelor I cannot tell : it must surely have been by especial indulgence.

BARROW. My dear Isaac ! do not be dispirited. The less intelligent of the examiners will break their beaks against the gravel, in trying to cure the indigestions and heartburnings your plenteousness has given them ; the more intelligent know your industry, your abilities, and your modesty : they would favour you if there were need of favour, but you, without compliment, surpass them all.

NEWTON. Oh sir ! forbear, forbear ! I fear I may have forgotten a good deal of what you taught me.

BARROW. I wonder at that. I am older than you by many years ; I have many occupations and distractions ; my memory is by nature less retentive : and yet I have not forgotten anything *you* taught *me*

NEWTON. Too partial tutor, too benevolent friend ! this unmerited praise confounds me. I cannot calculate the powers of my mind, otherwise than by calculating the time I require to compass anything.

BARROW. Quickness is among the least of the mind's properties, and belongs to her in almost her lowest state : nay, it doth not abandon her when she is driven from her house, when she is wandering and insane. The mad often retain it ; the liar has it, the cheat has it ; we find it on the race-course and at the card-table : education does not give it, and reflection takes away from it.

NEWTON. I am slow ; and there are many parts of ordinary learning yet unattained by me.

BARROW. I had an uncle, a sportsman, who said that the light dog beats over most ground, but the heavier finds the covey.

NEWTON. Oftentimes indeed have I submitted to you problems and possibilities——

BARROW AND NEWTON

BARROW. And I have made you prove them.

NEWTON. You were contented with me ; all may not be.

BARROW. All will not be : many would be more so if you could prove nothing. Men, like dogs and cats, fawn upon you while you leave them on the ground ; if you lift them up they bite and scratch ; and if you show them their own features in the glass, they would fly at your throat and tear your eyes out. This between ourselves : for we must not indulge in unfavourable views of mankind, since by doing it we make bad men believe that they are no worse than others, and we teach the good that they are good in vain. Philosophers have taken this side of the question to show their ingenuity : but sound philosophers are not ingenious. If philosophy can render us no better and no happier, away with it ! There are things that can ; and let us take them.

What dost thou sigh at, Isaac ?

NEWTON. At my ignorance, in some degree, of their writings.

BARROW. At your ignorance of the ignorant ? No man ever understood the things that are most admired in Plato and Aristoteles. In Plato there are incoherencies that fall to pieces at a touch : and Aristoteles lost himself in the involutions of his own web. What must we think of a philosopher, who promised to teach one pupil that which he withheld from the rest, although [1] these were more familiar with him, and more instructed ? And what must we think of a pupil, who was indignant that any others should partake in his sentiments and his knowledge ? Yet such men have guided the scientific, such men have ruled the world.

NEWTON. Not such was Bacon.

BARROW. No indeed. I told you, and I repeat it, I think the small volume of *Essays* in your hand, contains more wisdom and more genius than we can find in all the philosophers of antiquity ; with one exception, Cicero. On which I desired you to peruse it attentively, and to render me an account of it according to your opinion.

NEWTON. Sir, I have been induced to believe, but rather from the authority of my elders than from my own investigation, that Bacon is the more profound of the two, although not the more eloquent.

BARROW. If Bacon had written as easily and harmoniously as Cicero, he would have lost a portion of his weight with the generality

_____
[1] 1st ed. reads : " although more familiar."

of the learned, who are apt to conceive that in easy movement there is a want of solidity and strength.[1] We must confess that antiquity has darkened colleges and has distorted criticism. Very wise men, and very wary and inquisitive, walk over the earth, and are ignorant not only what minerals lie beneath, but what herbs and foliage they are treading. Some time afterward, and probably some distant time, a specimen of ore is extracted and exhibited ; then another ; lastly the bearing and diameter of the vein are observed and measured. Thus it is with writers who are to have a currency through ages. In the beginning they are confounded with most others ; soon they fall into some secondary class ; next, into one rather less obscure and humble ; by degrees they are liberated from the dross and lumber that hamper them ; and, being once above the heads of contemporaries, rise slowly and waveringly, then regularly and erectly, then rapidly and majestically, till the vision strains and aches as it pursues them in their ethereal elevation.

Neither you nor I have wasted our time in the cultivation of poetry ; but each of us hath frequently heard it discoursed on by those who have ; and, if it serves for nothing else, it serves for an illustration. In my early days he would have been scoffed out of countenance who should have compared the *Lycidas*, or the *Allegro* and *Penseroso*, of Mr. John Milton, to the sterling poetry (as it was called) of Dr. John Donne : and yet much may be said in favour of the younger : and there are those, and not only undergraduates, but bachelors and masters, who venture even to prefer him openly. Who knows but we may see him extolled to the level of Lucan and Statius, strong as is the sense of the University against all sorts of supplanters ! There are eyes that can not see print when near them ; there are men that can not see merit.

NEWTON. The [2] Latin secretary may be pardoned for many defects in his poetry, and even for many in his politics, in consideration of the reverence he bore toward the *Apocalypse*. I cannot think him a very irreligious man, although he does not attend divine service, we are told, so regularly as we [3] could have wished.

BARROW. Let us talk no more about him. I opposed his prin-

---

[1] 1st ed. reads : " strength. Take away all Cicero's wit and half his eloquence, and you leave a Bacon at bottom. Very wise," etc.

[2] 1st ed. reads : " The late Latin secretary."

[3] 1st ed. reads : " one."

ciples : nevertheless he may have acted conscientiously : and even his principles are now coming again into fashion, and among the sons of those very cavaliers who would have hanged him. Perhaps the most dangerous of his doctrines, the lawfulness of setting aside God's anointed for misconduct, may soon be the leading one in the front of our Constitution. Well! we are not met for politics: only it would be salutary to consider, if God's anointed will not be set aside, what must be done : how avoid the commission of a diabolical act.

NEWTON. Could we rightly understand the *Revelations*, I question not but every difficulty of this nature would be solved.

BARROW. May-be : let us trust in God.

NEWTON. We must have certain *data* for everything upon which we reason : the greater part of reasoners begin without them.

BARROW. I wish the event may answer your expectations ; that the *Apocalypse*, the *Argonautic Expedition*, and the *Siege of Troy*, form the trident which is to push away our difficulties in navigating through all the rocks and shoals of time ; all those of religion, and all those of history. Happen what may, I doubt nothing of your surpassing the foremost of your competitors ; of your [1] very soon obtaining a name in the University, little below Doctor Spry's of Caius, Doctor Brockhouse's of St. John's, Doctor Cockburn's of Emanuel, Doctor Turnbull's of Peter-house, or Doctor Cruikshank's of Bennet ; nay, a name which, within a few years, may reach even to Leyden and Paris, as that of a most studious young man, distinguished alike for application and invention.

NEWTON. Although I could not in conscience disclaim the small merit there may be in application, since I owe it to the encouragement of my tutor, I surely have no right or title to invention.

BARROW. You have already given proofs of it beyond any man I know. Your questions lead to great discoveries : whether it please God that you hereafter make them, or someone following you, is yet uncertain. We are silly enough to believe that the quality of invention, as applied to literature, lies in poetry and romance, mostly or altogether. I dare to speculate on discoveries in the subjects of your studies, every one far greater, every one far more wonderful, than all that lie within the range of fiction. In our days the historian is the only inventor : and it is ludicrous to see how busily and lustily he beats about, with his string and muzzle upon him. I wish we could

[1] 1st ed. reads : " your obtaining, at your decease, a name," etc.

drag him for a moment into philosophical life : it would be still more amusing to look at him, as he runs over this loftier and dryer ground, throwing up his nose and whimpering at the prickles he must pass through.

Few men are contented with what is strictly true concerning the occurrences of the world : it neither heats nor soothes. The body itself, when it is in perfect health, is averse to a state of rest. We wish our prejudices to be supported, our animosities to be increased, as those who are inflamed by liquor would add materials to the inflammation.

NEWTON. The simple verities, important perhaps in their consequences, which I am exploring, not only abstract me from the daily business of society, but exempt me from the hatred and persecution to which every other kind of study is exposed. In poetry a good pastoral would raise against one as vehement enemies as a good satire. A great poet in our country, like the great giant in Sicily, can never move without shaking the whole island ; while the mathematician and astronomer may pursue their occupations, and rarely be hissed or pelted from below. You spoke of historians : it would ill become a person of my small experience to discourse on them after you.

BARROW. Let me hear, however, what you have to say, since at least it will be dispassionate.

NEWTON. Those who now write history do certainly write it to gratify a party, and to obtain notoriety and money. The materials lie in the cabinet of the statesman, whose actions and their consequences are to be recorded. If you censure them, you are called ungrateful for the facilities he has afforded you ; and if you commend them, venal. No man, both judicious and honest, will subject himself to either imputation.

BARROW. Not only at the present day, but always, the indulgence of animosity, the love of gain, and the desire of favour, have been the inducements of an author to publish in his lifetime the history of his contemporaries. But there have been, and let us hope there may be, judicious and virtuous men, so inflamed by the glory of their country in their days, that, leaving all passions and prejudices, they follow this sole guide, and are crowned by universal consent for commemorating her recent exploits.

NEWTON. Here are reasons enough for me rather to apply my mind as you direct it, than to the examination of facts which never can be collected by one person ; or to poetry, for which I have no call ; or to the composition of essays, such as those of Montaigne and Bacon ; or dialogues, such as those of Cicero and Plato, and, nearer our times, of Erasmus and Galileo. You had furnished me before with arguments in abundance ; convincing [1] me that, even if I could write as well as they did, the reward of my labours would be dilatory and posthumous.

BARROW. I should entertain a mean opinion of myself, if all men or the most-part praised and admired me : it would prove me to be somewhat like them. Sad and sorrowful is it to stand near enough to people for them to see us wholly ; for them to come up to us and walk round us leisurely and idly, and pat us when they are tired and going off. That lesson which a dunce can learn at a glance, and likes mightily, must contain little, and not good. Unless it can be proved that the majority are not dunces, are not wilful, presumptuous, and precipitate, it is a folly to care for popularity. There are indeed those who must found their fortunes upon it ; but not with books in their hands. After the first start, after a stand among the booths and gauds and prostitutes of party, how few have lived contentedly, or died calmly ! One hath fallen the moment when he had reached the last step of the ladder, having undersawed it for him who went before, and forgotten that knavish act : another hath wasted away more slowly, in the fever of a life externally sedentary, internally distracted : a third, unable to fulfill the treason he had stipulated, and haunted by the terrors of detection, snaps the thread under the shears of the Fates, and makes even those who frequented him believe in Providence.

Isaac ! Isaac ! the climbing plants are slender ones. Men of genius have sometimes been forced away from the service of society into the service of princes ; but they have soon been driven out, or have retired. When shall we see again, in the administration of any country, so accomplished a creature as Wentworth*, the favourite of Charles ? Only light men recover false steps : his greatness crushed

---

[1] 1st ed. reads : " showing."

* He [1] far excelled in energy and capacity the other councillors of Charles ; but there was scarcely a crueller or (with the exception of his master) a more perfidious man on either side. Added to which, he was wantonly oppressive, and sordidly avaricious.—W. S. L.

---

[1] This note was added in 2nd ed.

him. Aptitude for serving princes is no proof or signification of genius, nor indeed of any elevated or extensive knowledge. The interests of many require a multiplicity of talents to comprehend and accomplish them. Mazarin and Richelieu were as little able as they were little disposed to promote the well-being of the community; both of them had keen eyes, and kept them on one object,[1] aggrandisement. We find the most trivial men in the streets pursuing an object through as many intricacies, and attaining it; and the schemes of children, though sooner dropped, are frequently as ingenious and judicious. No person can see more clearly than you do, the mortifications to which the ambitious are subject : but some may fall into the snares of ambition whose nature was ever averse to it, and whose wisdom would almost reach anything, and only seems too lofty to serve them watchfully as a guard. It may thus happen to such as have been accustomed to study and retirement, and fall unexpectedly on the political world by means of recommendations. There are those, I doubt not, who would gladly raise their name and authority in the state, by pushing you forward, as the phrase is, into Parliament. They seize any young man who has gained some credit at college, no matter for what, whether for writing an epigram or construing a passage in Lycophron ; and, if he succeeds to power, they and their family divide the patronage. The ambitious heart is liable to burst in the emptiness of its elevation : let yours, which is sounder, lie lower and quieter. Think how much greater is the glory you may acquire by opening new paths to science, than by widening old ones to corruption. I would not whisper a syllable in the ear of Faction : but the words of the intelligent, in certain times and on certain occasions, do not vary with parties and systems. The royalist and republican meet ; the difference lies merely in the intent, the direction, and the application. Do not leave the wise for the unwise, the lofty for the low, the retirement of a college for the turbulence of a House of Commons. Rise, but let no man lift you : leave that to the little and to the weak. Think within yourself, I will not say how impure are the sources of election to our Parliament, but how inconsiderable a distinction is conferred on the representative, even where it is not an individual who nominates, or only a few who appoint him, but where several hundreds are the voters. For who are they, and who direct them ? The roughest bear-guard, the most ferocious

---

[1] 1st ed. reads : " object, the aggrandizement of their master."

bull-baiter, the most impudent lawyer, the tinker that sings loudest, and the parson that sits latest at the alehouse, hitting them all by turns with his tobacco-pipe, calling them all sad dogs, and swearing till he falls asleep he will hear no more filthy toasts. Show me the borough where such people as these are not the most efficient in returning a candidate to Parliament; and then tell me which of them is fit to be the associate—it would be too ludicrous to say the patron —of a Euclid or an Archimedes ? My dear Newton ! the best thing is to stand above the world ; the next is, to stand apart from it on any side. You *may* attain the first : in trying to attain it, you are certain of the second.

NEWTON. I am not likely to be noticed by the great, nor favoured by the popular. I have no time for visiting : I detest the strife of tongues : all noises discompose me.

BARROW. We will then lay aside the supposition. The haven of philosophy itself is not free at all seasons from its gusts and swells. Let me admonish you to confide your secrets to few : I mean the secrets of science. In every great mind there are some : every deep inquirer hath discovered more than he thought it prudent to avow, as almost every shallow one throws out more than he hath well discovered. Among our learned friends we may be fully and unreservedly philosophical : in the company of others we must remember, first and chiefly, that discretion is a part of philosophy ; and we must let out only some glimpses of the remainder.

NEWTON. Surely no harm can befall us from following a chain of demonstrations in geometry, or any branch of the mathematics.

BARROW. Let us hope there may be none : nevertheless we can not but recollect how lately Galileo was persecuted and imprisoned for his discoveries.

NEWTON. He lived under a popish government.

BARROW. My friend ! my friend ! all the most eminently scientific, all the most eminently brave and daring in the exercise of their intellects, live, and have ever lived, under a popish government. There are popes in all creeds, in all countries, in all ages. Political power is jealous of intellectual ; often lest it expose and mar its plans and projects, and oftener lest it attract an equal share of celebrity and distinction. Whenever the literary man is protected by the political, the incitement to it is the pride of patronage, not the advancement of letters, nor the honour they confer on the cultivator or the country.

NEWTON. That is rational in England which beyond the Alps is monstrous. By God's blessing, I firmly believe in the *Holy Scriptures ;* yet, under your discretion and guidance, I would be informed if [1] the sun's rays in Syria could ever be above the horizon for twenty-four hours, without a material alteration, without an utter derangement, of our whole mundane system.*

BARROW. Reserve that question for a future time and a wiser teacher. At present I would only remark to you, that our mundane system *has* been materially altered ; and that its alterations may have been attributed to other causes than the true, and laid down by different nations as having taken place at different epochs and on different occasions, sometimes to gratify their pride, sometimes to conceal their ignorance.

NEWTON. I am not quite satisfied.

BARROW. Those who are quite satisfied, sit still and do nothing : those who are not quite satisfied, are the sole benefactors of the world.

NEWTON. And are driven out of it for their pains.

BARROW. Men seldom have loved their teachers.

NEWTON. How happens it then that you are loved so generally ? for who is there, capable of instruction, that you have not taught ? Never, since I have been at the University, have I heard of anyone being your enemy who was not a Calvinist ; a sect wherein good-humoured and gracefully-minded men are scanty.

BARROW. Do not attribute the failing to the sect, which hath many strong texts of Scripture for its support ; but rather think that the

---

[1] 1st ed. reads : " if the sun could stand stiller at one time than at another ; and if his rays in Syria," etc.

* Newton [1] was timid and reserved in expressing his opinions, and was more orthodox (in the Anglican sense of orthodoxy) early in life than later. What he thought at last is not clear ; and perhaps it was well for him that it was no clearer. Under his eyes, in the reign of William III., a youth of eighteen was punished with death for expressing such opinions as our philosopher hinted to Le Clerc. To remove and consume the gallows on which such men are liable to suffer, is among the principal aims and intents of these writings.—W. S. L.

---

[1] This note was added in 2nd ed., and refers to the case of Thomas Aikenhead, who was executed in Scotland in 1696 for denying the doctrine of the Trinity. Newton, in a letter which Locke passed on to Le Clerc, expressed doubt of the authenticity of 1 St. John v. 7. Le Clerc, not knowing Newton to be the author of the letter, intended publishing a French translation of it, and Newton, through Locke, restrained him. Later, upon learning that Newton was its writer, he published the letter with slight alterations.

doctrines are such as are most consentaneous to the malignant and morose. There are acrid plants that attract as many insects as the sweeter, but insects of another kind. All substances have their commodities, all opinions their partisans. I have been happy in my pupils ; but in none of them have I observed such a spirit of investigation as in you. Keep it, however, within the precincts of experimental and sure philosophy, which are spacious enough for the excursions of the most vigorous mind, and varied enough for the most inconstant and flighty. Never hate, never dislike men, for difference of religion. Some receive baleful impressions in it more easily than others, as they do diseases. We do not hate a child for catching the small-pox, but pity its sores and blemishes. Let the Calvinist hate us : he represents his God as a hater, he represents him as capricious. I wish he would love us, even from caprice ; but he seems to consider this part of the divine nature as a weakness.

Come ; unroll your paper ; let me hear what you have to say on Bacon's *Essays ;* a volume I place in the hand of those only who appear to me destined to be great.

NEWTON. He says in his Preface,

" I do now publish my Essays, which of all my *other* works have been most current."

How can the very thing of which you are speaking be *another ?*

BARROW. This is a chasm in logic, into which many have fallen.

NEWTON. I had scarcely begun the first Essay, when an elderly gentlemen of another college came into the room, took up the book, and read aloud,

" This same truth is a naked and open daylight, that doth not show the masks, and mummeries, and triumphs of the world half so stately and daintily as candle-lights. Truth may, perhaps, come to the price of a pearl, that showeth best by day, but it will not rise to the price of a diamond or carbuncle, that showeth best in varied lights. A mixture of a lie doth ever add pleasure. Doth any man doubt that, if there were taken out of men's minds vain opinions, flattering hopes, false valuations, imaginations as one would, and the like, but it would leave the minds of a number of men poor shrunken things, full of melancholy and indisposition, *and unpleasing to themselves ?* "

" One might well imagine," said he, " unpleasing to themselves, *if* full of melancholy and indisposition. But how much of truth and wisdom is compressed in these few sentences ! Do not you wonder that a man capable of all this, should likewise be capable of such foolery as the following ?

" ' First he breathed light upon the face of the matter, or chaos ; then he breathed light into the face of man ; and still he *breatheth and inspireth* light into the face of his chosen.' "

I looked with wonder at him, knowing his seriousness and gravity, his habits and powers of ratiocination, and his blameless life. But perhaps I owe to his question the intensity and sedulity with which I have examined every page of Bacon. He called the words I have quoted, dull and colourless bombast ; he declared them idle in allusion, and false, and impious. I was appalled. He added, " I do not know, Mr. Newton, whether you have brothers ; if you have, what would you think of your father, when he gave a cherry to one, a whipping to a second, and burnt the fingers of a third against the bars of his kitchen grate ; and vouchsafed no better reason for it, than that he had resolved to do so the very night he begot them ? Election [1] in such a case is partiality ; partiality is injustice. Is God unjust ? "

I could have answered him, by God's help, if he had given me time ; but he went on, and said, " Bacon had much sagacity, but no sincerity ; much force, but no firmness. It is painful to discover in him the reviler of Raleigh, the last relic of heroism in the dastardly court of James : it is horrible to hear him, upon another occasion, the apologist of a patron's disgrace and death : the patron's whose friendly hand had raised him to the first steps of the highest station."

" Sir," answered I, " his political conduct is not the question before us."

" It may, however," said he, " enlighten us in regard to his candour, and induce us to ask ourselves whether, in matters of religion, he delivered his thoughts exactly, and whether he may not have conformed his expression of them to the opinions of his master."

BARROW. I hope you dropped the discussion after this.

NEWTON. No ; I cried resolutely, " Sir, when I am better prepared for it, I may have something to say with you on your irreverent expressions."

BARROW. Mr. Newton, do not be ruffled. Bacon spoke figur-

---

[1] 1st ed. reads : " Election is," etc.

atively; so did Moses, to whom the allusion was made. Let the matter rest, my dear friend.

NEWTON. I told him plainly he was unfair : he was no friend to Bacon. He smiled at me and continued, " My good Newton, I am as ready to be told when I am unfair as you are to have your watch set right when it goes amiss. You say I am no friend to Bacon ; and in truth, after the experience he left us in the Earl of Essex, he is not precisely the man to place one's friendship on. Yet surely no folly is greater than hatred of those we never saw, and from whom we can have received no injury. Often do I wonder when I hear violent declamations against theories and opinions ; which declamations I think are as ill-directed as they would be against currents of air or water-courses. We may keep out of their way if we will. I estimate the genius of Bacon as highly as perhaps you do, and in this Essay I find a single sentence which I would rather have written than all the volumes of all the Greek philosophers : let me read it. ' Certainly, it is heaven upon earth to have a man's mind move in charity, rest in providence, and turn upon the poles of truth.' "

BARROW. Magnificent as Shakespeare.

NEWTON. He who wrote tragedies ?

BARROW. The same : I have lately been reading them.

NEWTON. Sir, should you have marked the truths he demonstrated, if any, I shall think it no loss of time to run over them, at my leisure. I have now a question to ask you on the third of these Essays. We find in it that " Quarrels and divisions about religion were evils unknown to the heathen : the reason was, because the religion of the heathen consisted rather in rites and ceremonies than in any constant belief." This is no truer of the old Paganism than of the later in the same country, which however burns men alive for slight divergencies.

" You may imagine," says Bacon, " what kind of faith theirs was, when the chief doctors and fathers of their church were the poets."

I read this loudly and triumphantly to my friend, who paused and smiled, and then asked me complacently, whether it were better to imprison, burn, and torture, or to send away the audience in good humour and good fellowship ; and whether I should prefer the conversation and conviction of Doctor Bonner and Doctor Gardiner to those of Doctor Tibullus and Doctor Ovid. I thought the question too flippant for an answer, which indeed was not quite at hand. He proceeded : " ' God has this attribute, that he is a jealous God, and therefore his worship and religion will endure no mixture.' His jealousy must be touched to the quick," said my friend ; " for every century there comes forth some new pretender, with his sect behind him in the dark passages : and his spouse was hardly at her own door after the nuptials, ere she cried out and shrieked against the filthiness of an intruder."

I was lifting up my eyes and preparing an ejaculation, when he interrupted me, and continued. " ' It is certain that heresies and schisms are *of all others* the greatest scandals ; yea, more than corruption of manners : for, as in the natural body a wound, or solution of continuity, is worse than a corrupt humour———' "

Here he laid down the volume, and said, " I will ask the professor of surgery whether a cut in the finger is worse than a scrofula : I will then go to the professor of divinity, and ask him, whether the best Christian in Cambridge ought to be hanged to-morrow morning."

I stared at him : whereupon he declared that every church on earth is heretical and schismatical, if the word of Christ is the foundation of the true ; and that the fellow who was hanged last week for *corruption of manners* had, according to the decision of Bacon, more Christianity in him than all the heads of colleges. " When he would follow theologians," said my friend, " he falls into gross absurdities : he corrects himself, or only trips harmlessly, when he walks alone."

I myself was obliged to agree with my disputant, in censuring an exception. Speaking of *sanguinary persecutions to force consciences*, the author blames them, " except it be in cases of *overt scandal*, *blasphemy*, &c." Now who shall decide what is *overt scandal*, or what is *blasphemy ?* That which is prodigiously so in one age and one country, is not at all in another. Such exceptions are the most pernicious things a great author can sanction.

BARROW. I side with you. We come now, I perceive, to the Essay *On Revenge*.

NEWTON. " There is no man doth a wrong for the wrong's sake, but thereby to purchase himself profit, or pleasure, or honour, *or the like :* therefore why should I be angry with a man for loving himself better than me ? "

If this be an excuse, why send a rogue to prison ? All the crimes that men commit, are committed because they love themselves better

122

than others ; and it is the direction and extent of this loving, to the detriment of others, that constitutes the magnitude of the crime. Cruelty is the highest pleasure to the cruel man : it is his love. Murder may ensue : and shall we not be *angry with him* for loving himself better than the murdered ?

On Simulation and Dissimulation, we are told, " The best composition and temperature is, to have a power to feign, if there be no remedy."

BARROW. In other words, to lie whenever we find it convenient. The two last decisions you have reported from him, as little become the chancellor as the philosopher ; as little the philosopher as the citizen. Why will you not read on ?

NEWTON. I am afraid to mention the remark of my visitor on a sentence in the Essay *Upon Goodness.*

BARROW. Fear not : what is it ?

NEWTON. " The desire of knowledge in excess caused man to fall."

BARROW. This is a sin the most rarely of all committed in our days. If the earth is to be destroyed by fire, the bottom of a rush-chair will serve to consume all who are guilty of it ; and what falls from heaven may fall upon other offenders.

NEWTON. " Do you believe," said my friend, " that God punished men for wishing to be wiser ? for wishing to follow him and to learn his pleasure ? for wishing that acquisition by which beneficence and charity may be the most luminously and extensively displayed ? No, Newton, no. The Jews, who invented this story, were envious of the scientific, for they were ignorant of the sciences. Astronomy, among the rest, was odious to them : and hence the fables stuck against the Tower of Babel, the observatory of a better and a wiser people, their enemy, their conqueror. Take care, or you may be hanged for shooting at the stars. If these fictions are believed and acted on, you must conceal your telescope and burn your observations."

On my representing to him the effects of Divine Justice, in casting down to earth the monument of human pride, he said, " The Observatory of Babylon was constructed of unbaked bricks, and upon an alluvial soil. Look at the Tower of Pisa : look at every tower and steeple in that city : you will find that they all lean, and all in one direction, that is, toward the river. Some have fallen ; many will fall. God would not have been so angry with the Tower of Babel, if it had been built of Portland stone a few weeks' journey to the westward, and you had been as importunate as the Babylonians were, in their attempts at paying him a visit."

He expressed his wonder that Bacon, in the reign of James, should have written, " A king is the servant of his people, *or else he were without a calling.*" In other words, whenever he ceases to be the *servant of the people*, he forfeits his right to the throne.

BARROW. Truth sometimes comes unaware upon Caution, and sometimes speaks in public as unconsciously as in a dream.

NEWTON. Sir, although you desired me rather to investigate and note the imperfections of my author, than what is excellent in him, as you would rather the opaquer parts of the sun, than what is manifest of his glory to the lowest and most insensible, yet, from the study of your writings, and from the traces of your hand in others, I am sometimes led to notice the beauties of his style. It requires the greatest strength to support such a weight of richness as we sometimes find in him. The florid grows vapid where the room is not capacious, and where perpetual freshness of thought does not animate and sustain it. Unhappily, it seems to have been taken up mostly by such writers as have least invention.

BARROW. Read to me the sentence or the paragraph that pleases you.

NEWTON. 'Tis *On Envy.*

" Lastly, near kinsfolks and fellows in office, and those that have been bred together, are more apt to envy their equals when they are raised ; for it doth upbraid unto them their own fortunes, and pointeth at them, and cometh oftener into their remembrance, and incurreth likewise more into the note of others ; and envy ever redoubleth from speech and fame."

BARROW. Very excellent. I wish, before he cast his invectives against Raleigh, he had reflected more on a doctrine in the next page. " Those that have joined with their honour great travels, cares, or perils, are less subject to envy : for men think that they earn their honours hardly, and pity them sometimes : and pity ever healeth envy." I am afraid it will be found on examination, that Bacon in his morality was too like Seneca ; not indeed wallowing in wealth and vice and crying out against them, but hard-hearted and hypocritical ; and I know not with what countenance he could have said, " By indignities men come to dignities."

NEWTON. I have remarked with most satisfaction those sentences in which he appears to have forgotten both the age and station wherein he lived, and to have equally overlooked the base and summit of our ruder institutions. " Power to do good," says he, as Euripides or Phocion might have said, and Pericles might have acted on it, " is the true and lawful end of aspiring ; for good thoughts (though God accept them) yet towards men are little better than good dreams, except they be put in act ; and that can not be without power and place, as the vantage and commanding ground."

And again, " Reduce things to the first institution, and observe wherein and how they have degenerated ! But yet ask counsel of both times ; *of the ancienter time what is best,* and of the latter time what is fittest."

BARROW. He spoke unadvisedly : for, true as these sentences are, they would lead toward republicanism, if men minded them. Of this however there is as little danger as that the servants of kings should follow the advice he gives afterward.

" Embrace and invite helps and advices, touching the execution of thy place ; and do not drive away such as bring thee information, as meddlers, but accept of them in good part."

NEWTON. *On Seditions,* he says the matter is of " two kinds ; much poverty and much discontentment." It appears to me that here is only one kind : for much discontentment may spring, and usually does, from much poverty.

BARROW. Certainly. He should not have placed cause and effect as two causes. You must however have remarked his wonderful sagacity in this brief essay, which I hesitate not to declare the finest piece of workmanship that ever was composed on any part of government. Take Aristoteles and Machiavelli, and compare the best sections of their works to this, and then you will be able, in some degree, to calculate the superiority of genius in Bacon.

NEWTON. I have not analysed the political works of Aristoteles ; but I find in Machiavelli many common thoughts, among many ingenious, many just,[1] many questionable, and many false ones.

BARROW. What are you turning over ? Do not let me lose anything you have remarked.

[1] 1st ed. reads : " just, and more perverse ones. Let the following serve for instances : and I hasten the sooner to the exposition of them, that I may raise no objection against any part of a treatise which you have commended so unexceptionally. BARROW. Nay, be candid with me and bring forward your objection. NEWTON. ' Money,' says," etc.

NEWTON. " Money," says my lord, " is like muck ; not good except it be spread." I am afraid this truth would subvert, in the mind of a reflecting man, all that has been urged by the learned author on the advantages of nobility, and even of royalty : for which reason I dare not examine it : only let me, sir, doubt before you, whether " this is to be done by suppressing, or at the least keeping a strait hand upon, the devouring trades of usury, engrossing, great pasturages, *and the like*."

BARROW. I wish he never had used, which he often does, those silly words, *and the like*.

NEWTON. *Great pasturages* are not *trades ;* and they must operate in a way directly opposite to the one designated.

BARROW. I know not whether a manifest fault in reasoning be not sometimes more acceptable than stale and worm-eaten and weightless truths. Heaps of these are to be found in almost every modern writer : Bacon has fewer of them than any.

Nicholas Machiavelli is usually mentioned as the deepest and acutest of the Italians : a people whose grave manner often makes one imagine there is more to be found in them than they possess. Take down that volume : read the examples I have transcribed at the end.

" The loss of every devotion and every religion draws after it infinite inconveniences and infinite disorders."

Inconveniences and disorders would follow, sure enough : the losses, being negatives, *draw* nothing.

" In a well-constituted government, war, peace, and amity, should be deliberated on, not for the gratification of a few, but for the common good.

" That war is just which is necessary.

" It is a cruel, inhuman, and impious thing, even in war, *stuprare le donne, viziare le vergini*, &c.

" Fraud is detestable in everything."

These most obvious truths come forward as if he had now dis-covered them for the first time. He tells us also that " A prince ought to take care that the people are not without food." He says with equal gravity that " Fraud is detestable in everything " : and that " A minister ought to be averse from public rapine, and should augment the public weal."

It would be an easy matter to fill many pages with flat and unprofitable sentences. I had only this blank one for it ; and there are many yet, the places of which are marked, with only the first words. Do not lose your time in looking for them : we must not judge of him from these defects.

NEWTON. Whenever I have heard him praised, it was for vigour of thought.

BARROW. He is strongest where he is most perverse. There are men who never show their muscles but when they have the cramp.

NEWTON. Consistency and firmness are not the characteristics of the Florentines, nor ever were. Machiavelli wished at one time to satisfy the man of probity, at another to conciliate the rogue and robber ; at one time to stand on the alert for the return of liberty, at another to sit in the portico of the palace, and trim the new livery of nascent princes. If we consider him as a writer, he was the acutest that had appeared since the revival of letters. None had reasoned so profoundly on the political interests of society, or had written so clearly or so boldly.[1]

BARROW. Nevertheless, the paper of a boy's cracker, when he has let it off, would be ill-used by writing such stuff upon it as that which you have been reading. The great merit of Machiavelli, in style, is the avoiding of superlatives. We can with difficulty find an Italian prose-writer who is not weak and inflated by the continual use of them, to give him pomp and energy, as he imagines.

NEWTON. Davila too is an exception.

BARROW. The little elegance there is among the Italians, is in their historians and poets : the preachers, the theologians, the ethic writers, the critics, are contemptible in the last degree. Well ; we will now leave the *Issimi* nation, and turn homeward.

You will find that Bacon, like all men conscious of their strength, never strains or oversteps.[2] While the Italians are the same in the church and in the market-place, while the preacher and policinello are speaking in the same key and employing almost the same language, while a man's God and his rotten tooth are treated in the same manner, we find at home convenience and proportion. Yet

---

[1] The following footnote appears in 1st ed. :—

" Those who have written since are worse stil. The glory of Italy, in recent times, is Gravina : next to him is Filangieri. This country has produced no periodical work above the lowest in England, France, Germany, and Holland."

[2] 1st ed. reads : " oversteps, and is frugal in the use of superlatives ; while the Italians," etc.

the French have taken more pains than we have done to give their language an edge and polish ; and, although we have minds in England more massy and more elevated than theirs, they may claim a nearer affinity to the greater of the ancients.

I have been the less unwilling to make this digression, as we are now come nigh the place where we must be slow and circumspect. The subject awes and confounds me. Human reason is a frail guide in our disquisitions on royalty, which requires in us some virtue like unto faith. We can not see into it clearly with the eyes of the flesh or of philosophy, but must humble and abase ourselves to be worthy of feeling what it is. For want whereof, many high and proud spirits have been turned aside from it, by the right hand of God, who would not lead them into its lights and enjoyments, because they came as questioners not as seekers, would have walked when they should have stood, and would have stood when they should have knelt.

NEWTON. Sir, I do not know whether you will condescend to listen with patience to the thoughts excited in me by Bacon's observations on the character of a king.

BARROW. He shocked me by what he said before on the fragility of his title : God forbid that common men should talk like the Lord High Chancellor !

NEWTON. I was shocked in a contrary direction, and, as it were, by a repercussion, at hearing him call a king a *mortal God on earth :* and I do not find anywhere in the Scriptures, that " the living God told him he should die, like a man, lest he should be proud, and flatter himself that God had, with his name, imparted unto him his nature also."

Surely, sir, God would repent as heartily of having made a king, as we know he repented of having made a man, if it were possible his king should have turned out so silly and irrational a creature. However vain and foolish, he must find about him, every day, such natural wants and desires as could not appertain to a God. I made the same remark to my visitor, who said calmly, " Bacon in the next sentence hath a saving grace ; and speaketh as wisely and pointedly as ever he did. He says, ' Of all kind of men, God is the least beholden to them ; for he doth most for them, and they do ordinarily least for him.' A sentence not very favourable to their admission as pastors of the people, and somewhat strong against them as visible heads of the Church. But, Mr. Newton, you will detect at once a

128

deficiency of logic in the words, ' That king that holds not religion the best reason of state, is void of all piety and justice, the supporters of a king.' Supposing a king soundly minded and well educated—a broad supposition, and not easily entering our preliminaries—may not he be just, be pious, be religious, without holding his religion as the best reason of state, or the best guide in it ? Must he be void of *all* piety, and *all* justice, who sometimes thinks other reasons of state more applicable to his purposes than religion ? Psalms and sack-cloth are admirable things ; but these, the last expedients of the most contrite religion, will not always keep an enemy from burning your towns and violating your women, when a few pieces of cannon, and loftiness of spirit instead of humiliation, will do it."

He went on, and asserted that the king is not the sole fountain of honour, as he is called in the Essay, and cannot be more fairly entitled so, than the doctors in Convocation. He remarked that the king had not made him master of arts ; which dignity, he said, requires more merit than the peerage ; whereupon he named several in that order, of whose learning or virtues I never heard mention, and even of whose titles I thought I never had, until he assured me I must, and expressed his wonder that I had forgotten them. When he came to the eighth section, ' he is the life of the law,' " the law leads a notoriously bad life," said he, " and therefore I would exempt his Majesty from the imputation : and indeed if ' he animateth the dead letter, making it active toward all his subjects,' the parliament and other magistratures are useless. In the ninth paragraph he makes some accurate observations, but ends weakly. ' He that changeth the fundamental laws of a kingdom, thinketh there is no good title to a crown but by conquest.' What ! if he changes them from the despotic to the liberal ? if, knowing the first possession to have been obtained by conquest, he convokes the different orders of his people, and requests their assent to the statutes he presents ? Nothing can be more pedantic than the whole of the sixteenth section."

BARROW. But there are sound truths in it, and advice too good to be taken every day.

NEWTON. *On Nobility.*

" A great and potent nobility . . . putteth life and spirit into the people, *but presseth their fortune.*"

" The man must have turned fool," said my friend, " to write thus. Are life and spirit put into people by the same means as their fortune is depressed ? "

On Atheism.

" ' The fool hath said in his heart there is no God.' It is not said, ' the fool hath *thought* in his heart.' "

No, nor is it necessary ; for, to say *in his heart*, is to think *within himself*, to be *intimately convinced.*

" It appeareth in nothing more, that atheism is rather in the lip than in the heart of man, than by this, that atheists will ever be talking of that their opinion, as if they fainted in it within themselves, and would be glad to be strengthened by the consent of others : nay more, you shall have atheists strive to get disciples, as it fareth with other sects."

So great is my horror at atheists, that I would neither reason *with* them nor about them ; but surely they are as liable to conceit and vanity as other men are, and as proud of leading us captive to their opinions. I could wish the noble author had abstained from quoting Saint Bernard, to prove the priesthood to have been, even in those days, more immoral than the laity ; and I am shocked-at hearing that " *learned times*," especially with peace and prosperity, tend toward atheism. Better blind ignorance, better war and pestilence and famine——

BARROW. Gently, gently ! God may forgive his creature for not knowing him when he meets him ; but less easily for fighting against him, after talking to him and supping with him ; less easily for breaking his image, set up by him at every door—and such is man ; less easily for a series of fratricides—and such is war.

NEWTON. I am wrong : and here again let me repeat the strange paradox of my visitor, rather than hazard another fault. In the words about *Superstition* he agreed that Bacon spoke wisely :

" It were better to have no opinion of God at all, than such an opinion as is unworthy of him ; for the one is unbelief, the other is contumely."

" And here," remarked my visitor, " it is impossible not to look back with wonder on the errors of some among the wisest men, following the drift of a distorted education, or resting on the suggestions of a splenetic disposition. I am no poet, and therefore am ill qualified to judge the merits of the late Mr. Milton in that capacity ;

BARROW AND NEWTON

yet, being of a serious and somewhat of a religious turn, I was shocked greatly more at his deity than at his devil. I know not what interest he could have in making Satan so august a creature, and so ready to share the dangers and sorrows of the angels he had seduced. I know not, on the other hand, what could have urged him to make the better ones so dastardly, that, even at the voice of their Creator, not one among them offered his service to rescue from eternal perdition the last and weakest of intellectual beings. Even his own Son sate silent, and undertook the mission but slowly, although the trouble was momentary if compared with his everlasting duration, and the pain small if compared with his anterior and future bliss. Far be it from me," cried he——

BARROW. Did he cry so ? then I doubt whatever he said ; for those are precisely the words that all your sanctified rogues begin their lies with. Well, let us hear however what he asserted.

NEWTON. " Far be it from me, Mr. Newton, to lessen the merits of our Divine Redeemer. I, on the contrary, am indignant that poets and theologians should frequently lean toward it."

BARROW. Did he look at all indignant ?

NEWTON. He looked quite calm.

BARROW. Ha ! I thought so. I doubt your friend's sincerity.

NEWTON. He is a very sincere man.

BARROW. So much the worse.

NEWTON. How ?

BARROW. We will discourse another time upon this. I meant only —what we may easily elucidate when we meet again. At present we have three-fourths of the volume to get through.

NEWTON. " Atheism leaves a man to sense, to philosophy, to natural piety, to laws, to reputation : all which may be guides to an outward moral virtue, though religion were not : but superstition dismounts all these, and erecteth an *absolute monarchy* in the minds of men : therefore atheism did never perturb states."

Again, " We see the times inclined to atheism . . . as the times of Augustus Cæsar—were civil times : but superstition hath been the confusion of many states."

I wish the noble author had kept to himself the preference he gives atheism over superstition : for, if it be just, as it seems to be, it follows that we should be more courteous and kind toward an atheist, than toward a loose catholic or rigid sectary.

131

IMAGINARY CONVERSATIONS : ENGLISH

BARROW. I see no reason why we should not be courteous and kind toward men of all persuasions, provided we are certain that, neither by their own inclination nor by the instigation of another, they would burn us alive to save our souls, or invade our conscience for the pleasure of carrying it with them at their girdles.

Atheism would make men have too little to do with others : superstition makes them wish to have too much. Atheism would make some fools : superstition makes many madmen. Atheism would oftener be in good humour than superstition is out of bad. I could bring many more and many stronger arguments in support of Bacon : and the danger would be little in adducing them : for the current runs violently in a contrary direction, and will have covered everything with slime and sand before atheism can have her turn against it.

NEWTON. If *atheism did never perturb states*,[1] as Bacon asserts, then nothing is more unjust than to punish it by the arm of the civil power. It was impolitic in him to remind the world that it was peaceful and happy for sixty years together, while those who ruled it were atheists ; when we must acknowledge that it never has been happy or peaceful for so many days, at a time, under the wisest and most powerful (as they call the present one) of the *Most Christian* kings. For, if the observation and the fact be true, and if it also be true that the most rational aim of man is happiness, then must it follow that his most rational wish, and, being his most rational, therefore his most innocent and laudable, is the return of such times.

BARROW. We will go forward to the Essay *On Empire*.

NEWTON. I do not think the writer is correct in saying that " kings want matter of desire." Wherever there is vacuity of mind, there must either be flaccidity or craving ; and this vacuity must necessarily be found in the greater part of princes, from the defects of their education, from the fear of offending them in its progress by interrogations and admonitions, from the habit of rendering all things valueless by the facility with which they are obtained, and transitory by the negligence with which they are received and holden.

---

[1] The following footnote appears in 1st ed. :—

" I was arguing at Pisa with Vacca Berlinghieri, an atheist, and the most acute and intelligent man in Italy, on the mischief of atheism to public morals, when hearing under the window the chains of the galley-slaves employed in sweeping the streets, he called to me to look out, and said, ' Of all these fellows there is not one atheist : they are all good catholics, who would have cut my throat for not fasting on Fridays.' "

132

BARROW AND NEWTON

" Princes many times make themselves desires, and set their hearts upon toys ; sometimes upon a building ; sometimes upon erecting of an order ; sometimes upon obtaining excellency in some art or feat of the hand."

On which my visitor said, " The latter desire is the least common among them. Whenever it does occur, it arises from idleness, and from the habitude of doing what they ought not. For, commendable as such exercises are, in those who have no better and higher to employ their time in, they are unbecoming and injurious in kings ; all whose hours, after needful recreation and the pleasures which all men share alike, should be occupied in taking heed that those under them perform their duties."

BARROW. Bacon lived in an age when the wisest men were chosen, from every rank and condition, for the administration of affairs. Wonderful is it, that one mind on this subject should have per vaded all the princes in Europe, not excepting the Turk, and that we can not point out a prime minister of any nation, at that period, deficient in sagacity or energy.* Yet that even the greatest, so much greater than any we have had since among us, did not come up to the standard he had fixed, is evident enough.

" The wisdom," says he, " of *all these latter times* in princes' affairs, is rather fine deliveries, and *shifting of dangers and mischiefs* when they are near, than solid and grounded courses to keep them aloof : but this is but to try masteries with fortune. And let men beware how they neglect and suffer matter of trouble to be prepared ; for no man can forbid the spark, nor tell whence it may come."

NEWTON. Sir, it was on this passage that my friend exclaimed, " The true philosopher is the only true prophet. From the death of this, the brightest in both capacities, a few years opened the entire scroll of his awful predictions. Yet age after age will the same truths be disregarded, even though men of a voice as deep, and a heart less hollow, should repeat them. Base men must raise new

* There is a remark in a preceding Essay which could not be noticed in the text.
" As for the acquaintance which is to be sought in travel, that which is most of all profitable, is acquaintance with the *secretaries and employed men* of embassadors ; for so, in travelling in one country, he shall suck the experience of many."
This, whatever it may appear to us, was not ludicrous nor sarcastic when Bacon wrote it, but might be applied as well to the embassadors and secretaries of England as of other states.—W. S. L.

families, though the venerable edifice of our constitution be taken down for the abutments ; and broken fortunes must be soldered in the flames of war blown up for the occasion."

On this subject he himself is too lax and easy. Among the reasons for legitimate war, he reckons the *embracing of trade*. He seems unwilling to speak plainly, yet he means to signify that we may declare war against a nation for her prosperity : a prosperity raised by her industry, by the honesty of her dealings, and by excelling us in the quality of her commodity, in the exactness of workmanship, in punctuality, and in credit.

BARROW. Hell itself, with all its jealousy and malignity and falsehood, could not utter a sentence more pernicious to the interests and improvement of mankind. It is the duty of every state, to provide and watch that not only no other in its vicinity, but that no other with which it has dealings, immediate or remoter, do lose an inch of territory or a farthing of wealth by aggression. Princes fear at their next door rather the example of good than of bad. Correct your own ill habits, and you need not dread your rival's. Let him have them, and wear them every day, if indeed a christian may propose it, and they will unfit him for competition with you.

NEWTON. I now come to the words, *On Counsel*. "The doctrine of Italy, and practice of France, in some kings' times, hath introduced *cabinet councils ;* a remedy worse than the disease."

Cabinet—council! It does indeed seem a strange apposition. One would sooner have expected *cabinet cards* and *counters, cabinet miniature pictures—*or what not !

BARROW. Isaac ! if you had conversed, as I have, with some of those persons who constitute such councils, you would think the word *cabinet* quite as applicable to them, as to cards or counters, or miniature pictures, or essences, or pots of pomatum.

NEWTON. How then, in the name of wonder, are the great matters of government carried on ?

BARROW. Great dinners are put upon the table, not by the entertainer but by the waiters. There are usually some dextrous hands accustomed to the business. The same weights are moved by the same ropes and pulleys. There is no vast address required in hooking them, and no mighty strength in the hawling.

NEWTON. I have taken but few notes of some admirable things in my way to the Essay *On Cunning*.

134

BARROW AND NEWTON

BARROW. I may remind you hereafter of some omissions in other places.

NEWTON. I find Bacon no despiser of books in men of business, as people mostly are.

BARROW. Because they know little of them, and fancy they could manage the whole world by their genius. This is the commonest of delusions in the shallows of society. Well doth Bacon say, " There be that can pack the cards and yet can not play well ; so there are some that are good in canvasses and factions that are otherwise weak men."

Fortunate the country that is not the dupe of these intruders and bustlers, who often rise to the highest posts by their readiness to lend an arm at every stepping-stone in the dirt, and are found as convenient in their way as the candle-snuffers in gaming-houses, who have usually their *rouleau* at the service of the half-ruined.

NEWTON. I am sorry to find my Lord High Chancellor wearing as little the face of an honest man as doth one of these.

BARROW. How so ?

NEWTON. He says, " If a man would cross a business, that he doubts some other would handsomely and effectually move, let him pretend to wish it well, and move it himself in such sort as may foil it."

What must I think of such counsel ?

BARROW. Bacon, as I observed before, often forgets his character. Sometimes he speaks the language of truth and honesty, with more freedom than a better man could do safely : again, he teaches a lesson of baseness and roguery to the public, such as he could intend only for the private ear of some young statesman, before his rehearsal on the stage of politics. The words from the prompter's book have crept into the text, and injure the piece. Bacon might not have liked to cancel the directions he had given so much to his mind : instead of which, he draws himself up and cries austerely, " But these small wares and petty points of cunning are infinite, and it were a good deed to make a list of them : for nothing doth more hurt in a state than that cunning men pass for wise."

NEWTON. He has other things about wisdom in another place : *On the wisdom for a man's self*.

BARROW. I must repeat one noble sentence ; for I fear, if you

135

begin to read it, I may interrupt you, not being master of my mind when his comes over it. " Divide with reason between self-love and society ; and be so true to thyself as thou be not false to others, especially to thy king and country. It is a poor centre of a man's actions, himself : it is right earth ; for that only stands fast upon his own centre ; whereas all things that have affinity with the heavens, move upon the centre of another, which they benefit."

What an imagination is Bacon's ! what splendid and ardent language ! In what prose-writer of our country, or of Rome, or of Greece, is there anything equal or similar to it ?

NEWTON. *On Innovations* I find the sentence which I have heard oftener quoted than any in the volume : " Time is the greatest innovator."

We take the axiom up without examination ; it is doubtful and inconsiderate. Does it mean much time or little time ? By a *great* innovator we must either signify an innovator in great matters, or in many at once, or nearly at once. Now Time is slow in innovation of any kind ; and all great innovations are violences, as it were, done to Time, crowding into a small space what would in ordinary cases occupy a larger. Time, without other agents, would innovate little : for the portions of Time are all the same, and being so, their forces must be the same likewise.

BARROW. That satisfies me.

NEWTON. Truth and falsehood are the two great innovators, always at work, and sometimes the one uppermost and sometimes the other.

BARROW. Let us engage ourselves in the service of Truth, where the service is not perilous ; and let us win Time to help us, for without him few can not stand against many.

NEWTON. *On Friendship* there are some things which sit loose upon the subject. The *utility* of it seems to be principally in the view of Bacon. Some positions are questionable.

" Certain it is that whosoever hath his mind fraught with many thoughts, his wits and understanding do clarify and break up in the communicating and discoursing with another ; he tosseth his thoughts more easily ; he marshalleth them more orderly ; he seeth how they look when they are turned into words ; finally, he waxeth wiser than himself, and that more by an hour's discourse than by a day's meditation."

BARROW AND NEWTON

This I conceive is applicable to one frame of mind, but not to another of equal capacity and elasticity. I admire the ingenuity of the thought, and the wording of it; nevertheless I doubt whether it suits not better the mind of an acute lawyer than of a contemplative philosopher. Never have I met with anyone whose thoughts are *marshalled more orderly* in conversation than in composition: nor am I acquainted in the University with any gentleman of fluent speech, whose ideas are not frequently left dry upon the bank. Cicero and Demosthenes were laborious in composition, and their replies were, I doubt not, as much studied as their addresses. For it was a part of the orator to foresee the points of attack to which his oration was exposed, and to prepare the materials, and the arrangement of them, for defending it.

"It was well said by Themistocles to the king of Persia, that speech was like cloth of *Arras*," &c.

Themistocles might as well have spoken of velvet of Genoa and satin of Lyons.

On Expense there is much said quite worthy of Bacon's experience and prudence: but he lays down one rule which I think I can demonstrate to be injurious in its tendency.

"If a man will keep but of even hand, his ordinary expenses ought to be but to the half of his receipts; and if he think to wax rich, but to the third part."

Should all private gentlemen, and others who are not gentlemen, but whose income is of the same value, spend only the third part of it, the nation would be more nearly ruined within the century, than it would be if every one of them mortgaged his property to half its amount.

A wiser saying comes soon afterward, where he speaks *On the true greatness of kingdoms and estates.*

"No people overcharged with tribute is fit for empire."

How happy, my dear sir, is our condition, in having been ever both generous and thrifty, ready at all times to succour the oppressed, and condescending on this holy occasion to ask the countenance of none! how happy, to have marched straight forward in the line of duty with no policy to thwart, no penury to enfeeble, and no debt to burthen us! Although our nobility is less magnificent than in the reign of the Tudors, I do verily believe it is as free and independent; and its hospitality so conducive (as Bacon says)

137

to martial greatness, is the same as ever, although the quality of the guests be somewhat changed.

BARROW. Isaac ! are you serious ?

NEWTON. Dear sir, the subject animates me.

BARROW. What sparkles is hardly more transparent than what is turbid. Your animation, my friend, perplexed me. I perceive you are vehemently moved by the glory of our country.

NEWTON. As we derive a great advantage from the nature of our nobility, so do we derive an equal one from the dispositions and occupations of the people. How unfortunate would it be for us, if we had artisans cooped up like tame pigeons in unwholesome lofts, bending over the loom by tallow-light, and refreshing their exhausted bodies at daybreak with ardent liquors ! Indeed, in comparison with this, the use of slaves itself, which Bacon calls a great advantage, was almost a blessing.

BARROW. Let us not speculate on either of these curses, which may not be felt as such when they come upon us, for we shall be stunned and torpefied by the greatness of our fall.

What have you next ?

NEWTON. *On Suspicion* I find an Italian proverb, which the learned author has misconstrued. " Sospetto licenzia fede " he translates, " Suspicion gives a passport to faith." The meaning is (my visitor tells me), " Suspicion dismisses fidelity." " Licenziare un servitore," is, to dismiss a servant. That the person suspected is no longer bound to fidelity, is the axiom of a nation, in which fidelity is readier to quit a man than suspicion is.

It cost me many hours of inquiry, to search into the propriety of his thoughts *Upon Ambition*. He says, " It is counted by some a weakness in princes to have favourites ; but it is *of all others* the best remedy against ambitious great ones : for when the way of pleasuring and displeasuring lieth by the favourite, it is impossible any other should be overgreat."

I hope, and am willing to believe, that my Lord Chancellor Bacon was a true and loyal subject ; yet one would almost be tempted to think in reading him, that there must be a curse in hereditary princes, and that he had set his private mark upon it when he praises their use of favourites, and supposes them surrounded by mean persons and ambitious ones, by poisons and counter-poisons. Sejanus and Tigellinus, our Gavestons and Mortimers, our Empsons and Dudleys, our Wolseys and Buckinghams, are like certain fumigations to drive away rats, which indeed do drive them out, but also make the house undesirable to inhabit. He recommends " the continual interchange of favours and disgraces, whereby they may not know what to expect, and be, as it were, in a wood."

BARROW. By the effect of this policy, we find the countenances of the statesmen and courtiers, who lived in his age, almost without exception, mean and suspicious. The greatest men look, in their portraits, as if they were waiting for a box on the ear, lowering their heads, raising their shoulders, and half-closing their eyes, for the reception of it.

NEWTON. What he says *Of nature in men*, seems spoken by some-one who saw through it from above : the same *On Custom and Education.* Here he speaks with more verity than consolation, when he says, " There be not two more fortunate properties, than to have a little of the fool and not too much of the honest : therefore extreme lovers of their country were never fortunate ; neither can they be ; for when a man placeth his thoughts without himself, he goeth not his own way."

In the Essay *On Youth and Age*, what can be truer, what can be more novel or more eloquent, than this sentence ?

" Men of age object too much, consult too long, adventure too little, repent too soon, and seldom drive business home to the full period, but content themselves with a mediocrity of success."

What he says *Of Beauty* is less considerate.

BARROW. I do not wonder at it : Beauty is not stript in a Court of Chancery, as Fortune is.

NEWTON. He is inconsequent in his reasoning when he says, " There is no excellent beauty that hath not some strangeness in the proportion. A man can not tell whether Apelles or Albert Dürer were the more trifler, *whereof* the one would make a personage by geometrical proportions ; the other, by taking the best parts out of divers faces to make one excellent."

BARROW. *Whereof* is of *which*, not of *whom*.

NEWTON. If " there is no excellent beauty that hath not some strangeness in the proportion," then Apelles was no trifler in taking the best parts of *divers faces*, which would produce *some strangeness in the proportion*, unless he corrected it.

BARROW. True : Bacon's first remark, however, is perfectly just and novel. What strikes us in beauty is that which we did not expect to find, from anything we had seen before : a new arrangement of excellent parts. The same thing may be said of genius ; the other great gift of the Divinity, not always so acceptable to his creatures ; but which however has this advantage, if you will allow it to be one, that, whereas beauty has most admirers at its first appearance, genius has most at its last, and begins to be commemorated in the period when the other is forgotten.

NEWTON. What you said of beauty, as striking us chiefly in being unexpected from anything we had seen before, is applicable no less to ugliness.

BARROW. I am not giving a definition, but recording an observation,[1] which would be inexact without the remaining words " *a new* arrangement of excellent parts."

NEWTON. Our author errs more widely than before ; not, as before, in drawing a false conclusion. " Such personages," he continues to remark, " I think would please nobody but the painter who made them : not but I think a painter may make a better face than ever was ; but he must do it by a kind of felicity (as a musician that maketh an excellent air in music), and not by rule." Nothing of excellent is to be done by felicity.

BARROW. Felicity and Excellence rarely meet, and hardly know one another.

NEWTON. Certainly no musician ever composed *an excellent air* otherwise than by rule : Felicity is without it.

BARROW. Beauty does not seem to dazzle but to deaden him. He reasons that the principal part of beauty lies in *decent motion*, and asserts that " No youthy person can be comely but by pardon, and by considering the youth as to make up the comeliness." Much of this reflection may have been fashioned and cast by the age of the observer ; much by the hour of the day : I think it must have been a rainy morning, when he had eaten unripe fruit for breakfast !

NEWTON. Perhaps sour grapes.

On Deformity I have transcribed a long sentence : here he seems more at home.

" Because there is in man an election touching the frame of his mind, and a necessity in the frame of his body, the stars of natural inclination are sometimes obscured by the sun of discipline and

---

[1] 1st ed. reads : " recording a fact. NEWTON. One which," etc.

virtue ; therefore it is good to consider of deformity, not as a sign which is most deceivable, but as a cause which seldom faileth of the effect."

Nothing can be truer in all its parts, or more magnificent in the whole.

BARROW. This short essay is worth many libraries of good books. Several hundreds of esteemed authors have not in them the substance and spirit of the sentence you recited.

NEWTON. *On Building* he says, " Houses are built to live in, and not to look on."

Half of this is untrue. Sheds and hovels, the first habitations (at least the first artificial ones) of men, were built to live in, and not to look on : but houses are built for both : otherwise why give directions for the proportions of porticoes, of columns, of intercolumniations, and of whatever else delights the beholder in architecture, and flatters the possessor ? Is the beauty of cities no honour to the inhabitants, no excitement to the defence ? External order in visible objects hath relation and intercourse with internal propriety and decorousness. I doubt not but the beauty of Athens had much effect on the patriotism, and some on the genius, of the Athenians. Part of the interest and animation men receive from Homer, lies in their conception of the magnificence of Troy. Even the little rock of Ithaca rears up its palaces sustained by pillars ; and pillars are that portion of an edifice on which the attention rests longest and most complacently. For we have no other means of calculating so well the grandeur of edifices, as by the magnitude of the support they need ; and it is the only thing about them which we measure in any way by our own.

" Neither do I reckon it an ill seat only where the air is unwholesome, but likewise where the air is unequal : as you shall see many fine seats set upon a knap of ground, environed with higher hills round about it, whereby the heat of the sun is pent in, and the wind gathereth as in troughs," &c.

Now surely this very *knap of ground* is the very spot to be chosen for the commodiousness of its situation, its salubrity, and its beauty. There is as little danger of the wind gathering in these *troughs* as in goat-skins. He must have taken his idea from some Italian work : the remark is suitable only to a southern climate.

BARROW. In one so rainy as ours is, it would have been more

judicious, I think, to have warned against building the house upon clay or marl, which are retentive of moisture, slippery nine months in the twelve, cracked the other three, of a colour offensive to the sight, of a soil little accommodating to garden-plants, the water usually unwholesome, and the roads impassable.

NEWTON. *On Negotiating* I am sorry to find again our lord chancellor a dissembler and a tutor to lies.

" To deal in person is good when a man's face breedeth regard, as commonly with inferiors ; or in tender cases, where a man's eye upon the countenance of him with whom he speaketh, may give him a direction how far to go ; *and generally where a man will reserve to himself liberty, either to disavow or to expound.*"

BARROW. Bad enough : but surely he must appear to you anything rather than knave, when he recommends *the employment of froward and absurd men,* be the business what it may.

NEWTON. He recommends them for *business which doth not well bear out itself ;* and in which, one would think, the wariest are the most wanted.

BARROW. But, like men who have just tripped, he walks the firmer and stouter instantly. The remainder of the essay is worthy of his perspicacity.

NEWTON. In the next, *On Followers and Friends,* I find the word *espial* used by him a second time, for a minister the French call *espion.* It appears to me that it should denote, not the *person* but the *action,* as the same termination is used in *trial.*

BARROW. Right. We want some words in composition as we want some side-dishes at table, less for necessity than for decoration. On this principle, I should not quarrel with a writer who had used the verb *originate;* on condition however that he used it as a neuter : none but a sugar-slave would employ it actively. It may stand opposite to *terminate.*

Bacon in the preceding sentence used *glorious* for *vain-glorious ;* a latinism among the many of the age, and among the few of the author. Our language bears gallicisms better than latinisms : but whoever is resolved to write soberly must be contented with the number of each that was found among us in the time of the Reformation. Little is to be rejected of what was then in use, and less of anything new is henceforward to be admitted. By which prudence and caution we may in time have writers as elegant as the Italian

BARROW AND NEWTON

and the French, whom already we exceed, as this little volume proves, in vigour and invention.

NEWTON. He says further on, " It is true that in government it is good to use men of one rank equally ; for to countenance some extraordinarily is to make them insolent, and the rest discontent ; because they may claim a due : but contrariwise in favour, to use men with much difference and election is good ; for it maketh the persons preferred more thankful, and the rest more officious ; because all is of favour."

Here again I am sorry so great an authority should, to use the words of my visitor, let his conscience run before his judgment, and his tongue slip in between. " In saying that all is of favour " (thus carps my visitor) " he gives a preference to another form of government over the monarchal ; another form indeed where all is not of favour ; where something may be attributed to virtue, something to industry, something to genius ; where something may accrue to us from the gratitude of our fellow-citizens ; and not everything drop and drivel from the frothy pulings of one swathed up in bandages never changed nor loosened ; of one held always in the same arms, and with its face turned always in the same direction."

BARROW. Hold ! hold ! this is as bad as Bacon or Milton : nay, Cicero and Demosthenes, in the blindness of their hearts, could scarcely have spoken, to the nations they guided, with more contemptuous asperity of royal power.

NEWTON. I venerate it, as coming of God.

BARROW. Hold again ! all things come from him : the hangman and the hanged are in the same predicament with the anointer and the anointed.

NEWTON. Sir, you remind me of an observation made in my father's house by the son of a republican, and who indeed was little better than one himself. My father had upbraided him on his irreverence to the Lord's anointed : he asked my father why he allowed his mind to be lime-twigged and ruffled and discomposed by words ; and whether he would feel the same awe in repeating the syllables, *God's greased*, as in repeating the syllables, *God's anointed*. If the Esquimaux heard them, said he, they would think the man no better reared than themselves, and worse dressed, as dressed by one less in practice.

BARROW. No men are so facetious as those whose minds are somewhat perverted. Truth enjoys good air and clear light, but no play-ground. Keep your eyes upon Bacon : we may more safely look on him than on thrones. How wise is all the remainder of the essay !

NEWTON. He says *On Suitors*, and truly, that " Private suits do putrefy the public good." Soon afterward, " Some embrace suits *which* never mean to deal effectually in them." This seems ordinary and flat ; but the words are requisite to a sentence founded (I fear) on a close observation of human nature, as courts render it. I noted them as presenting an incorrectness and indecision of language. *Who* is proper ; not *which ;* although *which* was used indiscriminately, as we find in the beginning of the ' Lord's Prayer ' : but in that place there could be no confusion.

BARROW. Among the few crudities and barbarisms that yet oppressed our language in his learned age, Bacon has this, " A man *were better rise* in his suit." Indeed he uses *were better* more than once ; with the simple verb after it, and without *to*.

NEWTON. *On Studies* he can not lose his road, having trodden it so frequently, and having left his mark upon so many objects all the way. Therefore it is no wonder that his genius points with a finger of fire to this subject.

He says *On Faction*, that " Many a man's strength is in opposi-tion,[1] and when that faileth he groweth out of use." He must have written from inspiration ; for in his age I find no person to whom he can have alluded.

BARROW. Perhaps not ; yet the preceding may have furnished him with examples.

NEWTON. In the first sentence *On Ceremonies and Respects*, are the words, " He that is only real had need have exceeding great parts of virtue." This weighty and sorrowful truth does not prevent me from questioning the expression, *had need have*.

BARROW. The true words, which all authors write amiss, are, *ha'* need *of*. *Ha' need* sounds like *had need*, and *have* sounds like *of*, in speaking quickly. Hence the wisest men have written the words improperly, by writing at once from the ear, without an appeal or reference to grammar.

---

[1] The following footnote appears in 1st ed. :—
" Fox and Mirabeau are illustrations of this position. They were superior to Pitt and Robespierre in reading and intellect, yet could not govern long with so much authority."

BARROW AND NEWTON

NEWTON. *On Praise* he says ingeniously, but not altogether truly, " Fame is like a river, that beareth up things light and swollen, and drowns things weighty and solid."

BARROW. This is true only of literary fame : and the drowned things are brought to light again, sometimes by the warmer season and sometimes by the stormier.

He uses *suspect* for *suspicion :* we retain *aspect, respect, retrospect, prospect :* I know not whether the chancellor's award in favour of *suspect* will be repealed or acquiesced in.

NEWTON. In the next Essay, *On Vain-glory*, he says, " In fame of learning the flight will be slow without some feathers of ostentation." That is hard, if true.

BARROW. There must be a good deal of movement and shuffling before there is any rising from the ground : and those who have the longest wings have the most difficulty in the first mounting. In literature, as at foot-ball, strength and agility are insufficient of themselves : you must have your *side*, or you may run till you are out of breath, and kick till you are out of shoes, and never win the game. There must be some to keep others off you, and some to prolong for you the ball's rebound. But your figures, dear Isaac, will serve as tenterhooks to catch the fingers of those who would meddle with your letters. Do not however be ambitious of an early fame : such is apt to shrivel and to drop under the tree.

NEWTON. The author continues the same subject in the next Essay, though under a different title. *Of Honour and Reputation* he says, " Discreet followers and servants help much to reputation." Then he who has no servant, or an indiscreet one, must be content to be helped to little of it.

BARROW.[1] Seeing that reputation is casual, that the wise may long want it, that the unwise may soon acquire it, that a servant may further it, that a spiteful man may obstruct it, that a passionate man may maim it, and that whole gangs are ready to waylay it as it mounts the hill, I would not wish greatly to carry it about me, but rather to place it in some safe spot, where few could find, and not many will look after it. But those who discover it, will try in their hands its weight and quality, and take especial care lest they injure it, saying, " It is his, and his only ; leave it to him and wish him increase in it."

NEWTON. Where Bacon is occupied " in the true marshalling of

---

[1] From " BARROW " to " language " added in 2nd ed.

sovran honour," he gives the third place to *liberatores* or *salvatores*. He wishes to speak in Latin ; one of these words belongs not to the language.

BARROW. His Latin is always void of elegance and grace ; but he had the generosity to write in it, that he might be useful the more extensively. We English are far below the Italians, French, Germans, and Dutch, in our latinity : yet we have Latin volumes written by our countrymen, each of which, in its matter, is fairly worth half theirs. They, like certain fine gentlemen, seem to found their ideas of elegance on slenderness, and in twenty or thirty of them we hardly find a thought or remark at all worthy of preservation. I remember but one sentence ; which however, if Cicero had written it, would be recorded among the best he ever wrote. " Valuit nimirum maledicentiâ, gratâ cunctis, etiam iis qui neque sibi maledici neque maledicere ipsi aliis velint."

NEWTON.[1] Permit me to inquire, sir, by whom was this strong and shrewd and truly Sallustian sentence written ?

BARROW. By Vavassor,[2] a Jesuit.

It may be remarked, and perhaps you have done it, that the title itself of this Essay, *The True Marshalling of Sovran Honour*, is incorrect. By *marshalling* he means *the giving of rates or degrees* : now what is *sovran* has no rates or degrees : he should have said " of titles assumed by sovran princes."

NEWTON. In the first sentence *On Judicature*, he uses the singular and plural in designating the same body : either is admissible, but not both.

" Else will it be like the authority claimed by the Church of Rome, which, under pretext of exposition of Scripture, *doth* not stick to add and alter, and to pronounce that which *they* do not find, and, by show of antiquity, to introduce novelty."

What gravity and wisdom is there in the remark that, " One foul sentence doth more hurt than many foul examples : for these do but corrupt the stream, the other corrupteth the fountain."

The worst, and almost the only bad sentence in the volume, is the childish antithesis, " There be, saith the Scripture, that turn judgment into wormwood—and surely there be also that turn it into vinegar : for injustice maketh it bitter, and delays make it sour."

---

[1] From " NEWTON " to " Jesuit " added in 2nd ed.
[2] Francois Vavasseur, 1605-1681.

BARROW AND NEWTON

On the Vicissitudes of Things he observes that " The true religion is built upon the rock, the rest are tossed upon the waves of Time." My [1] visitor said hereupon, " I doubt whether this magnificent figure has truth for its basis. If by true religion is meant the religion of our Saviour, as practised by his apostles, they outlived it. They complain that it never took firm possession even of their own auditors. Saint Peter himself was reproved by his master for using his sword too vigorously, after all he had said against any use of it whatever : yet, so little good did the reproof, he fell immediately to betraying the very man he had thus defended. But if by true religion we mean the Church of Rome, we come nearer the fact : for that religion, with patchings and repairings, with materials purloined from others, with piles driven under the foundation, and buttresses without that darken everything within, surmounted by pinnacles raised above the upper story, hath lasted long, and will remain while men are persuaded that wax and stockfish can atone for their vices. The obstacle to our acceptance of the meaning is, that it hath been convicted of many impostures in its claims and miracles, that it continues to insist on them, and that it uses violence (which is forbidden by Christ) against those who stumble or doubt."

BARROW. Deafness is not to be healed by breaking the head, nor blindness by pulling the eyes out : it is time the doctors should try new experiments : if they will not, it is time that the patients should try new doctors.

NEWTON. A bad religion may be kept afoot by the same means as other kinds of bad government ; by corruption and terror, by spies and tortures. No doubt it will please God to see all things set to rights : but we must acknowledge that the best religion, like the best men, has fared the worst.

Bacon says he " reckons martyrdoms among miracles, because they *seem* to exceed the strength of human nature." If they did *seem* to exceed the strength of human nature, this is no sufficient reason why they should be ranked with miracles : for martyrdoms have appertained to many religions, if we may call voluntary death to prove a misbeliever's sincerity a martyrdom, while we know that miracles belong exclusively to the Christian : and even in this faith there are degrees of latitude and longitude which they were never known to pass, although, humanly speaking, they were much wanted.

[1] From " My " to " hereupon " added in 2nd ed.

The Lithuanians, and other north-eastern nations, were long before they were reclaimed from paganism, for want of miracles. God's good time had not come ; and he fell upon different expedients for their conversion.

On the Vicissitudes of Things we find mention of Plato's great year. I think you once told me, Plato took more from others than he knew what to do with.

BARROW. Instead of simplifying, he involves and confounds.

NEWTON. I hope hereafter to study the heavenly bodies, with greater accuracy and on other principles than philosophers have done hitherto. The reasons of Bacon why " the northern tract of the world is the more martial region," are unworthy of his perspicacity. First he assigns the stars of the hemisphere ; then the greatness of the continent ; " whereas the south part is almost all sea " ; then, the cold of the northern parts, " which is that which, without aid of discipline, doth make the bodies hardest and the courage warmest." The stars can have no effect whatever on the courage or virtues of men, unless we call the sun one of them, as the poets do. The heat of the sun may produce effeminacy and sloth in many constitutions, and contrary effects in many : but I suspect that dryness and moisture are more efficient on the human body than heat and cold. Some races, as in dogs and horses, and cattle of every kind, are better than others, and do not lose their qualities for many ages, nor, unless others cross them, without the confluence of many causes. There may be as much courage in hot climates as in cold. The inhabitants of Madagascar and Malacca are braver than the Laplanders, and perhaps not less brave than the Londoners. The fact is this : people in warm climates are in the full enjoyment of all the pleasures that animal life affords, and are disinclined to toil after that which no toil could produce or increase : while the native of the north is condemned by climate to a life of labour, which oftentimes can procure for him but a scanty portion of what his vehement and exasperated appetite demands. Therefore he cuts it short with his sword, and reaps the field sown by the southern.

Bacon seems to me just in his opinion, if not that *ordnance*, at least that inflammable powder, and annoyance by its means, perhaps in rockets, was known among the ancients. He instances the Oxydraces in India. The remark is, I imagine, equally applicable to the priests of Delphi, who repelled the Gauls with it from the

148

temple of Apollo. This [1] is the more remarkable, as the Persians too encountered the same resistance, and experienced the double force of *thunderbolts and earthquake.* Whence we may surmise, that not only missiles, propelled by the combustion of powder, were aimed against them, but likewise that mines exploded. And perhaps other priests, the only people in most places who formerly had leisure for experiments, were equally acquainted with it, and used it, for their own defence only, and only in cases of extremity. Etruscan [2] soothsayers were appointed to blast the army of Alaric with lightning, and the Pope acceded to the proposal : but his Holiness, on reflection, was of opinion, that *aurum fulminans* was more effectual.

I wish the Essay *On Fame* had been completed : and even then its chief effect on me, perhaps, would be to excite another wish ; as gratification usually does. It would have made me sigh for the recovery of Cicero *On Glory*, that the two greatest of philosophers might be compared on the same ground.

BARROW. Let us look up at Fame without a desire or a repining ; and let us pardon all her falsehoods and delays, in remembrance that the best verse in Homer, and the best in Virgil, are on her. Virgil's is indeed but a feather from the wing of Homer.

NEWTON. You show a very forgiving mind, sir, and I hope she will be grateful to you. I do not know what these lines are worth, as they give me no equations.

BARROW. Nothing should be considered quite independently of everything else. We owe reverence to all great writers : but our reverence to one would be injustice to another, unless we collated and compared their merits.

NEWTON. Some are so dissimilar to others, that I know not how it can be done.

BARROW. Liquids and solids are dissimilar, yet may be weighed in the same scales. All things are composed of portions ; and all things bear proportions relatively ; mind to mind, matter to matter. Archimedes and Homer are susceptible of comparison : but the process would be long and tedious, the principles must be sought from afar, nor is the man perhaps at the next door who must be called for the operation. Bacon and Milton, Bacon and Shakespeare, may be compared with little difficulty, wide asunder as they appear to stand.

---

[1] From " This " to " exploded " added in 2nd ed.
[2] From " Etruscan " to " effectual " added in 2nd ed.

However, since the cogitative and imaginative parts of mind are exercised by both, in broad daylight and in open spaces, the degrees in which they are exercised are within our calculation. Until we bring together the weightiest works of genius from the remotest distances, we shall display no admirable power of criticism. None such hath been hitherto exhibited in the world, which stands, in relation to criticism, as it stood in relation to metaphysics until the time of Aristoteles. He left them imperfect ; and they have lain little better ever since. The good sense of Cicero led him to clearer studies and wholesomer exercise ; and where he could not pluck fruit he would not pluck brambles. In Plato we find only arbours and grottoes, with moss and shellwork all misplaced. Aristoteles hath built a solider edifice, but hath built it across our road : we must throw it down again, and use what we can of the materials elsewhere.

NEWTON. Bacon, seen only in his *Essays*, would have appeared to me (fresh as I come from the study of the ancients, and captivated as I confess I am by the graces of their language) the wisest and most instructive of writers.

BARROW. In calling him the wisest of writers, you must except those who wrote from inspiration.

NEWTON. Ha ! that is quite another thing.

BARROW. Henceforward I would advise you to follow the bent of your genius, in examining those matters principally which are susceptible of demonstration. Every young man should have some proposed end for his studies : let yours be philosophy : and principally those parts of it in which the ancients have done little, and the moderns less. And never be dejected, my dear Isaac, though it should enable you to throw but a scarcity of light on the *Revelation*, *The Rape of Helen*, and *The Golden Fleece*.

NEWTON. I hope by my labours I may find a clue to them in the process of time. But perhaps my conjectures may turn out wrong, as those on the book before me have.

BARROW. How ?

NEWTON. I should always have imagined, if you had not taught me the contrary, that there is more of genius and philosophy in Bacon's *Essays* than in all Cicero's works, however less there be of the scholastic and oratorical. Perhaps I, by being no estimator of style——

BARROW. Peace, peace ! my modest Newton ! Perhaps I, by being too much an estimator of it, have overvalued the clearest head and the purest tongue of antiquity. My [1] Lord Justice Coke, and probably the more learned Selden, would have ridiculed or reproved us, had we dared entertain in their presence a doubt of Cicero's superiority over Bacon. No very great man ever reached the standard of his greatness in the crowd of his contemporaries. This hath always been reserved for the secondary. There must either be something of the vulgar, something in which the commonalty can recognise their own features, or there must be a laxity, a jealousy, an excitement stimulating a false appetite. Your brief review of the *Essays* hath brought back to my recollection so much of shrewd judgment, so much of rich imagery, such a profusion of truths so plain, as (without his manner of exhibiting them) to appear almost unimportant, that, in the various high qualities of the human mind, I must acknowledge not only Cicero, but every prose-writer among the Greeks, to stand far below him. Cicero is least valued for his highest merits, his fulness and his perspicuity. Bad judges (and how few are not so !) desire in composition the concise and the obscure, not knowing that the one most frequently arises from paucity of materials, and the other from inability to manage and dispose them. Have you never observed that, among the ignorant in painting, dark pictures are usually called the finest in the collection, and grey-bearded heads, fit only for the garret, are preferred to the radiance of light and beauty ? Have you yourself never thought, before you could well measure and calculate, that books and furniture thrown about a room, appeared to be in much greater quantities than when they were arranged ? At every step we take to gain the approbation of the wise, we lose something in the estimation of the vulgar. Look within : can not we afford it ?

The minds of few can take in the whole of a great author, and fewer can draw him close enough to another for just commensuration. A fine passage may strike us less forcibly than one beneath it in beauty, from less sensibility in us at the moment ; whence less enthusiasm, less quickness of perception, less capacity, less hold. You have omitted to remark some of the noblest things in Bacon, often, I believe, because there is no power of judgment to be shown in the expression of admiration, and perhaps too sometimes from the repetition and intensity of delight.

NEWTON. Sir, I forbore to lift up my hands, as a mark of admira-

---

[1] From " My " to " below him " added in 2nd ed.

tion. You ordered me to demonstrate, if I could, the defects of this wonderful man, unnoticed hitherto.

BARROW. You have done it to my satisfaction. Cicero disdained not, in the latter days of his life, when he was highest in reputation and dignity, to perform a similar office in regard to Epicurus : and I wish he had exhibited the same accuracy and attention, the same moderation and respect. The objections of your friend and visitor are not altogether frivolous : take care however lest he, by his disceptations, move you from your faith. If you hold the faith, the faith will support you ; as, if you make your bed warm by lying in it, your bed will keep you so : never mind what the ticking or the wadding may be made of. There are few things against which I see need to warn you, and not many on which you want advice. You are not profuse in your expenditure : yet as you, like most of the studious, are inattentive to money-affairs, let me guard you against evils following on this negligence, worse than the negligence itself. Whenever a young man is remarked for it, a higher price is fixed on what he purchases ; and dishonest men of every description push themselves into his service, and often acquire his confidence, not only to the injury of his fortune, but likewise of his credit and respectability. Let a gentleman be known to have been cheated of twenty pounds, and it costs him forty a-year for the remainder of his life. Therefore, if you detect the cheat, the wisest thing is to conceal it ; both for fear of the rogues about your sideboard, and of those more dexterous ones round the green cloth, under the judge, in your county assize-room.

You will become an author ere long ; and every author must attend to the means of conveying his information. The plainness of your style is suitable to your manners and your studies. Avoid, which many grave men have not done, words taken from sacred subjects and from elevated poetry : these we have seen vilely prostituted. Avoid too the society of the barbarians who misemploy them : they are vain, irreverent, and irreclaimable to right feelings. The dialogues of Galileo, which you have been studying, are written with much propriety and precision. I do not urge you to write in dialogue, although the best writers of every age have done it : the best parts of Homer and Milton are speeches and replies, the best parts of every great historian are the same : the wisest men of Athens and of Rome converse together in this manner, as they are shown to us by

Xenophon, by Plato, and by Cicero. Whether you adopt such a form of composition, which, if your opinions are new, will protect you in part from the hostility all novelty (unless it is vicious) excites ; or whether you choose to go along the unbroken surface of the didactic ; never look abroad for any kind of ornament. Apollo, either as the God of day or the slayer of Python, had nothing about him to obscure his clearness or to impede his strength. To one of your mild manners, it would be superfluous to recommend equanimity in competition, and calmness in controversy. How easy is it for the plainest things to be misinterpreted by men not unwise, which a calm disquisition sets right ! and how fortunate and opportune is it to find in ourselves that calmness which almost the wisest have wanted, on urgent and grave occasions ! If others for a time are preferred to you, let your heart lie sacredly still ! and you will hear from it the true and plain oracle, that not for ever will the magistracy of letters allow the rancid transparencies of coarse colourmen to stand before your propylæa. It is time that Philosophy should have her share in our literature; that the combinations and appearances of matter be scientifically considered and luminously displayed. Frigid conceits on theological questions, heaps of snow on barren crags, compose at present the greater part of our domain : volcanoes of politics burst forth from time to time, and vary, without enlivening, the scene.

Do not fear to be less rich in the productions of your mind at one season than at another. Marshes are always marshes, and pools are pools ; but the sea, in those places where we admire it most, is sometimes sea and sometimes dry land ; sometimes it brings ships into port, and sometimes it leaves them where they can be refitted and equipt. The capacious mind neither rises nor sinks, neither labours nor rests, in vain. Even in those intervals when it loses the consciousness of its powers, when it swims as it were in vacuity, and feels not what is external nor internal, it acquires or recovers strength, as the body does by sleep. Never[1] try to say things admirably ; try only to say them plainly ; for your business is with the considerate philosopher, and not with the polemical assembly. If a thing can be demonstrated two ways, demonstrate it in both : one will please this man best, the other that ; and pleasure, if obvious and unsought, is never to be neglected by those appointed from above

---

[1] 1st ed. reads : " Never try to say things well ; try only to say them clearly ; for," etc.

to lead us into knowledge. Many will readily mount stiles and gates to walk along a footpath in a field, whom the very sight of a bare public road would disincline and weary ; and yet the place whereto they travel lies at the end of each. Your studies are of a nature unsusceptible of much decoration : otherwise it would be my duty and my care to warn you against it, not merely as idle and unnecessary, but as obstructing your intent. The fond of wine are little fond of the sweet or of the new : the fond of learning are no fonder of its must than of its dregs. Something of the severe hath always been appertaining to order and to grace : and the beauty that is not too liberal is sought the most ardently and loved the longest. The Graces have their zones, and Venus her cestus. In the writings of the philosopher are the frivolities of ornament the most ill-placed ; in you would they be particularly, who, promising to lay open before us an infinity of worlds, should turn aside to display the petals of a double pink.

It is dangerous to have any intercourse or dealing with small authors. They are as troublesome to handle, as easy to discompose, as difficult to pacify, and leave as unpleasant marks on you, as small children. Cultivate on the other hand the society and friendship of the higher ; first that you may learn to reverence them, which of itself is both a pleasure and a virtue, and then that on proper occasions you may defend them against the malevolent, which is a duty. And this duty can not be well and satisfactorily performed with an imperfect knowledge, or with an inadequate esteem. Habits of respect to our superiors are among the best we can attain, if we only remove from our bosom the importunate desire of unworthy advantages from them. They belong to the higher department of justice, and will procure for us in due time our portion of it. Beside, O Isaac ! in this affair our humanity is deeply concerned. Think, how gratifying, how consolatory, how all-sufficient, are the regards and attentions of such wise and worthy men as you, to those whom inferior but more powerful ones, some in scarlet, some in purple, some (it may be) in ermine, vilify or neglect. Many are there to whom we are now indifferent, or nearly, whom, if we had approached them as we ought to have done, we should have cherished, loved, and honoured. Let not this reflection, which on rude and unequal minds may fall without form and features, and pass away like the idlest cloud-shadow, be lost on you. Old literary men, beside age

154

and experience, have another quality in common with Nestor : they, in the literature of the country, are praisers of times past, partly from moroseness, and partly from custom and conviction. The illiterate, on the contrary, raise higher than the steeples, and dress up in the gaudiest trim, a maypole of their own, and dance round it while any rag flutters. So tenacious are Englishmen of their opinions, that they would rather lose their franchises and almost their lives. And this tenacity hath not its hold upon letters only, but likewise upon whatever is public. I have witnessed it in men guilty of ingratitude, of fraud, of peculation, of prevarication, of treachery to friends, of insolence to patrons, of misleading of colleagues, of abandonment of party, of renunciation of principles, of arrogance to honester men and wiser, of humiliation to strumpets for the obtainment of place and profit, of every villany in short which unfits not only for the honours of public, but rejects from the confidence of private life. And there have been people so maddened by faction, that they would almost have erected a monument to such persons, hoping to spite and irritate their adversaries, and unconscious or heedless that the inscription must be their own condemnation. Those who have acted in this manner will repent of it ; but they will hate you for ever if you foretell them of their repentance. It is not the fact nor the consequence, it is the motive that turns and pinches them ; and they would think it straightforward and natural to cry out against you, and a violence and a malady to cry out against themselves. The praises they have given they will maintain, and more firmly than if they were due ; as perjurers stick to perjury more hotly than the veracious to truth. Supposing there should be any day of your life unoccupied by study, there will not be one without an argument why parties, literary or political, should be avoided. You are too great to be gregarious ; and were you to attempt it, the gregarious in a mass would turn their heads against you. The greater who enter into public life are disposed at last to quit it : *retirement with dignity* is their device : the meaning of which is, retirement with as much of the public property as can be amassed and carried away. This race of great people is very numerous. I want before I die to see one or two ready to believe, and to act on the belief, that there is as much dignity in retiring soon as late, with little as with loads, with quiet minds and consciences as with ulcerated or discomposed. I have already seen some hundred sectaries of that pugnacious pope, who, being reminded that Christ commanded Peter to put up his sword, replied, " Yes, when he had cut the ear off."

To be in right harmony, the soul not only must be never out of time, but must never lose sight of the theme its Creator's hand hath noted. Why are you peeping over your forefinger into those pages near the beginning of the volume ?

NEWTON. I have omitted the notice of several Essays.

BARROW. There are many that require no observation for peculiarities ; though perhaps there is not one that any other man could have written.

NEWTON. I had something more, sir, to say—or rather—I had something more, sir, to ask—about Friendship.

BARROW. All men, but the studious above all, must beware in the formation of it. Advice or caution on this subject comes immaturely and ungracefully from the young, exhibiting a proof either of temerity or suspicion : but when you hear it from a man of my age, who has been singularly fortunate in the past, and foresees the same felicity in those springing up before him, you may accept it as the direction of a calm observer, telling you all he has remarked, on the greater part of a road which he has nearly gone through, and which you have but just entered. Never take into your confidence, or admit often into your company, any man who does not know, on some important subject, more than you do. Be his rank, be his virtues, what they may, he will be a hindrance to your pursuits, and an obstruction to your greatness. If indeed the greatness were such as courts can bestow, and such as can be laid on the shoulders of a groom, and make him look like the rest of the company, my advice would be misplaced : but since all transcendent, all true and genuine greatness, must be of a man's own raising, and only on the foundation that the hand of God has laid, do not let any touch it : keep them off civilly, but keep them off. Affect no stoicism ; display no indifference : let their coin pass current ; but do not you exchange for it the purer ore you carry, nor think the milling pays for the alloy. Greatly favoured and blest by Providence will you be, if you should in your lifetime be known for what you are : the contrary, if you should be transformed.

NEWTON. Better and more decorous would it be perhaps, if I filled up your pause with my reflections : but you always have permitted

BARROW AND NEWTON

me to ask you questions ; and now, unless my gratitude misleads me, you invite it.

BARROW. Ask me anything : I will answer it, if I can ; and I will pardon you, as I have often done, if you puzzle me.

NEWTON. Is it not a difficult and a painful thing to repulse, or to receive ungraciously, the advances of friendship ?

BARROW. It withers the heart, if indeed his heart were ever sound who doth it. Love, serve, run into danger, venture life, for him who would cherish you : give him everything but your time and your glory. Morning recreations, convivial meals, evening walks, thoughts, questions, wishes, wants, partake with him. Yes, Isaac ! there are men born for friendship ; men to whom the cultivation of it is nature, is necessity ; as the making of honey is to bees. Do not let them suffer for the sweets they would gather ; but do not think to live upon those sweets. Our corrupted state requires robuster food, or must grow more and more unsound.

NEWTON. I would yet say something ; a few words ; on this subject—or one next to it.

BARROW. *On Expense* then : that is the next : I have given you some warning about it, and hardly know what else to say. Can not you find the place ?

NEWTON. I had it under my hand. If—that is, provided—your time, sir !——

BARROW. Speak it out, man ! Are you in a ship of Marcellus under the mirror of Archimedes, that you fume and redden so ? Cry to him that you are his scholar, and went out only to parley.

NEWTON. Sir ! in a word—ought a studious man to think of matrimony ?

BARROW. Painters, poets, mathematicians, never ought : other studious men, after reflecting for twenty years upon it, may. Had I a son of your age, I would not leave him in a grazing country. Many a man hath been safe among corn-fields, who falls a victim on the grass under an elm. There are lightnings very fatal in such places.

NEWTON. Supposing me no mathematician, I must reflect then for twenty years !

BARROW. Begin to reflect on it after the twenty : and continue to reflect on it all the remainder ; I mean at intervals, and quite leisurely. It will save to you many prayers, and may suggest to you one thanksgiving.

XV. WALTON, COTTON, AND OLDWAYS

(Imag. Convers., v., 1829 ; *Wks.*, i., 1846 ; *Wks.*, iv., 1876.)

WALTON. God be with thee and preserve thee, old Ashbourne ! thou art verily the pleasantest place upon his earth, I mean from May-day till Michaelmas. Son Cotton, let us tarry a little here upon the bridge. Did you ever see greener meadows than these on either hand ? And what says that fine lofty spire upon the left, a trowling-line's cast from us ? It says methinks, " Blessed be the Lord for this bounty : come hither and repeat it beside me." How my jade winces ! I wish the strawberry-spotted trout, and ash-coloured grayling under us, had the bree that plagues thee so, my merry wench ! Look, my son, at the great venerable house opposite. You know these parts as well as I do, or better ; are you acquainted with the worthy who lives over there ?

COTTON. I can not say I am.[1]

WALTON. You shall be then. He has resided here forty-five years, and knew intimately our good Doctor Donne, and (I hear) hath some of his verses, written when he was a stripling or little better, the which we come after.

COTTON. That, I imagine, must be he ! the man in black, walking above the house.

WALTON. Truly said on both counts. Willy Oldways ; sure enough ; and he doth walk above his house-top. The gardens here, you observe, overhang the streets.

COTTON. Ashbourne, to my mind, is the prettiest town in England.

WALTON. And there is nowhere between Trent and Tweed a sweeter stream for the trout, I do assure you, than the one our horses are bestriding. Those in my opinion were very wise men who consecrated certain streams to the Muses : I know not whether I can say so much of those who added the mountains. Whenever I am beside a river or rivulet on a sunny day, and think a little while, and let images warm into life about me, and joyous sounds increase and

---

[1] 1st ed. reads : " am, tho' he visits my relatives when he rides so far."

158

multiply in their innocence, the sun looks brighter and feels warmer, and I am readier to live, and less unready to die.

> Son Cotton ! these light idle brooks,
> Peeping into so many nooks,
> Yet have not for their idlest wave
> The leisure you may think they have :
> No, not the little ones that run
> And hide behind the first big stone,
> When they have squirted in the eye
> Of their next neighbour passing by ;
> Nor yonder curly sideling fellow
> Of tones than Pan's own flute more mellow,
> Who learns his tune and tries it over
> As girl who fain would please her lover.
> Something has each of them to say,
> He says it and then runs away,
> And says it in another place,
> Continuing the unthrifty chase.
> We have as many tales to tell,
> And look as gay and run as well,
> But leave another to pursue
> What we had promised we would do,
> Till in the order God has fated,
> One after one precipitated,
> Whether we *would* on, or would *not* on,
> Just like these idle waves, son Cotton !

And now I have taken you by surprise, I will have (finished or unfinished) the verses you snatched out of my hand, and promised me another time, when you awoke this morning.

COTTON. If [1] you must have them, here they are.

WALTON (*reads*).

> Rocks under Okeover park-paling
> Better than Ashbourne suit the grayling.
> Reckless of people springs the trout,
> Tossing his vacant head about,
> And his distinction-stars, as one
> Not to be touched but looked upon,
> And smirks askance, as who should say
> " I 'd lay now (if I e'er *did* lay)
> The brightest fly that shines above,
> You know not what *I 'm* thinking of ;
> What *you* are, I can plainly tell,
> And so, my gentles, fare ye well ! "

---

[1] From " If " to " (*reads*) " added in 2nd ed.

IMAGINARY CONVERSATIONS : ENGLISH

Heigh! heigh! what have we here? a[1] double hook with a bait upon each side. Faith! son Cotton, if my friend Oldways had seen these, not[2] the verses I have been reading, but these others I have run over in silence, he would have reproved me, in his mild amicable way, for my friendship with one who, at two-and-twenty, could either know so much or invent so much about a girl. He remarked to me, the last time we met, that our climate was more backward and our youth more forward than anciently; and, taking out a newspaper from under the cushion of his arm-chair, showed me a paragraph, with a cross in red ink, and seven or eight marks of admiration, some on one side, some on the other, in which there was mention made of a female servant, who, hardly seventeen years old, charged her master's son, who was barely two older——

COTTON. Nonsense! nonsense! impossible!

WALTON. Why, he himself seemed to express a doubt; for beneath was written, " Qu: if perjured—which God forbid! May all turn out to his glory! "

COTTON. But really I do not recollect that paper of mine, if mine it be, which[3] appears to have stuck against the Okeover-paling lines.

WALTON. Look![4] they are both on the same scrap. Truly, son, there are girls here and there who might have said as much as thou,[5] their proctor, hast indited for them : they have such froward tongues in their heads, some of them. A breath keeps them in motion, like a Jew's harp, God[6] knows how long. If you do not or will not recollect the verses on this indorsement, I will read them again, and aloud.

COTTON. Pray do not baulk your fancy.

WALTON (*reads*).

> Where's[7] my apron ? I will gather
> Daffodils and kingcups, rather

---

1 From " a " to " side " added in 2nd ed.
2 From " not " to " silence " added in 2nd ed.
3 From " which " to " lines " added in 2nd ed.
4 From " Look ! " to " scrap " added in 2nd ed.
5 From " as thou " to " for them " added in 2nd ed.
6 From " God " to " (*reads*)" added in 2nd ed.
7 1st ed. reads :

> "In my bosom I would rather
> Daffodils and kingcups gather
> Than have fifty sighing souls
> False as cats and dull as owls."

> Than have fifty silly souls,
> False as cats and dull as owls,
> Looking [1] up into my eyes
> And half-blinding me with sighs.

Cats, forsooth ! *Owls*, and cry you mercy ! Have [2] they no better words than those for civil people ? Did any young woman really use the expressions, bating the metre, or can you have contrived them out of pure likelihood ?

COTTON. I will not gratify your curiosity at present.

WALTON. Anon then.

> Here I stretch myself along,
> Tell a tale or sing a song,
> By my cousin Sue or Bet—
> And for dinner here I get
> Strawberries, curds, or what I please,
> With my bread upon my knees ;
> And when I have had enough,
> Shake, and off to *blindman's buff*.[3]

Spoken [4] in the character of a maiden, it seems, who little knows, in her innocence, that *blind man's buff* is a perilous game.

[1] From " Looking " to " sighs " added in 2nd ed.

[2] From " Have " to " then " added in 2nd ed.

[3] 1st ed. adds following four lines and footnote :—

> " Which I cannot do if they
> Ever come across my way,
> They so puzzle me !—that tongue
> Always makes one cry out wrong !

" I cannot but think that I am indebted to a beautiful little poem of Redi, for the train of these ideas, though without a consciousness of it while I was writing. His sonnets are among the worst in the language : there is but one exception.

" I am likely to be a bad translator ; and moreover I must inform the reader that I am designedly an unfaithful one in the second line, of which the literal and entire version is ' who pass thro' *Pity-street*.' I have taken the elegiac measure as more becoming the subject.

> " Ye gentle souls, ye tenderer of the fair
> Who, passing by, to Pity's voice incline,
> O, stay a while and hear me ! then declare
> If ever there was grief that equal'd mine.

> " There was a woman to whose hallowed breast
> Faith had retired, and Honour fixed his throne—
> Pride, tho' upheld by Virtue, she repressed :
> Ye gentle souls, *that* woman was my own.

> " Her form was fill'd with beauty, from her face ;
> Grace was in all she did, in all she said,
> Grace in her pleasures, in her sorrows grace—
> Ye gentle souls, *that* gentle soul is fled."

[4] From " Spoken " to " church " added in 2nd ed.

You are looking, I perceive, from off the streamlet toward the church. In [1] its chancel lie the first and last of the Cockaynes. Whole races of men have been exterminated by war and pestilence ; families and names have slipped down and lost themselves by slow and imperceptible decay ; but I doubt whether any breed of fish, with heron and otter and angler in pursuit of it, hath been extinguished since the Heptarchy. They might humble our pride a whit, methinks, though they hold their tongues. The people here entertain a strange prejudice against the *nine-eyes*.

COTTON. What, in the name of wonder, is that ?

WALTON. At your years do not you know ? It is a tiny kind of lamprey, a finger long ; it sticketh to the stones by its sucker, and if you are not warier and more knowing than folks in general from the south, you might take it for a weed ; it wriggles its whole body to and fro so regularly, and is of that dark colour which subaqueous weeds are often of, as though they were wet through, which they are not any more than land-weeds, if one may believe young Doctor Plott, who told me so in confidence.

Hold my mare, son Cotton. I will try whether my whip can reach the window, when I have mounted the bank.

COTTON. Curious ! the middle of a street to be lower than the side by several feet. People would not believe it in London or Hull.

WALTON. Ho ! lass ! tell the good parson, your master, or his wife if she be nearer at hand, that two friends would dine with him ; Charles Cotton, kinsman of Mistress Cotton of the Peak, and his humble servant Izaak Walton.

GIRL. If you are come, gentles, to dine with my master, I will make another kidney-pudding first, while I am about it, and then tell him : not but we have enough and to spare, yet master and mistress love to see plenty, and to welcome with no such peacods as words.

WALTON. Go, thou hearty jade, trip it, and tell him.

COTTON. I will answer for it, thy friend is a good soul [2] : I perceive it in the heartiness and alacrity of the wench. She glories in his hospitality, and it renders her labour a delight.

WALTON. He wants nothing, yet he keeps the grammar-school,

[1] 1st ed. reads : " In the church, to our right, lie the Cockaynes. Whole races," etc.

[2] From " I " to " delight " added in 2nd ed. 1st ed. reads instead : " soul, although I know but little of him and have not met him for years. WALTON. He wants," etc.

and is ready to receive, as private tutor, any young gentleman in preparation for Oxford or Cambridge ; but only one. They live like princes, converse like friends, and part like lovers.*

COTTON. Here he comes : I never saw such a profusion of snow-white hair.

WALTON. Let us go up and meet him.

OLDWAYS. Welcome, my friends ! will you walk back into the house, or sit awhile in the shade here ?

WALTON. We will sit down in the grass, on each side of your arm-chair, good master William. Why, how is this ? here are tulips and other flowers by the thousand growing out of the turf. You are all of a piece, my sunny saint ; you are always concealing the best things about you, except your counsel, your raisin-wine, and your money.

OLDWAYS. The garden was once divided by borders : a young gentleman, my private pupil, was fond of leaping : his heels ruined my choicest flowers, ten or twenty at a time. I remonstrated : he patted me on the shoulder, and said, " My dear Mr. Oldways, in these borders if you miss a flower you are uneasy ; now, if the whole garden were in turf, you would be delighted to discover one. Turf it then, and leave the flowers to grow or not to grow, as may happen." I mentioned it to my wife: " Suppose we do," said she. It was done ; and the boy's remark, I have found by experience, is true.

WALTON. You have some very nice flies about the trees here, friend Oldways. Charles, do prythee lay thy hand upon that green one. He has it ! he has it ! bravely done, upon my life ! I never saw anything achieved so admirably—not a wing nor an antenna the worse for it. Put him into this box. Thou art caught, but shalt catch others : lie softly.

COTTON. The transport of dad Walton will carry him off (I would lay a wager) from the object of his ride.

OLDWAYS. What was that, sir ?

COTTON. Old Donne, I suspect, is nothing to such a fly.

* I pay this tribute to my worthy old tutor, Mr. Langley of Ashbourne, under whose tuition I passed a year between Rugby and Oxford. He would take only one private pupil, and never had but me. The kindness of him and his wife to me was parental. They died nearly together ; about five-and-twenty years ago.[1] Never was a youth blest with three such indulgent and affectionate private tutors as I was ; before by the elegant and generous Doctor John Sleath at Rugby, and after by the saintly Benwell at Oxford.—W. S. L.

[1] Footnote ends at "ago" in 1st ed.

WALTON. All things in their season.

COTTON. Come, I carried the rods in my hand all the way.

OLDWAYS. I never could have believed, master Izaak, that you would have trusted your tackle out of your own hand.

WALTON. Without cogent reason, no indeed: but—let me whisper. I told youngster it was because I carried a hunting-whip, and could not hold that and rod too. But why did I carry it, bethink you?

OLDWAYS. I can not guess.

WALTON. I must come behind your chair and whisper softlier. I have that in my pocket which might make the dogs inquisitive and troublesome—a rare paste, of my own invention. When son Cotton sees me draw up gill after gill, and he can do nothing, he will respect me : not that I have to complain of him as yet : and he shall know the whole at supper, after [1] the first day's sport.

COTTON. Have you asked ?

WALTON. Anon : have patience.

COTTON. Will no reminding do ? Not a rod or line, or fly of any colour, false or true, shall you have, dad Izaak, before you have made to our kind host here your intended application.

OLDWAYS. No ceremony with me, I desire. Speak and have.

WALTON. Oldways, I think you were curate to master Donne ?

OLDWAYS. When I was first in holy orders, and [2] he was ready for another world.

WALTON. I have heard it reported that you have some of his earlier poetry.

OLDWAYS. I have (I believe) a trifle or two : but if he were living he would not wish them to see the light.

WALTON. Why not ? he had nothing to fear: his fame was established ; and he was a discreet and holy man.

OLDWAYS. He was almost in his boyhood when he wrote it, being but in his twenty-third year, and subject to fits of love.

COTTON. This passion then can not have had for its object the daughter of Sir George More, whom he saw not until afterward.

OLDWAYS. No, nor was that worthy lady called Margaret, as was this, who scattered so many pearls in his path, he was wont to say, that he trod uneasily on them and could never skip them.

WALTON. Let us look at them in his poetry.

---

[1] From " after " to " sport " added in 2nd ed.
[2] From " and " to " world " added in 2nd ed.

WALTON, COTTON, AND OLDWAYS

OLDWAYS. I know not whether he would consent thereto, were he living, the lines running so totally on the amorous.

WALTON. Faith and troth ! we mortals are odd fishes. We care not how many see us in choler, when we rave and bluster and make as much noise and bustle as we can : but if the kindest and most generous affection comes across us, we suppress every sign of it, and hide ourselves in nooks and coverts. Out with the drawer, my dear Oldways ; we have seen Donne's sting ; in justice to him let us now have a sample of his honey.

OLDWAYS. Strange, that you never asked me before.

WALTON. I am fain to write his life, now one can sit by Dove-side and hold the paper upon one's knee, without fear that some unlucky catchpole of a rheumatism tip one upon the shoulder. I have many things to say in Donne's favour : let me add to them, by your assistance, that he not only loved well and truly, as was proved in his marriage, though like a good angler he changed his fly, and did not at all seasons cast his rod over the same water ; but that his heart opened early to the genial affections ; that his satire was only the overflowing of his wit ; that he made it administer to his duties ; that he ordered it to officiate as he would his curate, and perform half the service of the church for him.

COTTON. Pray, who was the object of his affections ?

OLDWAYS. The damsel was Mistress Margaret Hayes.

COTTON. I am curious to know, if you will indulge my curiosity, what figure of a woman she might be.

OLDWAYS. She was of lofty stature, red-haired (which some folks dislike), but with comely white eyebrows, a very [1] slender transparent nose, and elegantly thin lips, covering with due astringency a treasure of pearls beyond price, which, as her lover would have it, she never ostentatiously displayed. Her chin was somewhat long, with what I should have simply called a sweet dimple in it, quite proportionate ; but Donne said it was more than dimple ; that it was peculiar ; that her angelic face could not have existed without it, nor it without her angelic face ; that is, unless by a new dispensation. He was much taken thereby, and mused upon it deeply ; calling it in moments of joyousness the cradle of all sweet fancies, and in hours of suffering from her sedateness, the vale of death.

WALTON. So ingenious are men when the spring torrent of passion

[1] 1st ed. reads : " very slender nose, and thin lips. Her chin," etc.

165

shakes up and carries away their thoughts, covering (as it were) the green meadow of still homely life with pebbles and shingle, some colourless and obtuse, some sharp and sparkling.

COTTON. I hope he was happy in her at last.

OLDWAYS. Ha![1] ha! here we have 'em. Strong lines! Happy, no; he was not happy. He was forced to renounce her by what he then called his evil destiny; and wishing, if not to forget her, yet to assuage his grief under the impediments to their union, he made a voyage to Spain and the Azores with the Earl of Essex. When this passion first blazed out he was in his twentieth year; for the physicians do tell us that where the genius is ardent the passions are precocious. The lady had profited by many more seasons than he had, and carried with her manifestly the fruits of circumspection. No benefice falling unto him, nor indeed there being fit preparation, she submitted to the will of Providence. Howbeit, he could not bring his mind to reason until ten years after, when he married the daughter of the worshipful Sir George More.

COTTON. I do not know whether the arduous step of matrimony, on which many a poor fellow has broken his shin, is a step geometrically calculated for bringing us to Reason : but I have seen Passion run up it in a minute, and down it in half a one.

OLDWAYS. Young gentleman! my patron the doctor was none of the light-hearted and oblivious.

COTTON. Truly I should think it a hard matter to forget such a beauty as his muse and his chaplain have described; at least if one had ever stood upon the brink of matrimony with her. It is allowable, I hope, to be curious concerning the termination of so singular an attachment.

OLDWAYS. She would listen to none other.

COTTON. Surely she must have had good ears to have heard one.

OLDWAYS. No pretender had the hardihood to come forward too obtrusively. Donne had the misfortune, as he then thought it, to outlive her, after a courtship of about five years, which enabled him to contemplate her ripening beauties at leisure, and to bend over the opening flowers of her virtues and accomplishments. Alas! they were lost to the world (unless by example) in her forty-seventh spring.

COTTON. He might then leisurely bend over them, and quite as easily shake the seed out as smell them. Did she refuse him then ?

[1] From " Ha ! " to " obtrusively " added in 2nd ed.

WALTON, COTTON, AND OLDWAYS

OLDWAYS. He dared not ask her.

COTTON. Why, verily, I should have boggled at that said vale (I think) myself.

OLDWAYS. Izaak! our young friend master Cotton is not sedate enough yet, I suspect, for a right view and perception of poetry. I doubt whether these affecting verses on her loss will move him greatly : somewhat, yes ; there is in the beginning so much simplicity, in the middle so much reflection, in the close so much grandeur and sublimity, no scholar can peruse them without strong emotion. Take and read them.

COTTON. Come, come ; do not keep them to yourself, dad ! I have the heart of a man, and will bear the recitation as valiantly as may be.

WALTON. I will read aloud the best stanza only. What strong language !

> Her one hair would hold a dragon,
> Her one eye would burn an earth :
> Fall, my tears ! fill each your flagon !
> Millions fall ! A dearth ! a dearth !

COTTON. The Doctor must have been desperate about the fair Margaret.

WALTON. His verses are fine indeed : one feels for him, poor man !

COTTON. And wishes him nearer to Stourbridge, or some other glass-furnace. He must have been at great charges.

OLDWAYS. Lord help the youth ! tell him, Izaak, *that* is poetical, and means nothing.

WALTON. He has an inkling of it, I misgive me.

COTTON. How could he write so smoothly in his affliction, when he exhibited nothing of the same knack afterward ?

WALTON. I don't know ; unless it may be that men's verses like their knees stiffen by age.[1]

OLDWAYS. I do like vastly your glib verses ; but you can not be at once easy and majestical.

WALTON. It is only our noble rivers that enjoy this privilege. The greatest conqueror in the world never had so many triumphal arches erected to him as our middle-sized brooks have.

OLDWAYS. Now, master Izaak, by your leave, I do think you are

---

[1] 1st ed. reads : " age. COTTON. One would wish the stiffness somewhere else. OLDWAYS. Ay, truly, I do like," etc.

167

wrong in calling them triumphal. The ancients would have it that arches over waters were signs of subjection.

WALTON. The ancients may have what they will, excepting your good company for the evening, which (please God !) we shall keep to ourselves. They were mighty people for subjection and subjugation.

OLDWAYS. Virgil says, " Pontem indignatus Araxes."

WALTON. Araxes was testy enough under it, I dare to aver. But what have you to say about the matter, son Cotton ?

COTTON. I dare not decide either against my father or mine host.

OLDWAYS. So, we are yet no friends.

COTTON. Under favour then, I would say that we but acknowledge the power of rivers and runlets in bridging them ; for without so doing we could not pass. We are obliged to offer them a crown or diadem as the price of their acquiescence.

OLDWAYS. Rather do I think that we are feudatory to them much in the same manner as the dukes of Normandy were to the kings of France, pulling them out of their beds, or making them lie narrowly and uneasily therein.

WALTON. Is that between thy fingers, Will, another piece of honest old Donne's poetry ?

OLDWAYS. Yes ; these and one other are the only pieces I have kept : for we often throw away or neglect, in the lifetime of our friends, those things which in some following age are searched after through all the libraries in the world. What [1] I am about to read he composed in the meridian heat of youth and genius.

> She was so beautiful, had God but died
>   For her, and none beside,
> Reeling with holy joy from east to west
>   Earth would have sunk down blest ;
> And, burning with bright zeal, the buoyant Sun
>   Cried thro' his worlds *well done !*

He must have had an eye on the Psalmist ; for I would not asseverate that he was inspired, master Walton, in the theological sense of the word ; but I do verily believe I discover here a thread of the mantle.

COTTON. And with enough of the nap on it to keep him hot as a muffin when one slips the butter in.

---

[1] From " What " to " wish " added in 2nd ed.

WALTON, COTTON, AND OLDWAYS

OLDWAYS. True. Nobody would dare to speak thus but from authority. The Greeks and Romans, he remarked, had neat baskets, but scanty simples; and did not press them down so closely as they might have done; and were fonder of nosegays than of sweet-pots. He told me the rose of Paphos was of one species, the rose of Sharon of another. Whereat he burst forth to the purpose,

> Rather give me the lasting rose of Sharon,
> But dip it in the oil that oil'd thy beard, O Aaron!

Nevertheless, I could perceive that he was of so equal a mind that he liked them equally in their due season. These majestical verses——

COTTON. I am anxious to hear the last of 'em.

OLDWAYS. No wonder: and I will joyfully gratify so laudable a wish. He wrote this among the earliest:

> Juno was proud, Minerva stern,
> Venus would rather toy than learn.
> What fault is there in Margaret Hayes?
> Her high disdain and pointed stays.

I do not know whether, it being near our dinner-time, I ought to enter so deeply as I could into a criticism on it, which the Doctor himself, in a single evening, taught me how to do. Charley is rather of the youngest; but I will be circumspect. That Juno was proud may be learned from Virgil. The following passages in him and other Latin poets——

COTTON. We will examine them all after dinner, my dear sir.

OLDWAYS. The nights are not mighty long; but we shall find time, I trust.

> Minerva stern.

Excuse me a moment: my Homer is in the study, and my memory is less exact than it was formerly.

COTTON. O my good Mr. Oldways! do not let us lose a single moment of your precious company. Doctor Donne could require no support from these heathens, when he had the dean and chapter on his side.

OLDWAYS. A few parallel passages.—One would wish to write as other people have written.

COTTON. We must sleep at Uttoxeter.

OLDWAYS. I hope not.

WALTON. We must indeed ; and if we once get into your learning, we shall be carried down the stream, without the power even of wishing to mount it.

OLDWAYS. Well, I will draw in then.

Venus would rather toy than learn.

Now, Master Izaak, does that evince a knowledge of the world, a knowledge of men and manners, or not ? In our days we have nothing like it : exquisite wisdom ! Reason and meditate as you ride along, and inform our young friend here how the beautiful trust in their beauty, and how little they learn from experience, and how they trifle and toy. Certainly the Venus here is Venus Urania ; the Doctor would dissertate upon none other ; yet even she, being a Venus—the sex is the sex—ay, Izaak !

Her high disdain and pointed stays.

Volumes and volumes are under these words. Briefly, he could find no other faults in his beloved than the defences of her virgin chastity against his marital and portly ardour. What can be more delicately or more learnedly expressed !

WALTON. This is the poetry to reason upon from morning to night.

COTTON. By my conscience is it ! he wrongs it greatly who ventures to talk a word about it, unless after long reflection, or after the instruction of the profound author.

OLDWAYS. Izaak, thou hast a son worthy of thee, or about to become so—the son here of thy adoption—how grave and thoughtful !

WALTON. These verses are testimonials of a fine fancy in Donne ; and I like the man the better who admits Love into his study late and early : for which two reasons I seized the lines at first with some avidity. On second thoughts, however, I doubt whether I shall insert them in my biography, or indeed hint at the origin of them. In the whole story of his marriage with the daughter of Sir George More there is something so sacredly romantic, so full of that which bursts from the tenderest heart and from the purest, that I would admit no other light or landscape to the portraiture. For if there is aught, precedent or subsequent, that offends our view of an admirable character, or intercepts or lessens it, we may surely cast it down and suppress it, and neither be called injudicious nor disingenuous. I

170

think it no more requisite to note every fit of anger or of love, than to chronicle the returns of a hiccup, or the times a man rubs between his fingers a sprig of sweet-briar to extract its smell. Let the character be taken in the complex ; and let the more obvious and best peculiarities be markt plainly and distinctly, or (if those predominate) the worst. These latter I leave to others, of whom the school is full, who like anatomy the better because the subject of their incisions was hanged. When I would sit upon a bank in my angling I look for the even turf, and do not trust myself so willingly to a rotten stump or a sharp one. I am not among those who, speaking ill of the virtuous, say, " Truth obliges me to confess—the interests of Learning and of Society demand from me—" and such things ; when this Truth of theirs is the elder sister of Malevolence, and teaches her half her tricks ; and when the interests of Learning and of Society may be found in the printer's ledger, under the author's name, by the side of shillings and pennies.

OLDWAYS. Friend Izaak, you are indeed exempt from all suspicion of malignity ; and I never heard you intimate that you carry in your pocket the *letters patent* of Society for the management of her interests in this world below. Verily do I believe that both Society and Learning will pardon you, though you never talk of *pursuing*, or *exposing*, or *laying bare*, or *cutting up ;* or employ any other term in their behalf drawn from the woods and forests, the chase and butchery. Donne fell into unhappiness by aiming at espousals with a person of higher condition than himself.

WALTON. His affections happened to alight upon one who was ; and in most cases I would recommend it rather than the contrary, for the advantage of the children in their manners and in their professions.

Light and worthless men, I have always observed, choose the society of those who are either much above or much below them ; and, like dust and loose feathers, are rarely to be found in their places. Donne was none such : he loved his equals, and would find them where he could : when he could not find them he could sit alone. This seems an easy matter ; and yet, masters, there are more people who could run along a rope from yonder spire to this grass-plot, than can do it.

OLDWAYS. Come, gentles : the girl raps at the garden-gate. I hear the ladle against the lock : dinner waits for us.

XVI. ADMIRAL BLAKE AND HUMPHREY BLAKE

(Last Fruit, 1853 ; Wks., 1876.)

BLAKE. Humphrey ! it hath pleased God, upon this day, to vouchsafe unto the English arms a signal victory. Brother ! it grieves my heart that neither of us can rejoice in it as we should do. Evening is closing on the waters : our crews are returning thanks and offering up prayers to the Almighty. Alas ! alas ! that we, who ought to be the most grateful for his protection, and for the spirit he hath breathed into our people, should be the only men in this vast armament whom he hath sorely chastened ! that we of all others should be ashamed to approach the throne of grace among our countrymen and comrades ! There are those who accuse you, and they are brave and honest men—there are those, O Humphrey ! Humphrey !—was the sound ever heard in our father's house ?— who accuse you, brother ! brother !—how can I ever find utterance for the word ?—yea, of cowardice.

Stand off : I want no help : let me be.

HUMPHREY. To-day, for the first time in my life, I was in the midst of many ships of superior force firing upon mine, at once and incessantly.

BLAKE. The very position where most intrepidity was required. Were none with you ? were none in the same danger ? Shame ! Shame ! You owed many an example, and you defrauded them of it. They could not gain promotion, the poor seamen ! they could not hope for glory in the wide world : example they might have hoped for. You would not have robbed them of their prize-money——

HUMPHREY. Brother ! was ever act of dishonesty imputed to a Blake ?

BLAKE.—Until now. You have robbed them even of the chance they had of winning it : you have robbed them of the pride, the just and chastened pride, awaiting them at home : you have robbed their children of their richest inheritance, a father's good repute.

HUMPHREY. Despite of calumniators, there are worthy men ready to speak in my favour, at least in extenuation——

ADMIRAL BLAKE AND HUMPHREY BLAKE

BLAKE. I will hear them, as becomes me, altho I myself am cognizant of your default; for during the conflict how anxiously, as often as I could, did I look toward your frigate! Especial care could not be fairly taken that aid at the trying moment should be at hand: other vessels were no less exposed than yours; and it was my duty to avoid all partiality in giving my support.

HUMPHREY. Grievous as my short-coming may be, surely I am not precluded from what benefit the testimony of my friends may afford me.

BLAKE. Friends—ah thou hast many, Humphrey! and many hast thou well deserved. In youth, in boyhood, in childhood, thy honied temper brought ever warm friends about thee. Easiness of disposition conciliates bad and good alike: it draws affections to it, and relaxes enmities: but that same easiness renders us, too often, negligent of our graver duties. God knows, I may without the same excuse (if it is any) be impeached of negligence in many of mine; but never where the honour or safety of my country was concerned. Wherefore the Almighty's hand, in this last battle, as in others no less prosperous, hath conducted and sustained me.

Humphrey! did thy heart wax faint within thee through want of confidence in our sole Deliverer?

HUMPHREY. Truly I have no such plea.

BLAKE. It were none; it were an aggravation.

HUMPHREY. I confess I am quite unable to offer any adequate defence for my backwardness, my misconduct. Oh! could the hour return, the battle rage again. How many things are worse than death! how few things better! I am twelve years younger than you are, brother, and want your experience.

BLAKE. Is that your only want? Deplorable is it to know, as now I know, that you will never have it, and that you will have a country which you can never serve.

HUMPHREY. Deplorable it is indeed. God help me!

BLAKE. Worse evil soon may follow; worse to me, remembering thy childhood. Merciful Father! after all the blood that hath been shed this day, must I devote a brother's?

HUMPHREY. O Robert! always compassionate, always kind and generous! do not inflict on yourself so lasting a calamity, so unavailing a regret!

Listen!—not to me—but listen. I hear under your bow the

173

sound of oars. I hear them drawn into boats : verily do I believe that several of the captains are come to intercede for me, as they said they would do.

BLAKE. Intercession is vain. Honorable men shall judge you. A man to be honorable must be strictly just, at the least. Will brave men spare you ? It lies with them. Whatever be their sentence, my duty is (God give me strength !) to execute it.

Gentlemen ! who sent for you ?   [*Officers come aboard.*

SENIOR OFFICER. General ! we, the captains of your fleet, come before you upon the most painful of duties.

BLAKE (*to himself*). I said so : his doom is sealed. (*To* Senior Officer.) Speak, sir ! speak out, I say. A man who hath fought so bravely as you have fought to-day ought never to hesitate and falter.

SENIOR OFFICER. General ! we grieve to say that Captain Humphrey Blake, commanding a frigate in the service of the Commonwealth, is accused of remissness in his duty.

BLAKE. I know it. Where is the accuser ? What ! no answer from any of you ? Then I am he. Captain Humphrey Blake is here impleaded of neglecting to perform his uttermost in the seizure or destruction of the enemy's galloons. Is the crime—write it, write it down—no need to speak it here—capital ? Negligence ? no worse ? but worse can there be ?

SENIOR OFFICER. We would humbly represent——

BLAKE. Representations, if made at all, must be made elsewhere. He goes forthwith to England. Return each of you to his vessel. Delinquency, grave delinquency, there hath been, of what nature and to what extent, you must decide. Take him away. (*Alone.*) Just God ! am I the guilty man, that I should drink to the very dregs such a cup of bitterness ?

Forgive, forgive, O Lord ! the sinful cry of thy servant ! Thy will be done ! thou hast shown thy power this day, O Lord ! now show, and make me worthy of, thy mercy ! *

---

* Various and arduous as were Blake's duties, such on all occasions were his circumspection and discretion, that no fault could be detected or invented in him. His victories were won against all calculation but his own. Recollecting, however late, his services ; recollecting that in private life, in political, in military, his purity was ever the same ; England will place Robert Blake the foremost and the highest of her defenders. He was the archetype of her Nelsons, Collingwoods, and Pellews. Of all the men that ever bore a sword, none was worthier of that awful trust.—W. S. L.

174

XVII. MILTON AND ANDREW MARVEL *

(*Imag. Convers.*, ii., 1824 ; ii., 1826 ; *Wks.*, i., 1846 ; *Wks.*, iv., 1876.)

MILTON. Friend Andrew, I am glad to hear that you amuse your-self in these bad times by the composition of a comedy, and that you have several plans in readiness for others. Now let me advise you to copy the better part of what the Greeks and Romans called the *old*, and to introduce songs and music, which, suitable as they are to Tragedy, are more so to the sister Muse. Furthermore, I could desire to see a piece modeled [1] in every part on the Athenian scheme, with the names and characters and manners of times past. For surely you would not add to the immorality of the age, by represent-ing anything of the present mode upon the theatre. Although we are more abundant in follies, which rather than vices are the ground-work of comedy, we experience less disgust in touching those of other times than of our own ; and in a drama the most ancient would have the most novelty. I know that all the periods and all the nations of the world united, have less variety of character than we find in this one city ; yet, as you write to amuse yourself and a few learned friends, I am persuaded you would gladly walk out of it for once, and sit down to delineate a Momus or a Satyr with at least as much complacency as a vulgar fopling or a partycoloured buffoon.

O Andrew ! albeit [2] our learning raiseth up against us many enemies among the low, and more among the powerful, yet doth it invest us with grand and glorious privileges, and confer [3] on us a largeness [4] of beatitude. We enter our studies, and enjoy a society which we alone can bring together : we raise no jealousy by convers-ing with one in preference to another : we give no offence to the most

---

* Milton had given his opinion in full on government and religion, and on many kinds of poetry ; what he may be supposed to have thought on comedy was wanting.—W. S. L. [Added in 3rd ed.]

[1] 1st and 2nd eds. read : " modeled in all parts."
[2] 1st and 2nd eds. read : " although."
[3] 1st ed. reads " grant to " ; 2nd ed. reads : " conferr."
[4] 1st ed. reads : " largess."

illustrious by questioning him as long as we will, and leaving him as abruptly. Diversity of opinion raises no tumult in our presence : each interlocutor stands before us, speaks or is silent, and we adjourn or decide the business at our leisure. Nothing is past which we desire to be present ; and we enjoy by anticipation somewhat like the power which I imagine we shall possess hereafter, of sailing on a wish from world to world. Surely you would turn away as far as possible from the degraded state of our country ; you would select any vices and follies for description, rather than those that jostle us in our country-walks, return with us to our house-doors, and smirk on us in silks and satins at our churches.

Come, my old friend, take down your *hortus siccus :* the live plants you would gather do both stink and sting : prythee leave them to wither or to rot, or to be plucked and collated by more rustic hands.

MARVEL. I entertain an utter contempt for the populace, whether in robes or tatters ; whether the face be bedaubed with cinnabar or with dirt from the alleys and shops. It appears to me, however, that there is as much difference between tragedy and comedy as between the heavens and the clouds ; and that comedy draws its life from its mobility. We must take manners as we find them, and copy [1] from the individual, not the species ; into which fault Menander fell and seduced his followers. The characters whereon [2] he raised his glory are trivial and contemptible.

> Dum fallax servus, durus pater, improba lena
> Vivent, dum meretrix blanda, Menander erit.

His wisdom towered high above them, and he clothed [3] with smiles what Euripides charged with spleen. The beauty of his moral sentences was hurtful to the spirit of comedy, and I am convinced that, if we could recover his works, we should find them both less facetious and less dramatic than those of Plautus. Once, by way of experiment, I attempted to imitate his manner, as [4] far as I could judge of it from the fragments we possess. I will give you a specimen : it is the best I have.

> Friendship, in each successive stage of life,
> As we approach him, varies to the view :

---

[1] 1st and 2nd eds. read : " draw."
[2] 1st and 2nd eds. read : " characters on which . . . were trivial," etc.
[3] 1st and 2nd eds. read : " cloathed."
[4] From " as " to " possess " added in 3rd ed.

176

MILTON AND ANDREW MARVEL

In youth he wears the face of Love himself,
Of Love without his arrows and his wings ;
Soon afterward with Bacchus and with Pan
Thou findest him, or hearest him resign
To some dog-pastor by the quiet fire,
(With much good-will and jocular adieu)
His ageworn mule or brokenhearted steed.
Fly not, as thou wert wont, to his embrace,
Lest, after one long yawning gaze, he swear
Thou art the best good fellow in the world,
But he had quite forgotten thee, by Jove !
Or laughter wag his newly bearded chin
At recollection of his childish hours.
But wouldst thou see, young man, his latest form,
When e'en this laughter, e'en this memory fails ?
Look at yon figtree statue, golden once,
As all would deem it ; rottenness falls out
At every little chink the worms have made,
And if thou triest to lift it up again
It breaks upon thee.   Leave it, touch it not,
Its very lightness would encumber thee :
Come, thou hast seen it ; 'tis enough ; away !

MILTON. This indeed is in the manner I would propose.

MARVEL. Yet if it were spoken on our stage,[1] I should be condemned as a man ignorant of the art ; and justly too ; for it accords
not with its complexion.   Inevitable events and natural reflections,
but reflections not exhibited before, and events not expected, please
me better than the most demonstrable facts, the most sober truths,
the most clever improbabilities, and the most acute repartees.   In
comedy we should oftener raise reflections than present them.

Now for plot.

Intricacy [2] was always held necessary on the modern stage, and
the more so when delicacy was the least.   It was however so
difficult to make the audience keep watch and ward for it, and to
command an uninterrupted attention for five whole acts, that many
of the best writers, from Terence to the present age, have combined
two plots, hoping that what is twisted together will untwist together,
and leaving a great deal to the goodness of Providence, and to the
faith and charity of their fellow creatures.

MILTON. True enough.   Your plotters bring many great changes
into many whole families, and sometimes into several and distant

---

[1] 1st and 2nd eds. read : " theatre."   [2] See Forster's *Life*, 1st ed., p. 389.

countries, within the day ; and, what is more difficult and incredible, send off all parties well satisfied, excepting one scape-goat. For my own share I am content with seeing a fault wittily rebuked and checked effectually, and think *that* surprising enough, considering the time employed in doing it, without the formation of attachments, the begetting or finding of children, bickerings, buffetings, deaths, marriages, distresses, wealth again, love again, whims and suspicions, shaking heads, and shaking hands. These things are natural, I confess it ; but one would rather breathe between them, and perhaps one would think it no bad husbandry to put some of them off until another season. The combination of them, marvellous [1] as it appears, is less difficult to contrive than to credit.

MARVEL. I have always been an idle man, and have read or attended the greater part of the plays that are extant, and will venture to affirm that, exclusive of Shakespeare's and some Spanish pieces never represented nor translated, there are barely half a dozen plots among them, comic and tragic. So that it is evidently a much easier matter to run over the usual variations, than to keep entirely in another tune, and to raise up no recollections. Both in tragedies and comedies the changes are pretty similar, and nearly in the same places. You perceive the turns and windings of the road a mile before you, and you know exactly the precipice down which the hero or heroine must fall. You can discover with your naked eye, who does the mischief and who affords the help ; where the assassin bursts forth with the dagger, and where the old gentleman shakes the crabstick over the shoulder of his dissolute nephew.

MILTON. I do not wish direction-posts to perplexities and intrigues : I oppose this agrarian law, this general inclosure act : I would not attempt to square the circle of poetry : and am avowedly a nonjuror to the doctrine of grace and predestination in the drama.

MARVEL. In my project, one action leads to and brings about another, naturally but not necessarily. The event is the confusion of the evil-doer, whose machinations are the sole means of accomplishing what their motion seemed calculated to thwart and overthrow. No character is introduced that doth not tend toward the development [2] of the plot ; no one is merely prompter to a witticism, or master of the ceremonies to a repartee.

---

[1] 1st and 2nd eds. read : " marvelous."
[2] 1st and 2nd eds. read : " developement."

MILTON AND ANDREW MARVEL

Characters in general are made subservient to the plot : here the plot is made subservient to the characters. All are real : I have only invited them to meet, and bestowed on them those abilities for conversation, without which a comedy might be very natural, but would not possess the nature of a comedy. I expose only what arises from the headiness of unruly passions, or is precipitated by the folly that verges upon vice. This exposure is in the corner of a room, not in the stocks nor in the market-place. Comedy with me sits in an easy chair, as Menander is represented by the statuary : for it is as possible to be too busy on the scenic theatre as it is on the theatre of life. To those who admire the double plot and the machinery of the rope-walk, I only say, " Go to my betters, whom you have so long neglected ; carry off from them as much as you can bear ; you are then welcome to rip up my sheet, and to sew a scene in wherever the needle will go through. In this manner, the good may be made acceptable by the new, and the new can be no loser by the good."

MILTON. You say nothing about the chorus. I have introduced it, you know, in my *Samson Agonistes*, and intend to bring it forward in my *Macbeth*.

MARVEL. Dear John ! thou art lucky in having escaped two Stuarts ; and luckier wilt thou be if thou escapest one Macbeth. Contend with Homer, but let Shakespeare rest : drop that work ; prythee drop it for ever : thou mayest appear as high as he is (for who can measure either of you ?) if thou wilt only stand some way off.

In tragedy the chorusses [1] were grave people, called upon, or ready without it, to give advice and consolation in cases of need. To set them singing and moralising amid the dolefullest emergencies, when the poet should be *reporting progress*, is like sticking a ballad upon a turnstile to hasten folks on. The comic poet called out his regular chorus, in imitation of the tragic, till the genius of Menander took a middle flight between Aristophanes and Euripides. Comedy had among the ancients her ovations, but not her triumphs.

MILTON. Menander's form, which the Romans and French have imitated, pleases me less than the older. He introduced better manners, but employing no variety of verse, and indulging in few sallies of merriment, I incline to believe that he more frequently

---

[1] 2nd ed. reads : " choruses."

179

instructed than entertained. In[1] the joyous glades of Aristophanes the satyrs did not dance without the nymphs, and in the rich variety of the festival the purest and most refreshing water was mixed with the most sparkling wine. If it were not tedious to continue or take up again a metaphor, I should say that all the fruit of Jonson, and those like him, is mashed and mealy ; and, where there is any flavour at all, it is the strong flavour of fermentation or of mustiness.

The verse itself of Aristophanes is a dance of Bacchanals : one can not read it with composure. He had, however, but little true wit, whatever may be asserted to the contrary. There is abundance of ribaldry, and of that persecution by petulance which the commonalty call banter.

MARVEL. He takes delight in mocking and ridiculing the manner of Euripides. In my opinion, if a modern may form one upon the subject, he might with his ingenuity have seized more points to let his satire lighten on, and have bent them to his purpose with more dexterity and address.

MILTON. His ridicule on the poetry is misplaced, on the manners is inelegant. Euripides was not less wise than Socrates, nor less tender than Sappho. There is a tenderness which elevates the genius : there is also a tenderness which corrupts the heart. The latter, like every impurity, is easy to communicate ; the former is difficult to conceive. Strong minds alone possess it ; virtuous minds alone value it. I hold it abominable to turn into derision what is excellent. To render undesirable what ought to be desired, is the most mischievous and diabolical of malice. To exhibit him as contemptible, who ought, according to the conscience of the exhibitor, to be respected and revered, is a crime the more odious, as it can be committed only by violence to his feelings, against the reclamations of Justice, and among the struggles of Virtue. And what is the tendency of this brave exploit ? To cancel the richest legacy that ever was bequeathed to him, and to prove his own bastardy in relation to the most illustrious of his species. If it is disgraceful to demolish or obliterate a tombstone over the body of the most obscure among the dead, if it is an action for which a boy would be whipped as guilty of the worst idleness and mischief, what is it to overturn the monument that Gratitude has erected to Genius, and to break the lamp that is lighted by Devotion over against the image

[1] From " In " to " mustiness " added in 3rd ed.

of Love ? The writings of the wise are the only riches our posterity can not squander : why depreciate them ? To Antiquity again [1]; but afar from Aristophanes.

MARVEL. Our admiration of Antiquity is in part extraneous from her merits : yet even this part, strange as the assertion may appear, is well founded. We learn many things from the ancients which it cost them no trouble to teach, and upon which they employed no imagination, no learning, no time. Those among us who have copied them, have not succeeded. To produce any effect on morals or on manners, or indeed to attract any attention, which, whatever be the pretext, is the principal if not the only aim of most writers, and certainly of all the comic, we must employ the language and consult the habits of our age. We may introduce a song without retrospect to the old comedy ; a moral sentence, without authority from the new. The characters, even on their improved and purified stage, were, we know, of so vulgar and uncleanly a cast, that, with all their fine reflections, there was something like the shirt of Lazarus patched with the purple of Dives. Do not imagine I am a detractor from the glory of our teachers, from their grace, their elegance, and their careful weeding away of tiny starvling thoughts, that higher and more succulent may have room.

MILTON. No, Marvel, no. Between their poetry and ours you perceive as great a difference as between a rose and a dandelion. There is, if I may express myself so, without pursuing a metaphor till it falls exhausted at my feet, a sort of refreshing odour flying off it perpetually ; not enough to oppress or to satiate ; nothing is beaten or bruised ; nothing smells of the stalk ; the flower itself is half concealed by the Genius of it hovering round. Write on the same principles as guided them.

MARVEL. Yes ; but I would not imitate them further. I will not be pegged down to any plot, nor follow any walk, however well rolled, where the persons of the drama can not consistently lead the way.

MILTON. Reasonable enough : but why should not both comedy and tragedy be sometimes so disciplined as may better fit them for our closets ? I allow that their general intention is for action : it is also the nature of odes to be accompanied by voices and instruments. I only would suggest to you that a man of learning, with a genius suited to comedy, may as easily found it upon antiquity as

[1] 1st and 2nd eds. read : " to Antiquity again . . . but afar," etc.

the tragedian of equal abilities his tragedy, and that the one might be made as acceptable to the study as the other to the stage. I would not hamper you with rules and precedents. Comply with no other laws or limits than such as are necessary to the action. There may be occasion for songs, and there may not ; beside, a poet may be capable of producing a good comedy who is incapable of composing a tolerable stanza ; and, on the other hand, Pindar himself might have been lost in a single scene.

MARVEL. True : but tell me, friend John, are you really serious in your proposal of interspersing a few antiquated words, that my comedy may be acceptable to the readers of Plautus and Terence ? This I hear.

MILTON. I have, on several occasions, been a sufferer by the delivery of my sentiments to a friend. Antiquated words, used sparingly and characteristically, give often a force, and always a gravity, to composition. It is not every composition that admits them : a comedy *may* in one character, but charily and choicely.

There is in Plautus a great fund of language and of wit : he is far removed from our Shakespeare, but resembles him more than any other of the ancients. In reading him and Terence, my delight arises not so materially from the aptitude of character and expression, as from a clear and unobstructed insight into the feelings and manners of those ancient times, and an admission into the conversations to which Scipio and Lælius attended.

You [1] will carefully observe the proper and requisite unities, not according to the wry rigour of our neighbours, who never take up an old idea without some extravagance in its application. We would not draw out a conspiracy in the presence of those who are conspired against ; nor hold it needful to call a council of postilions, before we decide on the distance we may allow to our heroes between the acts. Let others treat them as monkeys and parrots, loving to hear them chatter, tied by the leg. The music renders a removal of twenty or thirty miles, during the action, probable enough, unless you take out your watch, and look upon it while you are listening. In that case, although you oblige the poet to prove the pedigree of the horses, and to bring witnesses that such horses might go thus far without drawing bit, your reasons are insufficient by fifty minutes or an hour.

The historical dramas of Shakespeare should be designated by

[1] From " You " to " partaken " added in 2nd ed.

that name only, and not be called tragedies, lest persons who reflect little (and how few reflect much ?) should try them by the rules of Aristoteles ; which would be as absurd as to try a gem upon a touchstone. Shakespeare, in these particularly, but also in the rest, can only be relished by a people which retains its feelings and character in perfection. The French, more than any other, are transmuted by the stream that runs over them, like the baser metals. Beautiful poems, in dialogue too, may be composed on the greater part of a life, if that life be eventful, and if there be a proper choice of topics. *Votivâ veluti depicta tabellâ.*

No other than Shakespeare hath ever yet been able to give unceasing interest to similar pieces : but he has given it amply to such as understand him. Sometimes his levity (we hear) is misplaced. Human life is exhibited not only in its calamities and its cares, but in the gay unguarded hours of ebullient and confident prosperity ; and we are the more deeply interested in the reverses of those whose familiarity we have long enjoyed, and whose festivity we have recently partaken.

MARVEL. Now, what think you about the number of acts ?

MILTON. There is no reason, in nature or in art, why a drama should occupy five. Be assured, my friend Andrew, the fifth-act-men will hereafter be thought as absurd as the fifth-monarchy-men. The number of acts should be optional, like the number of scenes, and the division of them should equally be subordinate to the convenience of the poet in the procession of his events. In respect to duration, nothing is requisite or reasonable but that it should not loiter nor digress, and that it should not exhaust the patience nor disappoint the expectation of the audience. Dramatists have gone to work in this business with so much less of wisdom than of system, that I question, when they say a comedy or tragedy in *five acts,* whether they should not rather say in *five scenes ;* whether, in fact, the scenes should not designate the divisions, and the acts the subdivisions ; for the *scene* usually changes to constitute a new *act,* and when a fresh *actor* enters we usually call it a new *scene.* I do not speculate on anyone carrying the identity of place strictly throughout a whole performance, least of all, a tragedy, unless for the purpose of ridiculing some late French critics. As a tragedy must consist of opposite counsels and unforeseen events, if the author should exhibit his whole action in one hall or chamber, he would be laughed to scorn. Comedy is not formed to astonish : she neither expects nor wishes great changes. Let her argue rarely ; let her remark lightly ; if she reasons too well, her audience will leave her, and reflect upon it. Those generally are the most temperate who have large and well-stored cellars. You have everything at home, Andrew, and need not step out of your way. Those show that they possess much who hold much back.

MARVEL. Be not afraid of me : I will not push my characters forward, and make them stare most one upon another when they are best acquainted. The union of wisdom with humour is unexpected enough for me. I would rather see it than the finest piece of arras slit asunder, or the richest screen in Christendom overturned ; than the cleverest trick that was ever played among the scenes, or than a marriage that should surprise me like an Abyssinian's with a Laplander.

———

SECOND CONVERSATION

(Athenæum, 1862 ; Wks., v., 1876.)

MARVEL. Years have passed over our heads, friend Milton, since the first conversation we held together on the subject of poetry. It was mainly, I think, if not entirely, on the dramatic. We will now exchange a few words, and more than a few if you are willing, on the other kinds of it. The desire was excited in me by your present of *Paradise Regained*, which I thanked you for by letter as soon as I had read it through ; and I now, in person, thank you for it again.

MILTON. Parents are usually the most fond of their last offspring, especially if the fruit of their declining years : I was of mine ; I now hesitate.

MARVEL. Be contented : you have fairly got the better of the Devil. There is little in either of your poems that the reader would wish out. This cannot be said of the great Italian. Nearly all the characters in the *Inferno* and *Purgatorio* are wretches who excite no sympathy, and forward no action. Marking, page after page, the good, bad, and indifferent, I find scarcely a fifth part noted for reading a second time. This is not the case in the *Iliad*, the *Æneid*, the *Paradise Lost*.

MILTON. The great poet of Italy—for great he was by intensity

184

MILTON AND ANDREW MARVEL

of thought and comprehension—constructed a hell and a purgatory for the accommodation of popes, prelates, and other dignitaries. Daring as he was, he was afraid of nearer fires than those below ; hence a compendious satire he entitled a divine comedy. Never was there so spacious a theatre with so many actors.

MARVEL. Faith ! it is a comedy in which the actors find no joke.

MILTON. Alighieri wanted flexibility of muscle, and wore an iron mask ; yet how warm are the tears which the lover of Beatrice shed over Francesca da Rimini and over the children of Ugolino ! I would rather have written two such scenes than twenty such poems as the *Faery Queen.*

MARVEL. Allegory grows tiresome: nevertheless, you have found, as I have heard you say, much to please you in Spenser. The heart, I confess it, is never toucht by him ; and he does not excite even a light emotion.

MILTON. He leads us into no walks of Nature. A poet must do that, or forfeit his right to a seat in the upper house.

MARVEL. Grave as you are, and ever were, you have exprest to me your delight in the *Canterbury Tales,* and in him

> who left untold
> The story of Cambuscan bold.

MILTON. Frequently do I read the *Canterbury Tales,* and with pleasure undiminisht.* They are full of character and of life. You would hardly expect in so early a stage of our language such harmony as comes occasionally on the ear ; it ceases with the verse, but we are grateful for it, shortly as it stays with us.

MARVEL. Happily you are now at leisure for a ramble in the open field of poetry, and to catch the Muses

> Dancing in the checker'd shade.

Think what a pleasure it is to have landed at last, after all the perils of a tempestuous sea.

MILTON. I would rather be on a tempestuous ocean than on a

* A Bachelor of Arts, a Mr. Pycroft, without any authority, classes W. S. Landor with Byron and Wordsworth, as holding Chaucer cheap. Let this Conversation indicate the contrary. There is one Art, namely, the Ars poetica, in which the Bachelor is unlikely to take his Master's degree.—W. S. L. [" a Mr. Pycroft " : the Rev. James Pycroft, in his *Course of English Reading.*]

pestilential marsh, knowing that the one will grow calm, and that the other will not grow salubrious.

Andrew ! we are sold like sheep, and we must not even bleat.

MARVEL. What you have done, both in poetry and prose, was enough to startle the salesmen. Into your prose an irruption was often made by your poetry.

MILTON. This is wrong. We should keep them distinct, however impetuous may be the loftier and the stronger.

MARVEL. If you could have done it, we should have lost the grandest piece of harmony that ever was uttered from the heart of man.

MILTON. Where is that ?

MARVEL. In your dissertation on Prelaty ; it is this—

> When God commands to take the trumpet
> And blow a louder and a shriller blast,
> It rests not in Man's will what he shall do
> Or what he shall forbear.

Isaiah seems to be speaking.

MILTON. The only resemblance is that Isaiah spoke also in vain.

The deafest man can hear praise, and is slow to think any an excess. Friendship may sometimes step a few paces in advance of Truth ; and who would check her ? I had neither will nor power to break the imperious words that you cite, over-ruling my prose.

MARVEL. Certainly they are not like the bleatings you have just now complained of. Your voice was never lowered to that key, my brave Milton.

MILTON. I might not have retained what is left to me of it, were it not for your intercession.

MARVEL. You over-rate my services. True, I did go to the Lord Chancellor, who knew me by name only, and who courteously said, " *Mr. Marvel, I will see about it.*" You know what that phrase means, spoken by high officials. He went immediately, with feather in hat above his embroidered robes, to " see about " the house he is building, which is to overtop the Somersets and Northumberlands. Lucky dog, lawyer Hyde !

Neither much disappointed nor at all discomfited, but well knowing that no time was to be lost, I went forthwith to my Lord Rochester, who noticed me when he was a stripling. He never lookt so grave as when he heard me mention the cause of my visit. He turned his peruke half-round, and said, "*My good Marvel! it is a ticklish thing.*" Without a moment's pause I replied, " Do you mean the halter, my Lord ? " The peruke was again in the first position, with a pleasant smile on each side of its exuberant curls. Patting me on the shoulder, he said, " Well, well, Marvel ! I do like a hearty friend, even in a quondam stickler to the old rebel Nol. Hangmanship is not a craft I would patronise. But master John Milton was bitter against us. He would even have set fire to the lawn sleeves, which I am in duty bound to reverence. ' But when the wicked man turneth away '—you can go on with it ; I may peradventure be at a fault. I hope our gracious king has forgotten the sad catastrophe of his father. If he has not he may haply be reminded that John Milton had a hand in it, and then filial affection may, and indeed necessarily must, lead his Majesty toward the rope-walk. He hath so many cares of state, and is occupied in them so constantly and incessantly, that the occurrence in front of Whitehall shall have dropt out of his memory. Let us hope for the best." My reply was, " I will hope it, my Lord, from your known humanity and good temper. If my old friend receives no pardon from his most gracious sovran, he will be the only blind man that a gracious sovran ever helped to mount the gallows."

Whereat his Lordship broke into a peal of laughter, which stopt suddenly, and he said, " Faith and troth ! blind ! stone blind ! It would be too bad. Charley must keep the long cap folded up, in readiness for some fellow whose eyes require it. You saw my coach at the door. I was going for a private audience. I will mention the matter the first thing I do." He did, and you know the result.

MILTON. The Presbyterians are now more unfriendly to me than the Episcopalians are.

MARVEL. Their tempers are sourer, and they are more exasperated by the persecutions they are suffering. You have become calmer and milder. The best apples, rough when they are first gathered, grow richer in flavour late. There are zealots who complain that you are lukewarm.

MILTON. It is better to be lukewarm than to boil over. My opinions in theology have undergone a change. What they are will be known hereafter ; I have written them in Latin and I shall leave them behind me. For I would not anger any on this side of the grave. Resentment and controversy cool in the churchyard.

IMAGINARY CONVERSATIONS : ENGLISH

MARVEL. There are temperate men in Italy, and perhaps elsewhere, so scandalized at the contests and cruelties of sects, that they almost doubt whether the death of the emperor Julian was not a calamity to the world, and whether what we call paganism was ever so uncharitable, in other words so unchristian, as some exclusive creeds.

MILTON. Physicians propose to cure the effect of one poison by administering another. Presbyterianism twisted back the neck of Prelaty and poured a strong drastic down her throat. She kickt and screamed, and, when she got on her legs again, swore bitterly and called her servants to kick the intruders down stairs.

MARVEL. The old religions on several accounts are better than the later. They are less profuse of foul language, they domineer less, and they cost less ; they withdraw none from agriculture or home. The priests exposed no wares for sale, and they kept to their own temples and their own houses. I am no customer of those chapmen whose glass and crockery are so brittle as to draw blood if you break it. I side neither with the cropt nor the periwigged. I will never deal with the dealers in damnation, while I can hear cursing and swearing gratis in the stable-yard.

MILTON. Men's curses are stored up for them in heaven.

MARVEL. Lucky fellows if they can get up there and find anything better. May they not catch their own tost back to them waiting below ?

MILTON. Andrew ! in sooth thou art a merry Andrew. Methinks thou knowest more about the poets than about the divines. Curious name ! as if the study and profession of what relates to divinity made the man himself divine, as the study and profession of physic entitles one, and justly, to be called a physician.

MARVEL. Now then, having had enough of both, I am ready to be as disputatious as the worst of them. I am about to find fault with you on the score of poetry.

Surgit amari aliquid quod in ipsis floribus angit.

MILTON. After the sweet I am prepared for the bitter, which often happens in life, and it is only children who take the bitter first.

MARVEL. Now for it. You were not a very young man when you wrote how

Sweetest Shakespeare, Fancy's child,
Warbled his native woodnotes wild.

188

MILTON AND ANDREW MARVEL

After acknowledging the prettiness of the verses, I deny the propriety of the application. No poet was ever less a warbler of " woodnotes wild." In his earliest poems he was elaborate, and not exempt from stiff conceits, the fault of the age as exemplified by Spenser.

MILTON. In his later he takes wing over the world, beyond human sight, but heard above the clouds.

MARVEL. His Muse, to be in the fashion of the day, wore a starcht ruff about her neck.

You have fringed Jonson's " learned sock." I never had patience to go through, or to speak more properly to *undergo*, his tragedies. In coarse comedy he succeeds better ; but comedy ought never to be coarse. Indelicate as was Aristophanes, there was an easy motion and an unaffected grace in every step he took. Plautus comes far behind, and Terence not quite up to Plautus. Be not angry with me if Molière is my delight.

MILTON. He has written since I was a reader ; and there is nobody in the house who can pronounce French intelligibly. My nephew reads Latin to me ; and he reminded me one day that Sir Philip Sidney tried his hand at turning our English into Latin hexameters. Some of the Germans have done likewise. English and German hexameters sound as a heavy cart sounds bouncing over boulders.

MARVEL. We often find in them a foot composed of two short syllables, instead of a spondee, and a trochee as often, which reminds us of a cripple, one of whose legs is shorter than the other, so that he cannot put it to the ground. I doubt whether in a hundred English hexameters there are three composed of dactyl and spondee.*

MILTON. I know not whether it ever has been observed that the final foot of the hexameter is a trochee. So it is, with only two or three exceptions, in Virgil where *mons*, and another monosyllable in another place, end the verse.

MARVEL. Why can not we be contented with our own measures, as establisht by law and custom ? None in Latin or Greek are more harmonious than several of them.

* Ovid was the first who subjected a strange language to Latin measures, and he acknowledges that he was ashamed of doing it.

> *Ah pudet !* et Getico scripsi sermone libellum
> Aptaque sunt nostris barbara verba modis.

Yet how would the philologist rejoice at the recovery of this *little book*, for a book there was of it, and not only one composition. The Jesuits, clever at Latin versification, have not yet introduced it into China.—W. S. L.

IMAGINARY CONVERSATIONS : ENGLISH

MILTON. Fond as I am of Latin, and many as are the verses I have written in it, never was I so rash and inconsiderate as to force its meters into our own language, which is infinitely more capable of stops and variations.

MARVEL. Not even the verses of Homer himself have that diversity of cadence which enchants us in *Paradise Lost*. Who was the blockhead who invented the word *blank* for its verse ? Never was anyone less appropriate. The Latin hexameter, closing with a disyllable or trisyllable, wants the variety of the Greek, and terminates too frequently with consonants, *ant*, *unt*, *am*, *um*, or *s*. To remove this obstruction from the sensitive ear we have recourse to Homer and Milton.

MILTON. Courtier ! courtier ! prythee hold thy tongue. Venerate one blind man and continue to love the other.

THIRD CONVERSATION

(*Athenæum*, 1862 ; *Wks.*, v., 1876.)

MILTON. Happy am I to see you here again, after a travel of so many weeks, and through a country where the roads, in many parts, are deep and difficult.

MARVEL. Truly since our late unhappy war they have been but little mended, and less before. The armies required a few of them to be rendered commodious for cannon and trains. How these were brought so far as to Kineton, and over Edge Hill, is wonderful.

MILTON. Yet you went beyond, even to the Upper Severn. How was this feat performed ?

MARVEL. Pondering the difficulties on one side and the conveniences on the other, I bought a palfrey at Highgate. Wink as the dealer might at him and me, I really found him fairly worth the eight guineas he cost me. He carried me to Oxford by the next nightfall, or soon after. Both of us rose and rested early, and neither had to complain of our provender. At Oxford we rested a whole day, it being the Sabbath.

MILTON. Virtuously and religiously done ! Whether men sit idle and morose for lack of amusement, or whether they enjoy the day in

MILTON AND ANDREW MARVEL

innocent pleasure among their children and friends, I do no longer censure them, as I did formerly.

MARVEL. Some lose their sourness by time, others become austere and crabbed. You once appeared too sedate, but never uncongenial.

MILTON. I have seen reason to change some of my old habits and some of my old opinions. I fear I am morose by nature : certain I am that the waters of Castalia are sweeter than the waters of Styx, and that the study, not of philosophy alone, but equally of poetry, corrects our evil humours. Any interesting book overlays and bluntens asperity. Music, in which I always have delighted, both calms and elevates.

What are you waiting for, so seriously ?

MARVEL. To hear more truths from you.

MILTON. You shall not, until you have reported to me somewhat more of your journey. As far as Edge Hill you have brought me, and no farther. Had the battle there been lost to us, the castle at Warwick would have suffered like its neighbour of Kenilworth, for the valiant Earl was the fast friend of Cromwell. Lord Brooke, as you remember, was killed by a shot from Lichfield minster by Dick Dyot, at the hall-door of Walter Noble in the close—his entrance had been watcht, and this fatal missive intercepted his return from the representative of the city.

MARVEL. We could have better spared another brave man. Brooke would never have betrayed us. Now enough for politics, usually ending hopelessly, often dishonourably, where the sharper keeps the winning card under his ruffle.

You have endured my company as far as Oxford. Few walled cities are less capable of resisting a siege. It is commanded by Shotover Hill, and the Cherwell at a short distance is so narrow, and there are so many trees on its banks, that it might be bridged within sunset and sunrise, unperceived. I am certain that orders were given to abstain from bombarding the town lest the colleges might suffer.

MILTON. Cathedrals were also spared, at the urgent instance of the Protector, hateful as was their service to the people at large. Westminster Abbey was under his guardian eye, and the towers of Windsor were left, for their beauty and their innocence in evil days.

MARVEL. I wish you could have seen with me those of Warwick, and the more graceful, though less august of Kenilworth. Their roofs are indeed battered down, and the chambers of the whole edifice are now tenanted by owls and daws. However, the windows are intact. None are so beautiful as they. Had they been inserted in the castle at Warwick it would be unequalled in beauty, as its towers are in magnificence.

MILTON. Rous, and Camden, and lately Dugdale, have rendered that county highly interesting. Yet rather would I see the chancel at Stratford than even the tower of Babel, had it been standing, or even the window of the Ark. Wretches so worthless as Dudley could erect the towers of Kenilworth. Who cares about him ? What human heart hath he ever warmed or moved ? Thousands will throb, age after age, at the very sound of our poet's name.

I might be glad to see these two castles, if sight were vouchsafed me, but neither of them or any other, so gladly as Ludlow, now (like the more gorgeous of the two) dilapidated.

MARVEL. I can easily believe it of you. It is an inheritance which you will bequeath to your country. The stones have fallen, but Comus stands above them, a warder who will never lose his office.

MILTON. We look complacently on our earlier handywork. The best sculptor might haply be glad to find in a corner some fragment of a clay model on which his fingers were employed before the knuckles were well knitted.

I am not dissatisfied, on the whole, with my *Mask of Comus :* yet there the scholar in his gown stood in the poet's way. I represented a boy talking like a philosopher, when he never could have heard even the name. I have often been too scholastic : yet I never brought Adam and Eve into the trim grove of Academus. It is almost as difficult to avoid faults in poetry as to reach beauties ; faults being multitudinous and lying under our feet in that quarter, attainable beauties few and over-head.

Your palfrey did not carry you to Ludlow ?

MARVEL. No, I stopt short ; yet I saw Sabrina before she had put her yellow cloak on for the fair at Bristow : I saw her where she met her brighter spouse Avon, fresh from watering the flowers under the chancel at Stratford. Pig-headed knaves have defaced the sacred image it contains. Who knows but in another age they may violate the tomb, fearless of the recorded curse denouncing such a sacrilege.

MILTON. It grieved me to see places of worship harmed in any sort. In the last century abbeys and convents were demolished, as

192

castles have been in ours. Never shall we or our children see such edifices as the abbeys of Evesham and Malmsbury, and some others. More is remaining of the rites there celebrated than of the walls under which bows and curtsies were made in bedizened frocks to dolls and candles. Puffy lawn is substituted for gold lace, but palaces and manors stand where they stood. The church " mutavit dominos et cedit in altera jura " : but milords are milords yet, and lawgivers, and offerers up of prayers for the murderers of nations. Glorious Reformation !

Will there never be a sanctuary in every private house ? Will there never be a time when every mother will be the priestess of her children and family ? Our duties are simple and learnt easily. No sunrise but awakens one or other of them into activity and growth. Boys are educated, girls are not ; yet girls should be educated first, and taught the most impressively. These slender and graceful columns are not only the ornament, but also the support, of society. Men are the braver for the reverence they bear toward them, and in them do they find their reward. I would that our cathedrals were turned into schoolrooms for the more advanced among the youths in age and study, and I would never grudge the bishops, then masters and ushers, a stipend of three or four hundred pounds a-year, with a commodious house and garden for each. I live comfortably within one hundred, and, after my decease, my children will not be reduced to starvation.

MARVEL. God forbid ! but must they not work for their bread ?

MILTON. Verily and indeed must they : and this, O Andrew, is among His other blessings. He taught me the rudiments of my craft ; they have learnt theirs. Those are happier who work for a family than those who work for a state. The poor have always their Commonwealth ; we have lost even the name.

MARVEL. Our most gracious king will take especial care that the people at large do not run riotous in wealth and be submerged in luxury. Perhaps, in the midst of his necessities, he may transfer the lawn sleeves to wearers on whom they would be more becoming, and of whom the most modest is a street-walking orange-girl.

MILTON. Charles may properly be called a sapper and miner. He thinks our earlier Constitution is just as deserving of overthrow as our later. I know not whether he has sold his regalia, I only know that he has sold his country. What must we think of a king who barters his patrimony for protection, or who recurs to any but his own people for protection ? Whenever the weak make an alliance with the strong they are the strong's dependants. A prudent nation will not permit its ruler to form a marriage with a foren potentate. There are daughters in England still worthy to wear a crown. A time there was, but it was a distant one, when feuds among the nobility would have exasperated the jealousy of most among them by the king's choice of a wife out of one baronial family. Such danger is now over. The heir to the throne is united to the daughter of a subject, a subject of mean family and powerless connections.

Such a peerage as is now patcht up will never stand between king and people as the old barons did, mainly, it is true, for their own ends. It grieves me that so many of their castles have been demolished. The ivy hath scarcely yet reacht the basement of Ludlow, and its longest eventide shadows fall short of the Severn below them. Cromwell has been called the destroyer of the most magnificent edifices : unjustly : the puritans were the carriers of this barbarous decree. The same ferocious men would have battered down the cathedrals. Our troopers did indeed stable their horses in some of them, ejecting idler and less serviceable cattle, and in several of them monuments were defaced. This was somewhat like tearing out a page from history, not indeed an important one, yet the deed was wanton mischief. Yet what is this in the sight of Wisdom and of our Creator if we compare it with the bloodshed of thousands, in one place, in one hour ? Men march into the field of battle in stately trim and after joyous music, and slay thousands to gratify one, the only one whom it would be innocent to slay. He who commands them to break God's image should experience God's vengeance where he has committed the offence. War will never cease, or long subside, while such creatures are permitted to exist. If two men quarrel and fight in the highway, there are many who come up and interpose ; can none be found to act likewise in a wider field ? Are there to be no restrictions on sturdier disturbers of the peace ?

MARVEL. Here I am quite in accord with you. Every parish should unite, and surround and hunt down the marauders, most Christian, Catholic, and Apostolic, cage them, and exhibit them in the market-place.

Italy has been parcelled out, bartered, and exchanged. I would treat them as they have treated the Italians, and as we do to other thieves and murderers, I would not draw and quarter them, but rather leave them whole in their deformity. Iron should hold what oaths could not. Italy, formed to be the Eden of the earth, is now torn to pieces by the bear and the monkey. In another age the beautiful Venice, which has flourished for the greater part of a thousand years, which is longer than any city ever did before, may peradventure be the prey of one barbarian—and be sold to another. Her people, the best governed and the happiest, may be made discontented by some crowned Jack Cade, and then handcuffed by their deliverer.

MILTON. No Demosthenes is living now.

MARVEL. While England was England there existed one, one only ; let me grasp his hand.

MILTON. Prythee, sit down ; let me be proud, but never vain. Demosthenes was superlatively μέγα κῦδος Ἀχαιῶν. Cicero was weaker in a weaker cause. He arraigned one powerful plunderer, but he left in his audience no few nearly as criminal. However, let not our admiration of so great a man fall off from him. He lived among and consorted with those, equally well educated as himself, who received a high gratification from the sight of their fellow creatures torn peacemele by wild beasts in the amphitheater. The Romans were never quite civilized or quite humanized. Even at this day the worship of a mother with an innocent babe, in her arms or at her breast, awakes no tenderness in them ; they stab one another on the church-steps as they leave her. The wolf nurtured more than one couple.

MARVEL. It is remarkable that the northern nations are less cruel and sanguinary than the southern. Where the air is keenest, it seems, the religion is purest.

MILTON. Idleness looks toward easy Gods and pardoners for pence. Popery will never flourish in Sweden and Norway, or the Gospel be preached openly, or even tolerated, in Rome. The followers of Christ must take refuge in the catacombs, among their elder brethren.

MARVEL. Fashions change perpetually. I should not wonder if, in the next reign, a slip from the robe of the scarlet lady becomes the general wear, instead of the magpie plumage now fluttering in churches.

MILTON. There may also be candles on what is called the *Communion-table* by protestants and *Altar* by papists, to commemorate the last supper of our Lord. Candles are unnecessary by daylight ;

and it was by daylight that our blessed Lord broke his last bread with his disciples. The principal meal, which the Romans called *cœna*, was taken before nightfall, as we may learn from Catullus, Horace, Petronius, and many others. The *Hall of Apollo*, in the house of Lucullus, was not lighted up when Cicero was invited to his table ; and no lamp shone down on the guests of Nasidienus.

MARVEL. Recurring to the Romans, it appears to me that the earlier cookt a dinner as badly as the later a religion. Some of their *receits* have been preserved, I would never have taken Apicius into my service at five farthings a day.

MILTON. Culinary may be called the lowest of the arts, yet men are slow and long in acquiring it. Wild men paint and carve the images of animals long before they have learnt to fry an omelet.

I know not what has brought us down into the kitchen.

MARVEL. The fault must have been mine. We were talking of castles and abbeys and cathedrals, and the lords of them in their several degrees. We began with what is high and have descended to what is low. It is difficult to find " from this lowest depth a lower depth."

MILTON. " Raccende il gusto il mutar esca," says Ariosto : and the words are very applicable. An imaginary line may be drawn between Conversation and Dialogue. In Conversation, as in the country, variety is pleasant and expected. We look from the ground before us into the remoter, and much of more than one quality lies between. In Conversation we ought not to be didactic, in Dialogue we may be : Galileo has done it. There are other authorities, but none so great.

I must now come back homeward from Italy.

If in the next or any remoter age our country should produce a sound historian, who holds up his head above his party, and sees clearly and widely, will he be believed when he records what we have witnessed within the last few years ? It will be called a traveller's *story*. Already a *story* is become a synonome for a *lie*. Herodotus, the most instructive of historians, when he relates a marvellous tale of some occurrence in a far country, gives it us as a report : how will our forthcoming writers manage what shall have fallen into their hands from their father's, the eyewitness ? Will they believe that a drop of Saxon blood is in their veins ?

MARVEL. Now you are speaking of history, let me express a wish that you had leisure or inclination to continue that which you began. Our own times do indeed seem as fabulous as the earlier. Did it never occur to you that many of us partake of the Roman ? that, although the legions had left Britain, many of the inhabitants, and especially the settlers on the coast, descended from the invader ?

MILTON. Doubtless in three centuries there must have been a large intermixture of the races. London was somewhat of a mercantile city and indeed an emporium, long before its occupation by the Romans. Tyre sent her merchants to the south of Ireland, and probably to the south of Britain, certainly to the west. An oyster was a bait to a Roman ; the rocks about our island were covered with them, while those on the Italian were scarce and worthless. Certainly few merchants would abandon their habitations when the legionaries left the land. Their ships were manned by the hardy sailors of the north, and the capital (as we call it) invested in them belonged in great measure to settlers from abroad, principally Roman, where it was safer than in their own city, where imperial purple was the merchandise, soldiers the salesmen and auctioneers.

We are a miscellaneous volume, the leaves well sewed together, Roman, Norwegian, Dane, Saxon, chapter after chapter.

MARVEL. It seems to me likely, that, when the Roman military were recalled they were prohibited from their usual rapine, and the wealthier townsmen took refuge in their ships. Many if not most of these were of half-breed. In Warwickshire I saw a lock of black hair, which had been taken from a tomb containing the bones of a Norman, buried in it within half a century of the invasion. There could scarcely have been time for an intermixture of Neustrian and Saxon. The Jutlanders and other Northerns were chiefly the crews of the wealthy Neustrian merchants, and soon were joined by their landsmen, who made several descents and occupied at last the whole country.

MILTON. Here is likelihood without record ; for the bowmen and swordsmen were no penmen. At the Conquest there were flocks of them. Ravens find food after battles. It is worthy of a thought and a reflection that a lock of hair, such as what you mention, should remain unchanged in colour and substance when body, bones, and brains, had become earth. Thus it often happens that the vile outlasts the valuable ; and what is shorn off and thrown away is gathered up and treasured. Gentlemen are usually proud of Norman origin :

none can prove unbroken in three generations : Dane and Saxon are interlopers. The absurd pretenders would go up higher if they knew how, and would thank you if you told and persuaded them that they quite as certainly had some particle of the Roman in them after so many crosses. The Northmen were as valiant as the Romans, and greatly more capable of true civilization. They never sent into the arena the bravest men to be devoured by wild beasts or to slaughter one another, as the most civilized of the Romans did, age after age. They worshipt false Gods ; what people has not ? and how few are there who do not even now ? But their priests were not hucksters of souls, nor covered sins with wafers. They never called their hearers *sheep*, and fleeced them as if they were. They never taught their fellow men that it was a duty or a privilege to kiss their toes, or that the seat was holy which they had squatted on. As they could not write, they could not forge wills had they been so minded.

MARVEL. I dare not follow where chemists are so expert in pharmacy. Even our own country bears hemlock and hensbane. We may walk more safely among the sticklers for antiquity of lineage, who probably have never learnt by heart the verse of that poet who, with all his levity, has more unobtrusively sage verses than any, be he Roman or Athenian. ―

> Genus et proavos et quæ non fecimus ipsi
> Vix ea nostra voco.[1]

Ulysses is here represented as the speaker, characteristically and worthily.

MILTON. We are all of the earth, earthly. They who are proud of family antiquity ought to be ashamed of beating a dog, who, we are certified, is of older creation. Probably the worms are of older still. Happily they are deaf and dumb ; if they had ears and tongues they would never so misapply them as we often do. We shall soon lie in the midst of them as quiet and mute as they are. We cause the bloodshed one of another, and often go far afield to chase the unoffending. The greediest worms are guiltless of the like ; they only exact what is their inheritance ; we must pay them the debt we owe them ; let it be unreluctantly !

[1] Ovid, *Metam.*, xiii. 140.

XVIII. OLIVER CROMWELL AND SIR OLIVER CROMWELL

(*Blackwood*, Feb. 1843 ; *Wks.*, ii., 1846 ; *Wks.*, iii., 1876.)

SIR OLIVER. How many saints and Sions [1] dost carry under thy cloak, lad ? Ay, what dost groan at ? What art about to be delivered of ? Troth, it must be a vast and oddly-shapen piece of roguery which findeth no issue at such capacious quarters. I never thought to see thy face again. Prythee what, in God's name, hath brought thee to Ramsey, fair Master Oliver ?

OLIVER. In his name verily I come, and upon his errand ; and the love and duty I bear unto my godfather and uncle have added wings, in a sort, unto my zeal.

SIR OLIVER. Take 'em off thy zeal and dust thy conscience with 'em. I have heard an account of a saint, one Phil Neri, who in the midst of his devotions was lifted up several yards from the ground. Now I do suspect, Nol, thou wilt finish by being a saint of his order ; and nobody will promise or wish thee the luck to come down on thy feet again, as he did. So ! because a rabble of fanatics at Huntingdon have equipped thee as their representative in Parliament, thou art free of all men's houses, forsooth ! I would have thee to understand, sirrah, that thou art fitter for the house they have chaired thee unto than for mine. Yet I do not question but thou wilt be as troublesome and unruly there as here. Did I not turn thee out of Hinchinbrook when thou wert scarcely half the rogue thou art latterly grown up to ? And yet wert thou immeasurably too big a one for it to hold.

OLIVER. It repenteth me, O mine uncle ! that in my boyhood and youth the Lord had not touched me.

SIR OLIVER. Touch thee ! thou wast too dirty a dog by half.

OLIVER. Yea, sorely doth it vex and harrow me that I was then of ill conditions, and that my name—even your godson's—stank in your nostrils.

---

[1] Thus in 1st ed. and successors ; Crump reads : " Zions."

SIR OLIVER. Ha ! polecat ! it was not thy name, although bad enough, that stank first ; in my house, at least.*   But perhaps there are worse maggots in stauncher mummeries.

OLIVER. Whereas in the bowels of your charity you then vouchsafed me forgiveness, so the more confidently may I crave it now in this my urgency.

SIR OLIVER. More confidently ! What ! hast got more confidence ? Where didst find it ? I never thought the wide circle of the world had within it another jot for thee. Well, Nol, I see no reason why thou shouldst stand before me with thy hat off, in the courtyard and in the sun, counting the stones in the pavement. Thou hast some knavery in thy head, I warrant thee. Come, put on thy beaver.

OLIVER. Uncle Sir Oliver ! I know my duty too well to stand covered in the presence of so worshipful a kinsman, who, moreover, hath answered at baptism for my good behaviour.

SIR OLIVER. God forgive me for playing the fool before Him so presumptuously and unprofitably ! Nobody shall ever take me in again to do such an absurd and wicked thing. But thou hast some left-handed business in the neighbourhood, no doubt, or thou wouldst never more have come under my archway.

OLIVER. These are hard times for them that seek peace. We are clay in the hand of the potter.

SIR OLIVER. I wish your potters sought nothing costlier, and dug in their own grounds for it. Most of us, as thou sayest, have been upon the wheel of these artificers ; and little was left but rags when we got off. Sanctified folks are the cleverest skinners in all Christendom, and their Jordan tans and constringes us to the averdupois of mummies.

OLIVER. The Lord hath chosen his own vessels.

SIR OLIVER. I wish heartily he would pack them off, and send them anywhere on ass-back or cart (cart preferably), to rid our country of 'em. But now again to the point : for if we fall among the potsherds we shall hobble on but lamely. Since thou art raised unto a high command in the army, and hast a dragoon to hold yonder thy solid and stately piece of horse-flesh, I can not but take it into my fancy that thou hast some commission of array or disarray to execute hereabout.

* See Forster's *Life of Cromwell.*—W. S. L.

CROMWELL AND SIR OLIVER CROMWELL

OLIVER. With a sad sinking of spirit, to the pitch well-nigh of swounding, and with a sight of bitter tears, which will not be put back nor staid in anywise, as you bear testimony unto me, uncle Oliver !

SIR OLIVER. No tears, Master Nol, I beseech thee ! Wet days, among those of thy kidney, portend the letting of blood. What dost whimper at ?

OLIVER. That I, that I, of all men living, should be put upon this work !

SIR OLIVER. What work, prythee ?

OLIVER. I am sent hither by them who (the Lord in his loving-kindness having pity and mercy upon these poor realms) do, under his right hand, administer unto our necessities, and righteously command us, *by the aforesaid as aforesaid* (thus runs the commission), hither am I deputed (woe is me !) to levy certain fines in this county, or shire, on such as the Parliament in its wisdom doth style malignants.

SIR OLIVER. If there is anything left about the house, never be over-nice : dismiss thy modesty and lay hands upon it. In this county or shire, we let go the civet-bag to save the weazon.

OLIVER. O mine uncle and godfather ! be witness for me.

SIR OLIVER. Witness for thee ! not I indeed. But I would rather be witness than surety, lad, where thou art docketed.

OLIVER. From the most despised doth the Lord ever choose his servants.

SIR OLIVER. Then, faith ! thou art his first butler.

OLIVER. Serving him with humility, I may peradventure be found worthy of advancement.

SIR OLIVER. Ha ! now if any devil speaks from within thee, it is thy own : he does not sniffle : to my ears he speaks plain English. Worthy or unworthy of advancement, thou wilt attain it. Come in ; at least for an hour's rest. Formerly thou knewest the means of setting the heaviest heart afloat, let it be sticking in what mud-bank it might : and my wet-dock at Ramsey is pretty near as commodious as that over-yonder at Hinchinbrook was erewhile. Times are changed, and places too ! yet the cellar holds good.

OLIVER. Many and great thanks ! But there are certain men on the other side of the gate, who might take it ill if I turn away and neglect them.

SIR OLIVER. Let them enter also, or eat their victuals where they are.

OLIVER. They have proud stomachs : they are recusants.

SIR OLIVER. Recusants of what ? of beef and ale ? We have claret, I trust, for the squeamish, if they are above the condition of tradespeople. But of course you leave no person of higher quality in the outer court.

OLIVER. Vain are they and worldly, although such wickedness is the most abominable in their cases. Idle folks are fond of sitting in the sun : I would not forbid them this indulgence.

SIR OLIVER. But who are they ?

OLIVER. The Lord knows. May-be priests, deacons, and such like.

SIR OLIVER. Then, sir, they are gentlemen. And the commission you bear from the parliamentary thieves, to sack and pillage my mansion-house, is far less vexatious and insulting to me, than your behaviour in keeping them so long at my stable-door. With your permission, or without it, I shall take the liberty to invite them to partake of my poor hospitality.

OLIVER. But, uncle Sir Oliver ! there are rules and ordinances whereby it must be manifested that they lie under displeasure—not mine—not mine—but my milk must not flow for them.

SIR OLIVER. You may enter the house or remain where you are, at your option ; I make my visit to these gentlemen immediately, for I am tired of standing. If ever thou reachest my age,* Oliver ! (but God will not surely let this be) thou wilt know that the legs become at last of doubtful fidelity in the service of the body.

OLIVER. Uncle Sir Oliver ! now that, as it seemeth, you have been taking a survey of the courtyard and its contents, am I indiscreet in asking your worship whether I acted not prudently in keeping the *men-at-belly* under the custody of the *men-at-arms ?* This pestilence,

---

* Sir Oliver, who died in 1655, aged ninety-three, might, by possibility, have seen all the men of great genius, excepting Chaucer and Roger Bacon, whom England has produced from its first discovery down to our own times. Francis Bacon, Shakespeare, Milton, Newton, and the prodigious shoal that attended these leviathans through the intellectual deep. Newton was but in his thirteenth year at Sir Oliver's death. Raleigh, Spenser, Hooker, Eliot,[1] Selden, Taylor, Hobbes, Sidney, Shaftesbury, and Locke, were existing in his lifetime ; and several more, who may be compared with the smaller of these.—W. S. L.

---

[1] 1st ed. reads : "Elliot."

CROMWELL AND SIR OLIVER CROMWELL

like unto one I remember to have read about in some poetry of Master Chapman's,* began with the dogs and the mules, and afterwards crope up into the breasts of men.

SIR OLIVER. I call such treatment barbarous ; their troopers will not let the gentlemen come with me into the house, but insist on sitting down to dinner with them. And yet, having brought them out of their colleges, these brutal half-soldiers must know that they are fellows.

OLIVER. Yea, of a truth are they, and fellows well met. Out of their superfluities they give nothing to the Lord or his Saints ; no, not even stirrup or girth, wherewith we may mount our horses and go forth against those who thirst for our blood. Their eyes are fat, and they raise not up their voices to cry for our deliverance.

SIR OLIVER. Art mad ? What stirrups and girths are hung up in college halls and libraries ? For what are these gentlemen brought hither ?

OLIVER. They have elected me, with somewhat short of unanimity, not indeed to be one of themselves, for of that distinction I acknowledge and deplore my unworthiness, nor indeed to be a poor scholar, to which, unless it be a very poor one, I have almost as small pretension, but simply to undertake a while the heavier office of burser for them ; to cast up their accounts ; to overlook the scouring of their plate ; and to lay a list thereof, with a few specimens, before those who fight the fight of the Lord, that his Saints, seeing the abasement of the proud and the chastisement of worldly-mindedness, may rejoice.

SIR OLIVER. I am grown accustomed to such saints and such rejoicings. But, little could I have thought, threescore years ago, that the hearty and jovial people of England would ever join in so filching and stabbing a jocularity. Even the petticoated torch-bearers from rotten Rome, who lighted the faggots in Smithfield some years before, if more blustering and cocksy, were less bitter and vulturine. They were all intolerant, but they were not all hypocritical ; they had not always " *the Lord* " in their mouth.

OLIVER. According to their own notions, they might have had, at an outlay of a farthing.

SIR OLIVER. Art facetious, Nol ? for it is as hard to find that out as anything else in thee, only it makes thee look, at times, a little the grimmer and sourer.

* Chapman's *Homer*, first Book.—W. S. L.

But, regarding these gentlemen from Cambridge. Not being such as, by their habits and professions, could have opposed you in the field, I hold it unmilitary and unmanly to put them under any restraint, and to lead them away from their peaceful and useful occupations.

OLIVER. I always bow submissively before the judgment of mine elders ; and the more reverentially when I know them to be endowed with greater wisdom, and guided by surer experience than myself. Alas ! those collegians not only are strong men, as you may readily see if you measure them round the waistband, but boisterous and pertinacious challengers. When we, who live in the fear of God, exhorted them earnestly unto peace and brotherly love, they held us in derision. Thus far indeed it might be an advantage to us, teaching us forbearance and self-seeking, but we can not countenance the evil spirit moving them thereunto. Their occupations, as you remark most wisely, might have been useful and peaceful, and had formerly been so. Why then did they gird the sword of strife about their loins against the children of Israel ? By their own declaration, not only are they our enemies, but enemies the most spiteful and untractable. When I came quietly, lawfully, and in the name of the Lord, for their plate, what did they ? Instead of surrendering it like honest and conscientious men, they attacked me and my people on horseback, with syllogisms and enthymemes, and the Lord knows with what other such gimcracks ; such venomous and rankling old weapons as those who have the fear of God before their eyes are fain to lay aside. Learning should not make folks mockers—should not make folks malignants—should not harden their hearts. We came with bowels for them.

SIR OLIVER. That ye did ! and bowels which would have stowed within them all the plate on board of a galloon. If tankards and wassail-bowls had stuck between your teeth, you would not have felt them.

OLIVER. We did feel them ; some at least : perhaps we missed too many.

SIR OLIVER. How can these learned societies raise the money you exact from them, beside plate ? dost think they can create and coin it ?

OLIVER. In Cambridge, uncle Sir Oliver, and more especially in that college named in honour (as they profanely call it) of the blessed

CROMWELL AND SIR OLIVER CROMWELL

Trinity, there are great conjurors or chemists. Now the said conjurors or chemists not only do possess the faculty of making the precious metals out of old books and parchments, but out of the skulls of young lordlings and gentlefolks, which verily promise less. And this they bring about by certain gold wires fastened at the top of certain caps. Of said metals, thus devilishly converted, do they make a vain and sumptuous use ; so that, finally, they are afraid of cutting their lips with glass. But indeed it is high time to call them.

SIR OLIVER. Well—at last thou hast some mercy.

OLIVER (aloud). Cuffsatan Ramsbottom ! Sadsoul Kiteclaw [1] ! advance ! Let every gown, together with the belly that is therein, mount up behind you and your comrades in good fellowship. And forasmuch as you at the country-places look to bit and bridle, it seemeth fair and equitable that ye should leave unto them, in full propriety, the mancipular office of discharging the account. If there be any spare beds at the inns, allow the doctors and dons to occupy the same—they being used to lie softly ; and be not urgent that more than three lie in each—they being mostly corpulent. Let pass quietly and unreproved any light bubble of pride or impetuosity, seeing that they have not always been accustomed to the service of guards and ushers. The Lord be with ye !—Slow trot ! And now, uncle Sir Oliver, I can resist no longer your loving-kindness. I kiss you, my godfather, in heart's and soul's duty ; and most humbly and gratefully do I accept of your invitation to dine and lodge with you, albeit the least worthy of your family and kinsfolk. After the refreshment of needful food, more needful prayer, and that sleep which descendeth on the innocent like the dew of Hermon, to-morrow at daybreak I proceed on my journey Londonward.

SIR OLIVER (aloud). Ho, there ! (To a servant.) Let dinner be prepared in the great dining-room ; let every servant be in waiting, each in full livery ; let every delicacy the house affords be placed upon the table in due courses ; arrange all the plate upon the sideboard : a gentleman by descent—a stranger—has claimed my hospitality. (Servant goes.)

Sir ! you are now master. Grant me dispensation, I entreat you, from a further attendance on you.

[1] 1st ed. reads : " Kitelau."

XIX. ANDREW MARVEL AND BISHOP PARKER [1] *

(*Wks.*, ii., 1846 ; *Wks.*, v., 1876.)

PARKER. Most happy am I to encounter you, Mr. Marvel. It is some time, I think, since we met. May I take the liberty of inquiring what brought you into such a lonely quarter as Bunhill-fields ?

MARVEL. My lord, I return at this instant from visiting an old friend of ours, hard-by, in Artillery-walk, who, you will be happy to hear, bears his blindness and asthma with truly Christian courage.

PARKER. And pray, who may that old friend be, Mr. Marvel ?

MARVEL. Honest John Milton.

PARKER. The same gentleman whose ingenious poem, on our first parents, you praised in some elegant verses prefixed to it ?

MARVEL. The same who likewise, on many occasions, merited and obtained your lordship's approbation.

PARKER. I am happy to understand that no harsh measures were taken against him, on the return of our most gracious sovran. And it occurs to me that you, Mr. Marvel, were earnest in his behalf.

---

[1] Parker was not raised to the Bishopric till after Marvel's death.

* He wrote a work entitled, as Hooker's was, *Ecclesiastical Polity*, in which are these words : " It is better to submit to the unreasonable impositions of Nero and Caligula than to hazard the dissolution of the state." It is plain enough to what *impositions* he recommended the duty of submission : for, in our fiscal sense of the word, none ever bore more lightly on the subject than Caligula's and Nero's : even the provinces were taxed very moderately and fairly by them. He adds, " Princes may with less danger give liberty to men's vices and debaucheries than to their consciences." Marvel answered him in his *Rehearsal Transposed*, in which he says of Milton,[1] " I well remember that, being one day at his house, I there first met you, and accidentally. Then it was that you wandered up and down Moor-fields, astrologising upon the duration of His Majesty's Government. You frequented John Milton incessantly, and haunted his house day by day. What discourses you there used he is too generous to remember : but, he never having in the least provoked you, it is inhumanely and inhospitably done to insult thus over his old age. I hope it will be a warning to all others, as it is to me, to avoid, I will not say such a Judas, but a man that creeps into all companies, to jeer, trepan, and betray them."—W. S. L.

---

[1] Landor has omitted some words in which Marvel made it plain that subsequent to the first meeting he had been " scarce four or five times " in Parker's company. See Thompson's *Life of Marvel*, iii.

ANDREW MARVEL AND BISHOP PARKER

Indeed I myself might have stirred upon it, had Mr. Milton solicited me in the hour of need.

MARVEL. He is grateful to the friends who consulted at the same time his dignity and his safety : but gratitude can never be expected to grow on a soil hardened by solicitation. Those who are the most ambitious of power are often the least ambitious of glory. It requires but little sagacity to foresee that a name will become invested with eternal brightness by belonging to a benefactor of Milton. *I might have served him !* is not always the soliloquy of late compassion or of virtuous repentance : it is frequently the cry of blind and impotent and wounded pride, angry at itself for having neglected a good bargain, a rich reversion. Believe me, my lord bishop, there are few whom God has promoted to serve the truly great. They are never to be superseded, nor are their names to be obliterated in earth or heaven. Were I to trust my observation rather than my feelings, I should believe that friendship is only a state of transition to enmity. The wise, the excellent in honour and integrity, whom it was once our ambition to converse with, soon appear in our sight no higher than the ordinary class of our acquaintance ; then become fit objects to set our own slender wits against, to contend with, to interrogate, to subject to the arbitration, not of their equals, but of ours ; and lastly, what indeed is less injustice and less indignity, to neglect, abandon, and disown.

PARKER. I never have doubted that Mr. Milton is a learned man ; indeed he has proven it : and there are many who, like yourself, see considerable merit in his poems. I confess that I am an indifferent judge in these matters : and I can only hope that he has now corrected what is erroneous in his doctrines.

MARVEL. Latterly he hath never changed a jot, in acting or thinking.

PARKER. Wherein I hold him blameable, well aware as I am that never to change is thought an indication of rectitude and wisdom. But if everything in this world is progressive ; if everything is defective ; if our growth, if our faculties, are obvious and certain signs of it ; then surely we should and must be different in different ages and conditions. Consciousness of error is, to a certain extent, a consciousness of understanding ; and correction of error is the plainest proof of energy and mastery.

MARVEL. No proof of the kind is necessary to my friend : and it was not always that your lordship looked down on him so magisterially in reprehension, or delivered a sentence from so commanding an elevation. I, who indeed am but a humble man, am apt to question my judgment where it differs from his. I am appalled by any supercilious glance at him, and disgusted by any austerity ill assorted with the generosity of his mind. When I consider what pure delight we have derived from it, what treasures of wisdom it has conveyed to us, I find him supremely worthy of my gratitude, love, and veneration ; and the neglect in which I now discover him, leaves me only the more room for the free effusion of these sentiments. How shallow in comparison is everything else around us, trickling and dimpling in the pleasure-grounds of our literature ! If we are to build our summer-houses against ruined temples, let us at least abstain from ruining them for the purpose.

PARKER. Nay, nay, Mr. Marvel ! so much warmth is uncalled for.

MARVEL. Is there anything offensive to your lordship in my expressions ?

PARKER. I am not aware that there is. But let us generalize a little : for we are prone to be touchy and testy in favour of our intimates.

MARVEL. I believe, my lord, this fault, or sin, or whatsoever it may be designated, is among the few that are wearing fast away.

PARKER. Delighted am I, my dear sir, to join you in your innocent pleasantry. But, truly and seriously, I have known even the prudent grow warm and stickle about some close affinity.

MARVEL. Indeed ? so indecorous before your lordship ?

PARKER. We may remember when manners were less polite than they are now ; and not only the seasons of life require an alteration of habits, but likewise the changes of society.

MARVEL. Your lordship acts up to your tenets.

PARKER. Perhaps you may blame me, and more severely than I would blame our worthy friend Mr. John Milton, upon finding a slight variation in my exterior manner, and somewhat more reserve than formerly : yet wiser and better men than I presume to call myself, have complied with the situation to which it hath pleased the Almighty to exalt them.

MARVEL. I am slow to censure anyone for assuming an air and demeanour which, he is persuaded, are more becoming than what he has left off. And I subscribe to the justice of the observation, that wiser and better men than your lordship have adapted their language and their looks to elevated station. But sympathy is charity, or engenders it : and sympathy requires proximity, closeness, contact : and at every remove, and more especially at every gradation of ascent, it grows a little colder. When we begin to call a man our *worthy friend*, our friendship is already on the wane. In him who has been raised above his old companions, there seldom remains more warmth than what turns everything about it vapid : familiarity sidles towards affability, and kindness curtseys into condescension.

PARKER. I see, we are hated for rising.

MARVEL. Many do really hate others for rising : but some who appear to hate them for it, hate them only for the bad effects it produces on the character.

PARKER. We are odious, I am afraid, sometimes for the gift, and sometimes for the giver : and Malevolence cools her throbs by running to the obscurity of neglected merit. We know whose merit that means.

MARVEL. What ! because the servants of a king have stamped no measure above a certain compass, and such only as the vulgar are accustomed to handle, must we disbelieve the existence of any greater in its capacity, or decline the use of it in things lawful and commendable ? Little men like these have no business at all with the mensuration of higher minds : gaugers are not astronomers.

PARKER. Really, Mr. Marvel, I do not understand metaphors.

MARVEL. Leaving out arithmetic and mathematics, and the sciences appertaining to them, I never opened a page without one : no, not even a title-page with a dozen words in it. Perhaps I am unfortunate in my tropes and figures : perhaps they come, by my want of dexterity, too near your lordship. I would humbly ask, is there any criminality in the calculation and casting up of manifold benefits, or in the employment of those instruments by which alone they are to be calculated and cast up ?

PARKER. Surely none whatever.

MARVEL. It has happened to me and my schoolfellows, that catching small fish in the shallows and ditches of the Humber, we called a minnow a perch, and a dace a pike ; because they pleased us in the catching, and because we really were ignorant of their quality. In like manner do some older ones act in regard to men. They who are caught and handled by them are treated with distinction, because they are so caught and handled, and because self-love and self-conceit dazzle and delude the senses ; while those whom they neither can handle nor catch are without a distinctive name. We are informed by Aristoteles, in his *Treatise on Natural History*, that solid horns are dropt and that hollow ones are permanent. Now, although we may find solid men cast on the earth and hollow men exalted, yet never will I believe in the long duration of the hollow, or in the long abasement of the solid. Milton, although the generality may be ignorant of it, is quite as great a genius as Bacon, bating the chancellorship, which goes for little where a great man is estimated by a wise one.

PARKER. Rather enthusiastic ! ay, Mr. Marvel ! the one name having been established for almost a century, the other but recently brought forward, and but partially acknowledged. By coming so much later into the world, he can not be quite so original in his notions as Lord Verulam.

MARVEL. Solomon said that, even in his time, there was nothing new under the sun : he said it unwisely and untruly.

PARKER. Solomon ? untruly ? unwisely ?

MARVEL. The spectacles, which by the start you gave, had so nearly fallen from the bridge of your nose, attest it. Had *he* any ? It is said, and apparently with more reason than formerly, that there are no new thoughts. What do the fools mean who say it ? They might just as well assert that there are no new men, because other men existed before, with eyes, mouth, nostrils, chin, and many other appurtenances. But as there are myriads of forms between the forms of Scarron and Hudson * on one side, and of Mercury and Apollo on the other, so there are myriads of thoughts, of the same genus, each taking its peculiar conformation. Æschylus and Racine, struck by the same idea, would express a sentiment very differently. Do not imagine that the idea is the thought : the idea is that which the thought generates, rears up to maturity, and calls after its own name. Every note in music has been sounded frequently ; yet a composition of Purcell may be brilliant by its novelty. There are extremely few roots in a language ; yet the language may be varied, and novel too, age after age. Chess-boards and numerals are less capable of exhibiting new combinations than poetry ; and prose likewise is equally capable of displaying new phases and phenomenons in images and

* A dwarf in that age.—W. S. L.

reflections. Good prose, to say nothing of the original thoughts it conveys, may be infinitely varied in modulation. It is only an extension of metres, an amplification of harmonies, of which even the best and most varied poetry admits but few. Comprehending at once the prose and poetry of Milton, we could prove, before " fit audience," that he is incomparably the greatest master of harmony that ever lived.

There may be, even in these late days, more originality of thought, and flowing in more channels of harmony, more bursts and breaks and sinuosities, than we have yet discovered.

The admirers of Homer never dreamt that a man more pathetic, more sublime, more thoughtful, more imaginative, would follow.

PARKER. Certainly not.

MARVEL. Yet Shakespeare came, in the memory of our fathers.

PARKER. Mr. William Shakespeare of Stratford upon Avon ? A remarkably clever man : nobody denies it.

MARVEL. At first people did not know very well what to make of him. He looked odd : he seemed witty ; he drew tears. But a grin and a pinch of snuff can do that.

Every great author is a great reformer ; and the reform is either in thought or language. Milton is zealous and effective in both.

PARKER. Some men conceive that, if their name is engraven in Gothic letters, it signifies and manifests antiquity of family ; and others, that a congestion of queer words and dry chopt sentences, which turn the mouth awry in reading, make them look like original thinkers. I have seen fantastical folks of this description who write *wend* instead of *go*, and are so ignorant of grammar as even to put *wended* for *went*. I do not say that Mr. Milton [1] is one of them ; but he may have led weak men into the fault.

MARVEL. Not only is he not one of them, but his language is never a patchwork of old and new : all is of a piece. Beside, he is the only writer whom it is safe to follow in spelling : others are inconsistent ; some for want of learning, some for want of reasoning, some for want of memory, and some for want of care. But there are certain words which ceased to be spelt properly just before his

---

[1] Compare the passage in the Conversation of Southey and Landor : " As some men conceive that, if their name is engraven in Gothic letters with several superfluous, it denotes antiquity of family," with subsequent reference to Milton, " his language is never a patchwork."

time : the substantives, *childe* and *wilde*, and the verbs *finde* and *winde*, for instance.

PARKER. Therein we agree. We ought never to have deviated from those who delivered to us our Litany, of which the purity is unapproachable and the harmony complete. Our tongue has been drooping ever since.

MARVEL. Until Milton touched it again with fire from heaven.

PARKER. Gentlemen seem now to have delegated the correction of the press to their valets, and the valets to have devolved it on the chambermaids. But I would not advise you to start a fresh reformation in this quarter ; for the round-heads can't spell, and the royalists won't : and if you bring back an ancient form retaining all its beauty, they will come forward from both sides against you on a charge of coining. We will now return, if you please, to the poets we were speaking of. Both Mr. Shakespeare and Mr. Milton have considerable merit in their respective ways ; but both surely are unequal. Is it not so, Mr. Marvel ?

MARVEL. Under the highest of their immeasurable Alps, all is not valley and verdure : in some places there are frothy cataracts, there are the fruitless beds of noisy torrents, and there are dull and hollow glaciers. He must be a bad writer, or however a very indifferent one, in whom there are no inequalities. The plants of such table-land are diminutive, and never worth gathering. What would you think of a man's eyes to which all things appear of the same magnitude and at the same elevation ? You must think nearly so of a writer who makes as much of small things as of great. The vigorous mind has mountains to climb and valleys to repose in. Is there any sea without its shoals ? On that which the poet navigates, he rises intrepidly as the waves rise round him, and sits composedly as they subside.

PARKER. I can listen to this : but where the authority of Solomon is questioned and rejected, I must avoid the topic. Pardon me ; I collect from what you threw out previously, that, with strange attachments and strange aversions, you cherish singular ideas about greatness.

MARVEL. To pretermit all reference to myself ; our evil humours, and our good ones too, are brought out whimsically. We are displeased by him who would be similar to us, or who would be near, unless he consent to walk behind. To-day we are unfriendly to a man of genius, whom ten days hence we shall be zealous in extolling : not because we know anything more of his works or his character, but because we have dined in his company and he has desired to be introduced to us. A flat ceiling seems to compress those animosities which flame out furiously under the open sky.

PARKER. Sad prejudices ! sad infirmities !

MARVEL. The sadder are opposite to them. Usually men, in distributing fame, do as old maids and old misers do : they give everything to those who want nothing. In literature, often a man's solitude, and oftener his magnitude, disinclines us from helping him if we find him down. We are fonder of warming our hands at a fire already in a blaze than of blowing one. I should be glad to see some person as liberal of fame in regard to Milton, as in regard to those literators of the town who speedily run it out.

PARKER. I have always called him a man of parts. But, Mr. Marvel ! we may bestow as injudiciously as we detract.

MARVEL. Perhaps as injudiciously, certainly not as injuriously. If indeed we are to be called to account for the misapplication of our bestowals, a heavy charge will lie against me for an action I committed in my journey hither from Hull. I saw an old man working upon the road, who was working upon the same road, and not far from the same spot, when I was first elected to represent that city in parliament. He asked me for *something to make him drink :* which, considering the heat of the weather and the indication his nose exhibited of his propensities, did appear superfluous. However, I gave him a shilling, in addition to as many good wishes as he had given me.

PARKER. Not reflecting that he would probably get intoxicated with it.

MARVEL. I must confess I had all that reflection with its whole depth of shade upon my conscience ; and I tried as well as I could to remove the evil. I inquired of him whether he was made the happier by the shilling. He answered that, if I was none the worse for it, he was none. " Then," said I, " honest friend ! since two are already the happier, prythee try whether two more may not become so : therefore drink out of it at supper with thy two best friends."

PARKER. I would rather have advised frugality and laying-by. Perhaps he might have had a wife and children.

MARVEL. He could not then, unless he were a most unlucky man, be puzzled in searching for his two best friends. My project gave him more pleasure than my money : and I was happy to think that he had many hours for his schemes and anticipations between him and sunset.

PARKER. When I ride or walk, I never carry loose money about me, lest, through an inconsiderate benevolence, I be tempted in some such manner to misapply it. To be robbed would give me as little or less concern.

MARVEL. A man's self is often his worst robber. He steals from his own bosom and heart what God has there deposited, and he hides it out of his way, as dogs and foxes do with bones. But the robberies we commit on the body of our superfluities, and store up in vacant places, in places of poverty and sorrow, these, whether in the dark or in the daylight, leave us neither in nakedness nor in fear, are marked by no burning-iron of conscience, are followed by no scourge of reproach; they never deflower prosperity, they never distemper sleep.

PARKER. I am ready at all times to award justice to the generosity of your character, and no man ever doubted its consistency. Believing you to be at heart a loyal subject, I am thrown back on the painful reflection that all our acquaintance are not equally so. Mr. Milton, for example, was a republican, yet he entered into the service of a usurper : you disdained it.

MARVEL. Events proved that my judgment of Cromwell's designs was correcter than his : but the warier man is not always the wiser, nor the more active and industrious in the service of his country.

PARKER. His opinions on religion varied also considerably, until at last the vane almost wore out the socket, and it could turn no longer.

MARVEL. Is it nothing in the eyes of an Anglican bishop to have carried the gospel of Christ against the Talmudists of Rome ; the Word of God against the traditions of men ; the liberty of conscience against the conspiracy of tyranny and fraud ? If so, then the Protector, such was Milton, not of England only, but of Europe, was nothing.

PARKER. You are warm, Mr. Marvel.

MARVEL. Not by any addition to my cloth, however.

PARKER. He hath seceded, I hear, from every form of public worship : and doubts are entertained whether he believes any longer in the co-equality of the Son with the Father, or indeed in his atonement for our sins. Such being the case, he forfeits the name and privileges of a Christian.

ANDREW MARVEL AND BISHOP PARKER

MARVEL. Not with Christians, if they know that he keeps the ordinances of Christ. Papists, Calvinists, Lutherans, and every other kind of scoria, exploding in the furnace of zeal, and cracking off from Christianity, stick alike to the side of this gloomy, contracted, and unwholesome doctrine. But the steadiest believer in the divinity of our Lord, and in his atonement for us ; if pride, arrogance, persecution, malice, lust of station, lust of money, lust of power, inflame him ; is incomparably less a Christian than he who doubteth all that ever was doubted of his genealogy and hereditary rights, yet who never swerveth from his commandments. A wise man will always be a Christian, because the perfection of wisdom is to know where lies tranquillity of mind, and how to attain it, which Christianity teaches ; but men equally wise may differ and diverge on the sufficiency of testimony, and still farther on matters which no testimony can affirm, and no intellect comprehend. To strangle a man because he has a narrow swallow, shall never be inserted among the " infallible cures " in my *Book of Domestic Remedies*.

PARKER. We were talking gravely : were it not rather more seemly to continue in the same strain, Mr. Marvel ?

MARVEL. I was afraid that my gravity might appear too specific : but, with your lordship's permission and exhortation, I will proceed in serious reflections, to which indeed, on this occasion, I am greatly more inclined. Never do I take the liberty to question or examine any man on his religion, or to look over his shoulder on his account-book with his God. But I know that Milton, and every other great poet, must be religious : for there is nothing so godlike as a love of order, with a power of bringing great things into it. This power, unlimited in the one, limited (but incalculably and inconceivably great) in the other, belongs to the Deity and the Poet.

PARKER. I shudder.

MARVEL. Wherefore ? at seeing a man, what he was designed to be by his Maker, his Maker's image ? But pardon me, my lord ! the surprise of such a novelty is enough to shock you.

Reserving to myself for a future time the liberty of defending my friend on theology, in which alone he shifted his camp, I may remark what has frequently happened to me. I have walked much : finding one side of the road miry, I have looked toward the other and thought it cleaner : I have then gone over, and when there I have found it just as bad, although it did not seem nearly so, until it was tried. This however has not induced me to wish that the overseer would bar it up; but only to wish that both sides were mended effectually with smaller and more binding materials, not with large loose stones, nor with softer stuff, soon converted into mud.

PARKER. Stability then and consistency are the qualities most desirable, and these I look for in Mr. Milton. However fond he was of Athenian terms and practices, he rejected them after he had proved them.

MARVEL. It was not in his choice to reject or establish. He saw the nation first cast down and lacerated by Fanaticism, and then utterly exhausted by that quieter blood-sucker, Hypocrisy. A powerful arm was wanted to drive away such intolerable pests, and it could not but be a friendly one. Cromwell and the saner part of the nation were unanimous in beating down Presbyterianism, which had assumed the authority of the Papacy without its lenity.

PARKER. He, and those saner people, had subverted already the better form of Christianity which they found in the Anglican church. Your Samson had shaken its pillars by his attack on Prelaty.

MARVEL. He saw the prelates, in that reign, standing as ready there as anywhere to wave the censer before the king, and under its smoke to hide the people from him. He warned them as an angel would have done, nay, as our Saviour has done, that the wealthy and the proud, the flatterer at the palace and the flatterer at the altar, in short the man for the world, is not the man for heaven.

PARKER. We must lay gentle constructions and liberal interpretations on the Scriptures.

MARVEL. Then let us never open them. If they are true we should receive them as they are; if they are false we should reject them totally. We can not pick and choose; we can not say to the Omniscient, " We think you right here; we think you wrong there; however, we will meet you half-way and talk it over with you." This is such impiety as shocks us even in saying we must avoid it : yet our actions tend to its countenance and support. We clothe the ministers of Christ in the same embroidery as was worn by the proudest of his persecutors, and they mount into Pilate's chair. The Reformation has effected little more than melting down the gold lace of the old wardrobe, to make it enter the pocket more conveniently.

PARKER. Who would have imagined Mr. John Milton should ever have become a seceder and sectarian ! he who, after the days of

216

adolescence, looked with an eye of fondness on the idle superstitions of our forefathers, and celebrated them in his poetry.

MARVEL. When superstitions are only idle it is wiser to look on them kindly than unkindly. I have remarked that those which serve best for poetry have more plumage than talon, and those which serve best for policy have more talon than plumage. Milton never countenanced priestcraft, never countenanced fraud and fallacy.

PARKER. The business is no easy one to separate devotion from practices connected with it. There is much that may seem useless, retained through ages in an intermixture with what is better : and the better would never have been so good as it is if you had cast away the rest. What is chaff when the grain is threshed, was useful to the grain before its threshing.

MARVEL. Since we are come unaware on religion, I would entreat of your lordship to enlighten me, and thereby some others of weak minds and tender consciences, in regard to the criminality of pretence to holiness.

PARKER. The Lord abominates, as you know, Mr. Marvel, from the Holy Scriptures, all hypocrisy.

MARVEL. If we make ourselves or others, who are not holy, seem holy, are we worthy to enter his kingdom ?

PARKER. No ; most unworthy.

MARVEL. What if we set up, not only for good men, but for exquisitely religious, such as violate the laws and religion of the country ?

PARKER. Pray, Mr. Marvel, no longer waste your time and mine in such idle disquisitions. We have beheld such men lately, and abominate them.

MARVEL. Happily for the salvation of our souls, as I conceive, we never went so far as to induce, much less to authorise, much less to command, anyone to fall down and worship them.

PARKER. Such insolence and impudence would have brought about the blessed Restoration much earlier.

MARVEL. We are now come to the point. It seems wonderful to pious and considerate men, unhesitating believers in God's holy word, that although the Reformation, under his guidance, was brought about by the prayers and fasting of the bishops, and others well deserving the name of saints, chiefly of the equestrian order, no place in the Kalendar hath ever been assigned to them.

PARKER. Perhaps, as there were several, a choice might have seemed particular and invidious. Perhaps also the names of many as excellent having been removed from the Rubric, it was deemed unadvisable to inaugurate them.

MARVEL. Yet, my lord bishop, we have inserted Charles the Martyr. Now there have been saints not martyrs, but no martyr not a saint.

PARKER. Do you talk in this manner ? you who had the manliness to praise his courage and constancy to Cromwell's face.

MARVEL. Cromwell was not a man to undervalue the courage and constancy of an enemy : and, had he been, I should have applauded one in his presence. But how happens it that the bishops, priests, and deacons, throughout England, treat Charles as a saint and martyr, and hold his death-day sacred, who violated those ecclesiastical ordinances, the violation whereof you would not only reprobate in another, but visit with exemplary punishment ? Charles was present at plays in his palace on the sabbath. Was he a saint in his life-time ? or only after his death ? If in his life-time, the single miracle performed by him was, to act against his established church without a diminution of holiness. If only in his death, he holds his canonization by a different tenure from any of his blessed predecessors.

It is curious and sorrowful that Charles the Martyr should have suffered death on the scaffold, for renewing the custom of arbitrary loans and forced benevolences, which the usurper Richard III. abolished. Charles, to be sure, had the misfortune to add the practice of torture and mutilation, to which those among the English who are most exposed to it bear a great dislike. Being a martyr, he is placed above the saints in dignity : they tortured only themselves.

PARKER. Let me bring to your recollection, that plays were not prohibited on the sabbath by our great Reformers.

MARVEL. But if it is unchristianlike now, it was then ; and a saint must have been aware of it, although it escaped a reformer.

PARKER. You scoff, Mr. Marvel ! I never answer the scoffer.

MARVEL. I will now be serious. Is the canonization of Charles the effect of a firm conviction that he was holier than all those ejected from the Kalendar ? or is it merely an ebullition of party spirit, an ostentatious display of triumphant spite against his enemies ? In this case, and there are too many and too cogent reasons for believing it, would it not be wiser never to have exhibited to the scrutinizing church of Rome a *consecration* more reprehensible than the former *desecrations?* Either you must acknowledge that saints are not always to be followed in their practices, or you must allow men, women, and children, to dance and frequent the play-houses on Sundays, as our martyr did before he took to mutilating and maiming; and he never left off the custom by his own free will.

PARKER. I think, Mr. Marvel, you might safely leave these considerations to us.

MARVEL. Very safely, my lord! for you are perfectly sure never to meddle with them : you are sure to leave them as they are ; solely from the pious motive that there may be peace in our days, according to the Litany. On such a principle there have been many, and still perhaps there may be some remaining, who would not brush the dust from the bench, lest they should raise the moths and discover the unsoundness and corrosions. But there is danger lest the people at some future day should be wiser, braver, more inquisitive, more pertinacious ; there is danger lest, on finding a notorious cheat and perjurer set up by Act of Parliament among the choice and sterling old saints, they undervalue not only saints but Parliaments.

PARKER. I would rather take my ground where politics are unmingled with religion, and I see better reason to question the wisdom of Mr. Milton than the wisdom of our most gracious King's Privy Council. We enjoy, thank God! liberty of conscience. I must make good my objection on the quarter of consistency, lest you think me resolute to find fault where there is none. Your friend continued to serve the Protector when he had reconstructed a house of Lords, which formerly he called an abomination.

MARVEL. He never served Cromwell but when Cromwell served his country ; and he would not abandon her defence for the worst wounds he had received in it. He was offended at the renewal of that house, after all the labour and pains he had taken in its demolition : and he would have given his life, if one man's life could have paid for it, to throw down again so unshapely and darkening an obstruction. From his youth upward he had felt the Norman rust entering into our very vitals ; and he now saw that, if we had received from the bravest of nations a longer sword, we wore a heavier chain to support it. He began his *History* from a love of the Saxon institutions, than which the most enlightened nations had contrived none better ; nor can we anywhere discover a worthier object for the meditations of a philosophical or for the energies of a poetical mind.

PARKER. And yet you republicans are discontented even with this.

MARVEL. We are not mere Saxons. A wise English republican will prefer (as having grown up with him) the Saxon institutions generally and mainly, both in spirit and practice, to those of Rome and Athens. But the Saxon institutions, however excellent, are insufficient. The moss must be rasped off the bark, and the bark itself must be slit, to let the plant expand. Nothing is wholesomer than milk from the udder : but would you always dine upon it ? The seasons of growth, physical and intellectual, require different modes of preparation, different instruments of tillage, different degrees of warmth and excitement. Whatever is bad in our constitution we derive from the Normans, or from the glosses put against the text under their Welsh and Scotch successors : the good is thrown back to us out of what was ours before. Our boasted Magna Charta is only one side of the old Saxon coat ; and it is the side that has the broken loopholes in it. It hangs loose, and at every breeze 'tis a hard matter to keep it on. In fact the Magna Charta neither is, nor ever was long together, of much value to the body of the people. Our princes could always do what they wished to do, until lately ; and this palladium was so light a matter, that it was easily taken from the town-hall to the palace. It has been holden back or missing whenever the people most loudly called for it. Municipalities, in other words small republics, are a nation's main-stay against aristocratical and regal encroachments.

PARKER. If I speak in defence of the peerage, you may think me interested.

MARVEL. Bring forward what may fairly recommend the institution, and I shall think you less interested than ingenious.

PARKER. Yet surely you, who are well connected, cannot be insensible of the advantages it offers to persons of family.

MARVEL. Is that any proof of its benefit to the public ? And persons of family ! who are they ? Between the titled man of ancient and the titled man of recent, the difference, if any, is in favour of the last. Suppose them both raised for merit (here indeed we do come to theory !), the benefits that society has received from him are nearer us. It is probable that many in the poor and abject are of very ancient families, and particularly in our county, where the contests

220

of the York and Lancaster broke down, in many places, the high and powerful. Some of us may look back six or seven centuries, and find a stout ruffian at the beginning: but the great ancestor of the pauper, who must be somewhere, may stand perhaps far beyond.

PARKER. If we ascend to the tower of Babel and come to the confusion of tongues, we come also to a confusion of ideas. A man of family, in all countries, is he whose ancestor attracted, by some merit, real or imputed, the notice of those more eminent, who promoted him in wealth and station. Now, to say nothing of the humble, the greater part even of the gentry had no such progenitors.

MARVEL. I look to a person of very old family as I do to anything else that is very old, and I thank him for bringing to me a page of romance which probably he himself never knew or heard about. Usually, with all his pride and pretensions, he is much less conscious of the services his ancestor performed, than my spaniel is of his own when he carries my glove or cane to me. I would pat them both on the head for it ; and the civiler and more reasonable of the two would think himself well rewarded.

PARKER. The additional name may light your memory to the national service.

MARVEL. We extract this benefit from an ancient peer ; this phosphorus from a rotten post.

PARKER. I do not complain or wonder that an irreligious man should be adverse not only to prelaty, but equally to a peerage.

MARVEL. Herodotus tells us that among the Egyptians a herald was a herald because he was a herald's son, and not for the clearness of his voice. He had told us before that the Egyptians were worshippers of cats and crocodiles ; but he was too religious a man to sneer at that. It was an absurdity that the herald should hold his office for no better reason than because his father held it. Herodotus might peradventure have smiled within his sleeve at no other being given for the privileges of the peer ; unless he thought a loud voice, which many do, more important than information and discretion.

PARKER. You will find your opinions discountenanced by both our universities.

MARVEL. I do not want anybody to corroborate my opinions. They keep themselves up by their own weight and consistency. Cambridge on one side and Oxford on the other could lend me no effectual support ; and my skiff shall never be impeded by the sedges of Cam, nor grate on the gravel of Isis.

PARKER. Mr. Marvel, the path of what we fondly call patriotism is highly perilous. Courts at least are safe.

MARVEL. I would rather stand on the ridge of Etna than lower my head in the Grotto del Cane. By the one I may share the fate of a philosopher, by the other I must suffer the death of a cur.

PARKER. We are all of us dust and ashes.

MARVEL. True, my lord ! but in some we recognise the dust of gold and the ashes of the phœnix ; in others the dust of the gateway and the ashes of turf and stubble. With the greatest rulers upon earth, head and crown drop together, and are overlooked. It is true, we read of them in history ; but we also read in history of crocodiles and hyænas. With great writers, whether in poetry or prose, what falls away is scarcely more or other than a vesture. The features of the man are imprinted on his works ; and more lamps burn over them, and more religiously, than are lighted in temples or churches. Milton, and men like him, bring their own incense, kindle it with their own fire, and leave it unconsumed and unconsumable : and their music, by day and by night, swells along a vault commensurate with the vault of heaven.

PARKER. Mr. Marvel, I am admiring the extremely fine lace of your cravat.

MARVEL. It cost me less than lawn would have done : and it wins me a reflection. Very few can think that man a great man, whom they have been accustomed to meet, dressed exactly like themselves ; more especially if they happen to find him, not in park, forest, or chase, but warming his limbs by the reflected heat of the bricks in Artillery-walk. In England a man becomes a great man by living in the middle of a great field ; in Italy by living in a walled city ; in France by living in a courtyard : no matter what lives they lead there.

PARKER. I am afraid, Mr. Marvel, there is some slight bitterness in your observation.

MARVEL. Bitterness it may be from the bruised laurel of Milton. What falsehoods will not men put on, if they can only pad them with a little piety ! And how few will expose their whole faces, from a fear of being frost-bitten by poverty ! But Milton was among the few.

222

ANDREW MARVEL AND BISHOP PARKER

PARKER. Already have we had our Deluge: we are now once more upon dry land again, and we behold the same creation as rejoiced us formerly. Our late gloomy and turbulent times are passed for ever.

MARVEL. Perhaps they are, if anything is for ever : but the sparing Deluge may peradventure be commuted for unsparing Fire, as we are threatened. The arrogant, the privileged, the stiff upholders of established wrong, the deaf opponents of equitable reformation, the lazy consumers of ill-requited industry, the fraudulent who, unable to stop the course of the sun, pervert the direction of the gnomon, all these peradventure may be gradually consumed by the process of silent contempt, or suddenly scattered by the tempest of popular indignation. As we see in masquerades the real judge and the real soldier stopped and mocked by the fictitious, so do we see in the carnival of to-day the real man of dignity hustled, shoved aside, and derided, by those who are invested with the semblance by the milliners of the court. The populace is taught to respect this livery alone, and is proud of being permitted to look through the grating at such ephemeral frippery. And yet false gems and false metals have never been valued above real ones. Until our people alter these notions ; until they estimate the wise and virtuous above the silly and profligate, the man of genius above the man of title ; until they hold the knave and cheat of St. James's as low as the knave and cheat of St. Giles's ; they are fitter for the slave-market than for any other station.

PARKER. You would have no distinctions, I fear.

MARVEL. On the contrary, I would have greater than exist at present. You can not blot or burn out an ancient name : you can not annihilate past services : you can not subtract one single hour from eternity, nor wither one leaf on his brow who hath entered into it. Sweep away from before me the soft grubs of yesterday's formation, generated by the sickliness of the plant they feed upon : sweep them away unsparingly ; then will you clearly see distinctions, and easily count the men who have attained them worthily.

PARKER. In a want of respect to established power and principles, originated most of the calamities we have latterly undergone.

MARVEL. Say rather, in the averseness of that power and the inadequacy of those principles to resist the encroachment of injustice: say rather, on their tendency to distort the poor creatures swaddled up in them : add moreover the reluctance of the old women who rock

223

and dandle them, to change their habiliments for fresh and wholesome ones. A man will break the windows of his own house that he
may not perish by foul air within ; now, whether is he, or those who
bolted the door on him, to blame for it ? If he is called mad or
inconsiderate, it is only by those who are ignorant of the cause and
insensible of the urgency. I declare I am rejoiced at seeing a gentleman, whose ancestors have signally served their country, treated
with deference and respect : because it evinces a sense of justice and
of gratitude in the people, and because it may incite a few others,
whose ambition would take another course, to desire the same.
Different is my sentence, when he who has not performed the action
claims more honour than he who performed it, and thinks himself the
worthier if twenty are between them than if there be one or none.
Still less accordant is it with my principles, and less reducible to my
comprehension, that they who devised the ruin of cities and societies
should be exhibited as deserving much higher distinction than they
who have corrected the hearts and enlarged the intellects, and have
performed it not only without the hope of reward, but almost with
the certainty of persecution.

PARKER. Ever too hard upon great men, Mr. Marvel !

MARVEL. Little men in lofty places, who throw long shadows
because our sun is setting : the men so little and the places so lofty,
that, casting my pebble, I only show where they stand. They would
be less contented with themselves if they had obtained their prefer-
ment honestly. Luck and dexterity always give more pleasure than
intellect and knowledge ; because they fill up what they fall on to the
brim at once, and people run to them with acclamations at the splash.
Wisdom is reserved and noiseless, contented with hard earnings, and
daily letting go some early acquisition, to make room for better
specimens. But great is the exultation of a worthless man, when
he receives, for the chips and raspings of his Bridewell logwood, a
richer reward than the best and wisest, for extensive tracts of well-
cleared truths ; when he who has sold his country——

PARKER. Forbear, forbear, good Mr. Marvel !

MARVEL. When such is higher in estimation than he who would
have saved it ; when his emptiness is heard above the voice that hath
shaken Fanaticism in her central shrine, that hath bowed down
tyrants to the scaffold, that hath raised up nations from the dust, that
alone hath been found worthy to celebrate, as angels do, creating and

224

redeeming Love, and to precede with its solitary sound the trumpet that will call us to our doom.

PARKER. I am unwilling to feign ignorance of the gentleman you designate : but really now you would make a very Homer of him.

MARVEL. It appears to me that Homer is to Milton what a harp is to an organ ; though a harp under the hand of Apollo.

PARKER. I have always done him justice : I have always called him a learned man.

MARVEL. Call him henceforward the most glorious one that ever existed upon earth. If two, Bacon and Shakespeare, have equalled him in diversity and intensity of power, did either of these spring away with such resolution from the sublimest highths of genius, to liberate and illuminate with patient labour the manacled human race ? And what is his recompense ? The same recompense as all men like him have received, and will receive for ages. Persecution follows Righteousness : the Scorpion is next in succession to Libra. The fool however who ventures to detract from Milton's genius, in the night which now appears to close on him, will, when the dawn has opened on his dull ferocity, be ready to bite off a limb, if he might thereby limp away from the trap he has prowled into. Among the gentler, the better, and the wiser, few have entered yet the awful structure of his mind : few comprehend, few are willing to contemplate, its vastness. Politics now occupy scarcely a closet in it. We seldom are inclined to converse on them : and, when we do, it is jocosely rather than austerely. For even the bitterest berries grow less acrid when they have been hanging long on the tree. Beside, it is time to sit with our hats between our legs, since so many grave men have lately seen their errors, and so many brave ones have already given proofs enough of their bravery, and trip aside to lay down their laurels on gilt tables and velvet cushions. If my friend condemns anyone now, it is Cromwell ; and principally for reconstructing a hereditary house of peers. He perceives that it was done for the purpose of giving the aristocracy an interest in the perpetuation of power in his family, of which he discovered the folly just before his death. He derides the stupidity of those who bandy about the battered phrase of *useful checks and necessary counterpoises.* He would not desire a hinderance on his steward in the receipt of his rent, if he had any, nor on his attorney in prosecuting his suit : he would not recommend any interest in opposition to that of the people :

he would not allow an honest man to be arrested and imprisoned for debt, while a dishonest one is privileged to be exempt from it : and he calls that nation unwise, and those laws iniquitous, which tolerate so flagrant an abuse. He would not allow a tradesman, who lives by his reputation for honesty, to be calumniated as dishonest, without the means of vindicating his character, unless by an oppressive and dilatory procedure, while a peer, who perhaps may live by dishonesty, as some are reported to have done in former reigns, recurs to an immediate and uncostly remedy against a similar accusation. He would not see Mother Church lie with a lawyer on the woolsack, nor the ministry of the apostles devolve on the Crown, sacred and uncontaminated as we see it is.

PARKER. No scoffs at the Crown, I do beseech you, Mr. Marvel ! whatever enmity you and Mr. Milton may bear against the peers. He would have none of them, it seems.

MARVEL. He would have as many as can prove by any precedent or argument, that virtue and abilities are hereditary ; and I believe he would stint them exactly to that number. In regard to their services, he made these observations a few days ago : " Why, in God's name, friend Andrew, do we imagine that a thing can be made stabile by pulling at it perpetually in different directions ? Where there are contrary and conflicting interests, one will predominate at one time, another at another. Now, what interest at any time ought to predominate against the public ? We hear indeed that when the royal power is oppressive to them, the peers push their horns against the Leopards ; but did they so in the time of James or his son ? And are not the people strong enough to help and right themselves, if they were but wise enough ? And if they were wise enough, would they whistle for the wolves to act in concert with the shepherd-dogs ? Our consciences tell us," added he, " that we should have done some good, had our intentions been well seconded and supported. Collegians and barristers and courtiers may despise the poverty of our intellects, throw a few of their old scraps into our satchels, and send the beadle to show us the road we ought to take : nevertheless we are wilful, and refuse to surrender our old customary parochial footpath."

PARKER. And could not he let alone the poor innocent collegians ?

MARVEL. Nobody ever thought them more innocent than he, unless when their square caps were fanning the flames round heretics :

and every man is liable to be a heretic in his turn. Collegians have always been foremost in the cure of the *lues* of heresy by sweating and caustic.

PARKER. Sir! they have always been foremost in maintaining the unity of the faith.

MARVEL. So zealously, that whatever was the king's faith was theirs. And thus it will always be, until their privileges and immunities are in jeopardy; then shall you see them the most desperate incendiaries.

PARKER. After so many species of religion, generated in the sty of old corruptions, we return to what experience teaches us is best. If the Independents, or any other sect, had reason on their side, and truly evangelical doctrine, they would not die away and come to nothing as they have done.

MARVEL. Men do not stick very passionately and tenaciously to a pure religion : there must be honey on the outside of it, and warmth within, and latitude around, or they make little bellow and bustle about it. That Milton has been latterly no frequenter of public worship, may be lamented, but is not unaccountable. He has lived long enough to perceive that all sects are animated by a spirit of hostility and exclusion, a spirit the very opposite to the Gospel. There is so much malignity, hot-blooded and cold-blooded, in zealots, that I do not wonder at seeing the honest man, who is tired of dissension and controversy, wrap himself up in his own quiet conscience, and indulge in a tranquillity somewhat like sleep, apart. Nearly all are of opinion that devotion is purer and more ardent in solitude, but declare to you that they believe it to be their duty to set an example by going to church. Is not this pride and vanity ? What must they conceive of their own value and importance, to imagine that others will necessarily look up to them as guides and models ! A hint of such an infirmity arouses all their choler ; and from that moment we are unworthy of being saved by them. But if they abandon us to what must appear to them so hopeless a condition, can we doubt whether they would not abandon a babe floating like Moses in a basket on a wide and rapid river ? I have always found these people, whatever may be the sect, self-sufficient, hard-hearted, intolerant, and unjust ; in short, the opposite of Milton. What wonder then if he abstain from their society ? particularly in places of worship, where it must affect a rational and religious man the most painfully.

He thinks that churches, as now constituted, are to religion what pest-houses are to health : that they often infect those who ailed nothing, and withhold them from freedom and exercise. Austerity hath oftener been objected to him than indifference. That neither of the objections is well-founded, I think I can demonstrate by an anecdote. Visiting him last month, I found him hearing read by his daughter the treatise of Varro *On Agriculture :* and I said, laughingly, " We will walk over your farm together." He smiled, although he could not see that I did ; and he answered, " I never wish to possess a farm, because I can enjoy the smell of the hay and of the hawthorn in a walk to Hampstead, and can drink fresh milk there." After a pause he added, " I can not tell (for nobody is more ignorant in these matters) in what our agriculture differs from the ancient : but I am delighted to be reminded of a custom which my girl has been recalling to my memory ; the custom of crowning with a garland of sweet herbs, once a year, the brink of wells. Andrew ! the old moss-grown stones were not neglected, from under which the father and son, the wife and daughter, drew the same pure element with the same thankfulness as their hale progenitors." His piety is infused into all the moods of his mind. Here it was calm and gentle, at other times it was ardent and enthusiastic. The right application of homely qualities is of daily and general use. We all want glass for the window, few want it for the telescope.

PARKER. It is very amiable to undertake the defence of a person who, whatever may be his other talents, certainly has possessed but in a moderate degree the talent of making or of retaining friends.

MARVEL. He, by the constitution of the human mind, or rather by its configuration under those spiritual guides who claim the tutelage of it, must necessarily have more enemies than even another of the same principles. The great abhor the greater, who can humble but can not raise them. The king's servants hate God's as much (one would fancy) as if he fed them better, drest them finelier, and gave them more plumy titles. Poor Milton has all these against him ; what is wanting in weight is made up by multitude and multiformity. Judges and privy counsellors throw axes and halters in his path : divines grow hard and earthy about him : slim, straddling, blotchy writers, those of quality in particular, feel themselves cramped and stunted under him : and people of small worth, in every way, detract from his, stamping on it as if they were going to spring over it.

228

ANDREW MARVEL AND BISHOP PARKER

Whatever they pick up against him they take pains to circulate ; and are sorrier at last that the defamation is untrue than that they helped to propagate it. I wish Truth were as prolific as Falsehood, and as many were ready to educate her offspring. But although we see the progeny of Falsehood shoot up into amazing stature, and grow day by day more florid, yet they soon have reached their maturity, soon lose both teeth and tresses. As the glory of England is in part identified with Milton's, his enemies are little less than parricides. If they had any sight beyond to-day, what would they give, how would they implore and supplicate, to be forgotten ?

PARKER. Very conscientious men may surely have reprehended him, according to the lights that God has lent them.

MARVEL. They might have burnt God's oil in better investigations. Your conscientious men are oftener conscientious in withholding than in bestowing.

PARKER. Writers of all ranks and conditions, from the lowest to the highest, have disputed with Mr. Milton on all the topics he has undertaken.

MARVEL. And I am grieved to think that he has noticed some of them. Salmasius alone was not unworthy *sublimi flagello.* But what would your lordship argue from the imprudence and irreverence of the dwarfs ? The most prominent rocks and headlands are most exposed to the violence of the sea ; but those which can repell the waves are in little danger from the corrosion of the limpets.

PARKER. Mr. Milton may reasonably be censured for writing on subjects whereof his knowledge is imperfect or null : on courts, for instance. The greater part of those who allow such a license to their pens, and he among the rest, never were admitted into them. I am sorry to remark that our English are the foremost beagles in this cry.

MARVEL. If Milton was never admitted within them, he never was importunate for admittance : and if none were suffered to enter but such as are better and wiser than he, the gates of Paradise are themselves less glorious, and with less difficulty thrown open. The great, as we usually call the fortunate, are only what Solomon says about them, " the highest part of the dust of the world," and this highest part is the lightest. Do you imagine that all the ministers and kings under the canopy of heaven are, in the sight of a pure Intelligence, equivalent to him whom this pure Intelligence hath enabled to penetrate with an unfailing voice the dense array of distant generations ?

229

Can princes give more than God can ? or are their gifts better ?
That they are usually thought so, is no conclusive proof of the fact.
On the contrary, with me at least, what is usually thought on any
subject of importance, and on many of none, lies under the suspicion
of being wrong : for surely the number of those who think correctly
is smaller than of those who think incorrectly, even where passions
and interests interfere the least. Of those who appear to love God,
and who sincerely think they do, the greater part must be conscious
that they are not very fond of the men whom he hath shown himself
the most indulgent to, and the most enriched with abilities and
virtues. Among the plants of the field we look out for the salubrious,
and we cultivate and cull them ; to the wholesomer of our fellow-
creatures we exhibit no such partiality : we think we do enough when
we only pass them without treading on them : if we leave them to
blossom and run to seed, it is forbearance.

PARKER. Mr. Milton hath received his reward from his employers.

MARVEL. His services are hardly yet begun ; and no mortal man,
no series of transitory generations, can repay them. God will not
delegate this ; no, not even to his angels. I venture no longer to
stand up for him on English ground : but, since we both are Englishmen by birth, I may stand up for the remainder of our countrymen.
Your lordship is pleased to remark that they are the first *beagles* in
the cry against courts. Now I speak with all the freedom and all the
field-knowledge of a Yorkshireman, when I declare that your lordship
is a bad sportsman, in giving a *hound's* title to dogs that hunt vermin.

PARKER. Mr. Marvel ! a person of your education should abstain
from mentioning thus contemptuously men of the same rank and
condition as yourself.

MARVEL. All are of the same rank and condition with me, who
have climbed as high, who have stood as firmly, and who have never
yet descended. Neglect of time, subserviency to fortune, compliance
with power and passions, would thrust men far below me, although
they had been exalted higher, to the uncalculating eye, than mortal
ever was exalted. Sardanapalus had more subjects and more
admirers than Cromwell, whom nevertheless I venture to denominate
the most sagacious and prudent, the most tolerant and humane, the
most firm and effective prince, in the annals of our country.

PARKER. Usurpers should not be thus commended.

MARVEL. Usurpers are the natural and imprescriptable successors of imbecile, unprincipled, and lawless kings. In general they too are little better furnished with virtues, and even their wisdom seems to wear out under the ermine. Ambition makes them hazardous and rash : these qualities raise the acclamations of the vulgar, to whom meteors are always greater than stars, and the same qualities which raised them, precipitate them into perdition. Sometimes obstreperous mirth, sometimes gipsy-like mysteriousness, sometimes the austerity of old republicanism, and sometimes the stilts of modern monarchy, come into play, until the crowd hisses the actor off the stage, pelted, broken-headed, and stumbling over his sword. Cromwell used none of these grimaces. He wore a mask while it suited him ; but its features were grave ; and he threw it off in the heat of action.

PARKER. On the whole, you speak more favourably of a man who was only your equal, than of those whom legitimate power has raised above you.

MARVEL. Never can I do so much good as he did. He was hypocritical, and, in countermining perfidy, he was perfidious ; but his wisdom, his valour, and his vigilance saved the nation at Worcester and Dunbar. He took unlawful and violent possession of supreme authority ; but he exercised it with moderation and discretion. Even Fanaticism had with him an English cast of countenance. He never indulged her appetite in blood, nor carried her to hear the music of tortures reverberated by the arch of a dungeon. He supplied her with no optical glass at the spectacle of mutilations : he never thought, as Archbishop Laud did, he could improve God's image by amputating ears and slitting noses ; he never drove men into holy madness with incessant howlings, like the lycanthropic saints of the north.

Having then before me not only his arduous achievements, but likewise his abstinence from those evil practices in which all our sovrans his predecessors had indulged, I should be the most insolent and the most absurd of mortals if I supposed that the Protector of England was only my equal. But I am not obliged by the force of truth and duty, to admit even to this position those whom court servility may proclaim to the populace as my superiors. A gardener may write *sweet lupin* on the cover of rape-seed ; but the cover will never turn rape-seed into sweet lupin. Something more than a couple of beasts, couchant or rampant, blue or blazing, or than a brace of birds with a claw on a red curtain, is requisite to raise an earl or a marquis up to me, although lion-king-at-arms and garter-king-at-arms equip them with all their harness, and beget them a grandfather each. I flap down with the border of my glove, and brush away and blow off these gossamer pretentions ; and I take for my motto, what the king bears for his, I hope as a model for all his subjects, " Dieu et mon droit."

PARKER. Mr. Marvel ! Mr. Marvel ! I did not think you so proud a man.

MARVEL. No, my lord ? not when you know that Milton is my friend ? If you wish to reduce me and others to our level, pronounce that name, and we find it. The French motto, merely from its being French, recalls my attention to what I was about to notice, when your lordship so obligingly led me to cover. I will now undertake to prove that the English beagles are neither the first nor the best in scenting what lieth about courts. A French writer, an ecclesiastic, a dignitary, a bishop, wrote lately :

" Courts are full of ill offices : it is there that all the passions are in an uproar * : it is there that hatred and friendship change incessantly for interest, and nothing is constant but the desire of injuring. Friend, as Jeremiah says, is fraudulent to friend, brother to brother. The art of ensnaring has nothing dishonourable in it excepting ill success. In short, Virtue herself, often false, becomes more to be dreaded than Vice."

Now, if there were any like place upon earth, would not even the worst prince, the worst people, insist on its destruction ? What brothel, what gaming-house, what den of thieves, what wreck, what conflagration, ought to be surrounded so strictly by the protectors of property, the guardians of morals, and the ministers of justice ? Should any such conspirator, any aider or abettor, any familiar or confidant of such conspiracy, be suffered to live at large ? Milton, in the mildness of his humanity, would at once let loose the delinquents, and would only nail up for ever the foul receptacle.

PARKER. The description is exaggerated.

MARVEL. It is not a schoolboy's theme, beginning with, " Nothing is more sure," or " Nothing is more deplorable " ; it is not an undergraduate's exercise, drawn from pure fresh thoughts, where there are

---

* The original is defective in logic. " C'est là que toutes les passions se réunissent pour s'entre-chocquer et se détruire." So much the better, were it true.—W. S. L.

only glimpses through the wood before him, or taken up in reliance on higher men to whom past ages have bowed in veneration : no ; the view is taken on the spot by one experienced and scientific in it ; by the dispassionate, the disinterested, the clear-sighted, and clear-souled Massillon.

PARKER. To show his eloquence, no doubt.

MARVEL. No eloquence is perfect, none worth showing, none becoming a Christian teacher, but that in which the postulates are just, and the deductions not carried beyond nor cast beside them, nor strained hard, nor snatched hastily. I quote not from stern republicans : I quote not from loose lay people : but from the interior of the court, from the closet of the palace, from under the canopy and cope of Episcopacy herself. In the same spirit the amiable and modest Fénelon speaks thus : " Alas ! to what calamities are kings exposed ! The wisest of them are often taken by surprise : men of artifice, swayed by self-interest, surround them : the good retire from them, because they are neither supplicants nor flatterers, and because they wait to be inquired for : and princes know not where they are to be found. O ! how unhappy is a king, to be exposed to the designs of the wicked ! "

It is impossible to draw any other deduction from this hypothesis, than the necessity of abolishing the kingly office, not only for the good of the people, but likewise of the functionaries. Why should the wisest and the best among them be subject to so heavy a calamity ? a calamity so easily avoided. Why should there be tolerated a focus and point of attraction for wicked men ? Why should we permit the good to be excluded, whether by force or shame, from any place which ought to be a post of honour ? Why do we suffer a block to stand in their way, which by its nature hath neither eyes to discern them, nor those about it who would permit the use of the discovery if it had ?

PARKER. Horrible questions ! leading God knows whither !

MARVEL. The questions are originally not mine. No person who reasons on what he reads can ever have read the works of Fénelon and not have asked them. If what he says is true, they follow necessarily : and the answer is ready for every one of them. That they are true we may well surmise : for surely nobody was less likely to express his sentiments with prejudice or precipitancy, or passion. He and Massillon are such witnesses against courts and royalty as can not be rejected. They bring forward their weighty and conclusive evidence, not only without heat, but without intention, and disclose what they overheard as they communed with their conscience. There may be malice in the thoughts, and acrimony in the expressions, of those learned men who, as you remark, were never admitted into courts ; although malice and acrimony are quite as little to be expected in them as in the spectators at a grand amphitheatre, because they could only be retired and look on, and were precluded from the arena in the combat of man and beast.

PARKER. There may be malice where there is no acrimony : there may be here.

MARVEL. The existence of either is impossible in well-regulated minds.

PARKER. I beg your pardon, Mr. Marvel.

MARVEL. What ! my lord ! do you admit that even in well-regulated minds the worst passions may be excited by royalty ? It must then be bad indeed ; worse than Milton, worse than Massillon, worse than Fénelon, represent it. The frugal republican may detest it for its vicious luxury and inordinate expenditure ; the strict religionist, as one of the worst curses an offended God inflicted on a disobedient and rebellious people ; the man of calmer and more indulgent piety may grieve at seeing it, with all its devils, possess the swine, pitying the poor creatures into which it is permitted to enter, not through their fault, but their infirmity ; not by their will, but their position.

PARKER. And do you imagine it is by their will that what is inrooted is taken away from them ?

MARVEL. Certainly not. Another proof of their infirmity. Did you ever lose a rotten tooth, my lord, without holding up your hand against it ? or was there ever one drawn at which you did not rejoice when it was done ? All the authorities we have brought forward may teach us, that the wearer of a crown is usually the worse for it : that it collects the most vicious of every kind about it, as a nocturnal blaze in uncultivated lands collects poisonous reptiles : and that it renders bad those who, without it, might never have become so. But no authority, before your lordship, ever went so far as to throw within its noxious agency the little that remained uncorrupted : none ever told us, for our caution, that it can do what nothing else can ; namely, that it can excite the worst passions in well-regulated minds.

234

ANDREW MARVEL AND BISHOP PARKER

O Royalty ! if this be true, I, with my lord bishop, will detest and abhor thee as the most sweeping leveller ! Go, go, thou indivisible in the infernal triad with Sin and Death !

PARKER. I must not hear this.

MARVEL. I spoke hypothetically, and stood within your own premises, referring to no actual state of things, and least of all inclined to touch upon the very glorious one in which we live. Royalty is in her place and sits gracefully by the side of our second Charles.

PARKER. Here, Mr. Marvel, we have no divergence of opinion.

MARVEL. Enjoying this advantage, I am the more anxious that my friend should partake in it, whose last political conversation with me was greatly more moderate than the language of the eloquent French bishops. " We ought," said he, " to remove anything by which a single fellow-creature may be deteriorated : how much rather then that which deteriorates many millions, and brands with the stamp of servitude the brow of the human race ! "

PARKER. Do you call this more moderate ?

MARVEL. I call it so, because it is more argumentative. It is in the temper and style of Milton to avoid the complaining tone of the one prelate, and the declamatory of the other. His hand falls on his subject without the softener of cuff or ruffle.

PARKER. So much the worse. But better as it is than with an axe in it ; for God knows where it might fall.

MARVEL. He went on saying that the most clear-sighted kings can see but a little way before them and around them, there being so many mediums, and that delegated authority is liable to gross abuses.

PARKER. Republics too must delegate a portion of their authority to agents at a distance.

MARVEL. Every agent in a well-regulated republic is a portion of itself. Citizen must resemble citizen in all political essentials ; but what is privileged bears little resemblance to what is unprivileged. In fact, the words *privilege* and *prerogative* are *manifestos* of injustice, without one word added.

PARKER. Yet the people would not have your republic when they had tried it ?

MARVEL. Nor would the people have God when they had tried him. But is this an argument why we should not obey his ordinances, and serve him with all our strength ?

235

PARKER. O strange comparison! I am quite shocked, Mr. Marvel!

MARVEL. What! at seeing any work of the Deity at all resemble the maker, at all remind us of him? May I be often so shocked! that light thoughts and troublesome wishes and unworthy resentments may be shaken off me; and that the Giver of all good may appear to me and converse with me in the garden he has planted.

PARKER. Then walk humbly with him, Mr. Marvel.

MARVEL. Every day I bend nearer to the dust that is to receive me: and, if this were not sufficient to warn me, the sight of my old friend would. I repress my own aspirations that I may continue to repeat his words, tending to prove the vast difference between the administration of a kingly government and a commonwealth, where all offices in contact with the people are municipal, where the officers are chosen on the spot by such as know them personally, and by such as have an immediate and paramount interest in giving them the preference. This, he insisted, is the greatest of all advantages; and this alone (but truly it is *not* alone) would give the republican an incontestable superiority over every other system.

PARKER. Supposing it in theory to have its merits, the laws no longer permit us to recommend it in practice.

MARVEL. I am not attempting to make or to reclaim a convert. The foot that has slipped back is less ready for progress than the foot that never had advanced.

PARKER. Sir! I know my duty to God and my king.

MARVEL. I also have attempted to learn mine, however unsuccessfully.

PARKER. There is danger, sir, in holding such discourses. The cause is no longer to be defended without a violation of the statutes.

MARVEL. I am a republican, and will die one; but rather, if the choice is left me, in my own bed; yet on turf or over the ladder unreluctantly, if God draws thitherward the cause and conscience, and strikes upon my heart to waken me. I have been, I will not say tolerant and indulgent (words applicable to children only), but friendly and cordial toward many good men whose reason stood in opposition and almost (if reason can be hostile) in hostility to mine. When we desire to regulate our watches, we keep them attentively before us, and touch them carefully, gently, delicately, with the finest and best-tempered instrument, day after day. When we would

236

ANDREW MARVEL AND BISHOP PARKER

manage the minds of men, finding them at all different from our own, we thrust them away from us with blind impetuosity, and throw them down in the dirt to make them follow us the quicklier. In the turbulence of attack from all directions, our cause hath been decried by some, not for being bad in itself, but for being supported by bad men. What! are there no pretenders to charity, to friendship, to devotion? Should we sit uneasy and shuffling under it, and push our shoulders against every post to rub it off, merely for the Scotch having worn it in common with us, and for their having shortened, unstitched, and sold it?

PARKER. Their history is over-run more rankly than any other, excepting the French, with blood and treachery.*

MARVEL. Half of them are Menteiths.† Even their quietest and most philosophical spirits are alert and clamorous in defence of any villany committed by power or compensated by wealth. In the degeneracy of Greece, in her utter subjugation, was there one historian or one poet vile enough to represent as blameless the conduct of Clytemnestra? Yet what labours of the press are bestowed on a queen of Scotland, who committed the same crime without the same instigation, who had been educated in the principles of Christianity, who had conversed from her girlhood with the polite and learned, and who had spent only a very few years among the barbarians of the north!

PARKER. Her subjects were angry, not that she was punished, but that she was unpaid for. They would have sold her cheaper than they sold her grandson : and, being so reasonable, they were outrageous that there were no bidders. Mr. Marvel! the Scotch have always been cringing when hungry, always cruel when full : their avarice is without satiety, their corruption is without shame, and their ferocity is without remorse.

MARVEL. Among such men there may be demagogues, there can not be republicans ; there may be lovers of free quarters, there can not be of freedom. Reverencing the bold and the sincere, and in them the character of our country, we Englishmen did not punish

* Undoubtedly such were the sentiments of Milton and Marvel; and they were just. But Scotland in our days has produced not only the calmest and most profound reasoners, she has also given birth to the most enlightened and energetic patriots.—W. S. L.

† Menteith was the betrayer of Wallace, the bravest hero, the hero in most points, our island has gloried in since Alfred.—W. S. L.

237

those ministers who came forth uncited, and who avowed in the House of Commons that they had been the advisers of the Crown in all the misdemeanours against which we brought the heaviest charges. We bethought us of the ingratitude, of the injuries, of the indignities, we had sustained : we bethought us of our wealth transferred from the nation to raise up enemies against it : we bethought us of patient piety and of tranquil courage, in chains, in dungeons, tortured, maimed, mangled, for the assertion of truth and of freedom, of religion and of law.

PARKER. Our most gracious king is disposed to allow a considerable latitude, repressing at the same time that obstinate spirit which prevails across the Border.   Much of the Scottish character may be attributed to the national religion, in which the damnatory has the upper hand of the absolving.

MARVEL. Our judges are merciful to those who profess the king's reputed and the duke's acknowledged tenets: but let a man stand up for the Independents, and out pops Mr. Attorney General, throws him on his back, claps a tongue-scraper into his mouth, and exercises it resolutely and unsparingly.

PARKER. I know nothing of your new-fangled sects : but the doctrines of the Anglican and the Romish church approximate.

MARVEL. The shepherd of the seven hills teaches his sheep in what tone to bleat before him, just as the Tyrolean teaches his bullfinch ; first by depriving him of sight, and then by making him repeat a certain series of notes at stated intervals.   Prudent and quiet people will choose their churches as they choose their ale-houses ; partly for the wholesomeness of the draught and partly for the moderation of the charges : but the host in both places must be civil, and must not damn you, body and soul, by way of invitation.   The wheat-sheaf is a very good sign for the one, and a very bad one for the other.   Tythes are more ticklish things than tenets, when men's brains are sound : and there are more and worse stumbling-blocks at the barn-door than at the church-porch.   I never saw a priest, Romanist or Anglican, who would tuck up his surplice to remove them.   Whichever does it first, will have the most voices for him: but he must be an Englishman, and serve only Englishmen : he must resign the cook's perquisites to the Spaniard : he must give up not only the fat but the blood, and he must keep fewer faggots in the kitchen.   Since, whatever the country, whatever the state of civilization, the Church of Rome remains the same ; since under her influence the polite Louis at the present day commits as much bloodshed and perfidy, and commands as many conflagrations and rapes to her honour and advancement, as the most barbarous kings and prelates in times past; I do hope that no insolence, no rapacity, no profligacy, no infidelity, in our own lords spiritual, will render us either the passive captives of her insinuating encroachments, or the indifferent spectators of her triumphal entrance.   We shall be told it was the religion of Alfred, the religion of the Plantagenets.   There may be victory, there may be glory, there may be good men, under all forms and fabrics of belief.   Titus, Trajan, the two Antonines, the two Gordians, Probus, Tacitus, rendered their countrymen much happier than the Plantagenets, or the greater and better Alfred could do. Let us receive as brethren our countrymen of every creed, and reject as Christians those only who refuse to receive them.

PARKER. Most willingly ; if such is the pleasure of the King and Privy Council.   And I am delighted to find you, who are so steadfast a republican, extolling the emperors.

MARVEL. Your idea of *emperor* is incorrect or inadequate.   Cincinnatus and Cato were emperors in the Roman sense of the word. The Germans and Turks and Marocchines cut out theirs upon another model.   These Romans, and many more in the same station, did nothing without the consent, the approbation, the *command* (for such was the expression), of the senate and the people.   They lived among the wiser and better citizens, with whom they conversed as equals, and where it was proper (for instance on subjects of literature), as inferiors.   From these they took their wives, and with the sons and daughters of these they educated their children.   In the decline of the Commonwealth, kings themselves, on the boundaries of the empire, were daily and hourly conversant with honest and learned men.   All princes in our days are so educated, as to detest the unmalleable and unmelting honesty which will receive no impression from them : nor do they even let you work for them unless they can bend you double.   We must strip off our own clothes, or they never will let us be measured for their livery, which has now become our only protection.

PARKER. It behoves us to obey ; otherwise we can expect no forbearance and no tranquillity.

MARVEL. I wish the tranquillity of our country may last beyond our time, although we should live, which we can not expect to do, twenty years.

PARKER. God grant we may !

MARVEL. Life clings with the pertinacity of an impassioned mistress to many a man who is willing to abandon it, while he who too much loves it, loses it.

PARKER. Twenty years !

MARVEL. I have enjoyed but little of it at a time when it becomes a necessary of life, and I fear I shall leave as little for a heritage.

PARKER. But in regard to living—we are both of us hale men : we may hope for many days yet : we may yet see many changes.

MARVEL. I have lived to see one too many.

PARKER. Whoever goes into political life must be contented with the same fare as others of the same rank who embark in the same expedition.

MARVEL. Before his cruise is over, he learns to be satisfied with a very small quantity of fresh provisions. His nutriment is from what is stale, and his courage from what is heady ; he looks burly and bold, but a fatal disease is lying at the bottom of an excited and inflated heart. We think to thrive by surrendering our capacities : but we can no more live, my lord bishop, with breathing the breath of other men, than we can by not breathing our own. Compliancy will serve us poorly and ineffectually. Men, like columns, are only strong while they are upright.

PARKER. You were speaking of other times ; and you always speak best among the Greeks and Romans. Continue ; pray !

MARVEL. Sovranty, in the heathen world, had sympathies with humanity ; and Power never thought herself contaminated by touching the hand of Wisdom. It was before Andromache came on the stage painted and patched and powdered, with a hogshead-hoop about her haunches and a pack-saddle on her pole, surmounted with upright hair larded and dredged : it was before Orestes was created monsigneur : it was before there strutted under a triumphal arch of curls, and through a Via Sacra of plumery, Louis the fourteenth.

PARKER. The ally of His Majesty——

MARVEL. And something more. A gilded organ-pipe, puffed from below for those above to play.

PARKER. Respect the cousin——

MARVEL. I know not whose cousin ; but the acknowledged brat

ANDREW MARVEL AND BISHOP PARKER

of milliner and furrier, with perruquier for godfather. And such forsooth are the *make-believes* we must respect! A nucleus of powder! an efflorescence of frill!

PARKER. Subject and prince stand now upon another footing than formerly.

MARVEL. Indeed they do. How dignified is the address of Plutarch to Trajan! how familiar is Pliny's to Vespasian! how tender, how paternal, is Fronto's to Antoninus! how totally free from adulation and servility is Julius Pollux to the ungentle Commodus! Letters were not trampled down disdainfully either in the groves of Antioch or under the colonnades of Palmyra. Not pleasure, the gentle enfeebler of the human intellect; not tyranny and bigotry, its violent assailants; crossed the walk of the philosopher, to stand between him and his speculations. What is more; two ancient religions, the Grecian and Egyptian, met in perfectly good temper at Alexandria, lived and flourished there together for many centuries, united in honouring whatever was worthy of honour in each communion, and never heard of persecution for matters of opinion, until Christianity came and taught it. Thenceforward, for fifteen hundred years, blood has been perpetually spouting from underneath her footsteps; and the wretch, clinging exhausted to the Cross, is left naked by the impostor, who pretends to have stript him only to heal his wounds.

PARKER. Presbyterians, and other sectaries, were lately as cruel and hypocritical as any in former times.

MARVEL. They were certainly not less cruel, and perhaps even more hypocritical. English hearts were contracted and hardened by an open exposure to the north: they now are collapsing into the putridity of the south. We were ashamed of a beggarly distemper, but parasitical and skin-deep; we are now ostentatious of a gentlemanly one, eating into the very bones.

PARKER. Our children may expect from lord Clarendon a fair account of the prime movers in the late disturbances.

MARVEL. He knew but one party, and saw it only in its gala suit. He despises those whom he left on the old litter; and he fancies that all who have not risen want the ability to rise. No doubt, he will speak unfavourably of those whom I most esteem: be it so: if their lives and writings do not controvert him, they are unworthy of my defence. Were I upon terms of intimacy with him, I would render

him a service, by sending him the best translations, from Greek and
Latin authors, of maxims left us by the wisest men ; maxims which
my friends held longer than their fortunes, and dearer than their
lives. And are the vapours of such quagmires as Clarendon to
overcast the luminaries of mankind ? Should a Hyde lift up, I will
not say his hand, I will not say his voice, should he lift up his eyes,
against a Milton ?

PARKER. Mr. Milton would have benefited the world much more
by coming into its little humours, and by complying with it cheerfully.

MARVEL. As the needle turns away from the rising sun, from the
meridian, from the occidental, from regions of fragrancy and gold
and gems, and moves with unerring impulse to the frosts and deserts
of the north, so Milton and some few others, in politics, philosophy,
and religion, walk through the busy multitude, wave aside the importunate trader, and, after a momentary oscillation from external
agency, are found in the twilight and in the storm, pointing with
certain index to the polestar of immutable truth.

PARKER. The nation in general thanks him little for what he has
been doing.

MARVEL. Men who have been unsparing of their wisdom, like
ladies who have been unfrugal of their favours, are abandoned by
those who owe most to them, and hated or slighted by the rest. I
wish beauty in her lost estate had consolations like genius.

PARKER. Fie, fie ! Mr. Marvel ! Consolations for frailty !

MARVEL. What wants them more ? The reed is cut down, and
seldom does the sickle wound the hand that cuts it. There it lies ;
trampled on, withered, and soon to be blown away.

PARKER. We should be careful and circumspect in our pity, and
see that it falls on clean ground. Such a laxity of morals can only
be taught in Mr. Milton's school. He composed, I remember, a
Treatise on Divorce, and would have given it great facilities.

MARVEL. He proved by many arguments what requires but few :
that happiness is better than unhappiness ; that, when two persons
can not agree, it is wiser and more christianlike that they should not
disagree ; that, when they cease to love each other, it is something if
they be hindered by the gentlest of checks, from running to the
extremity of hatred ; and lastly, how it conduces to circumspection
and forbearance to be aware that the bond of matrimony is not indis-
soluble, and that the bleeding heart may be saved from bursting.

ANDREW MARVEL AND BISHOP PARKER

PARKER. Monstrous sophistry! abominable doctrines! What more, sir? what more?

MARVEL. He proceeds to demonstrate that boisterous manners, captious contradictions, jars, jealousies, suspicions, dissensions, are juster causes of separation than the only one leading to it through the laws. Which fault, grievous as it is to morality and religion, may have occurred but once, and may have been followed by immediate and most sorrowful repentance, and by a greater anxiety to be clear of future offence than before it was committed. In itself it is not so irreconcilable and inconsistent with gentleness, good-humour, generosity, and even conjugal affection.

PARKER. Palpable perversion!

MARVEL. I suppose it to have been committed but once, and then there is the fairest inference, the most reasonable as well as the most charitable supposition, nay, almost the plainest proof, of the more legitimate attachment.

PARKER. Fear, apprehension of exposure, of shame, of abandonment, may force the vagrant to retrace her steps.

MARVEL. God grant, then, the marks of them never may be discovered!

PARKER. Let the laws have their satisfaction.

MARVEL. Had ever the Harpies theirs, or the Devil his? and yet when were they stinted? Are the laws or are we the better or the milder for this satisfaction? or is keenness of appetite a sign of it?

PARKER. Reverence the laws of God, Mr. Marvel, if you contemn those of your country. Even the parliament, which you and Mr. Milton must respect, since no king was coexistent with it, discountenanced and chastised such laxity.

MARVEL. I dare not look back upon a parliament which was without the benefit of a king, and had also lost its spiritual guides, the barons of your bench: but well do I remember that our blessed Lord and Saviour was gentler in his rebuke to the woman who had offended, than he was to Scribes and Pharisees.

PARKER. There is no argument of any hold on men of slippery morals.

MARVEL. My morals have indeed been so slippery that they have let me down on the ground and left me there. Every year I have grown poorer; yet never was I conscious of having spent my money among the unworthy, until the time came for them to show it by their ingratitude. My morals have not made me slip into an episcopal throne——

PARKER. Neither have mine me, sir! and I would have you to know it, Mr. Marvel!

MARVEL. Your lordship has already that satisfaction.

PARKER. Pardon my interruption, my dear sir! and the appearance of warmth, such as truth and sincerity at times put on.

MARVEL. It belongs to your lordship to grant pardon ; it is ours who have offended, to receive it.

PARKER. Mr. Marvel! I have always admired your fine gentlemanly manners, and regretted that you never have turned your wit to good account, in an age when hardly anything else is held of value. Sound learning rises indeed, but rises slowly : piety, although in estimation with the king, is less prized by certain persons who have access to the presence : wit, Mr. Marvel, when properly directed, not too high nor too low, will sooner or later find a patron. It is well at all times to avoid asperity and acrimony, and to submit with a willing mind to God's dispensations, be what they may. Probably a great part of your friend's misfortunes may be attributed to the intemperance of his rebukes.

MARVEL. Then what you call immoral and impious did him less harm ?

PARKER. I would not say *that* altogether. To me indeed his treatise on *Divorce* is most offensive : the treatise on *Prelaty* is contemptible.

MARVEL. Nevertheless, in the narrow view of my humble understanding, there is no human eloquence at all comparable to certain parts of it. And permit me to remind your lordship that you continued on the most friendly terms with him long after its publication.

PARKER. I do not give up a friend for a trifle.

MARVEL. Your lordship, it appears, must have more than a trifle for the surrender. I have usually found that those who make faults of foibles, and crimes of faults, have within themselves an impulse toward worse, and give ready way to such impulse whenever they can secretly or safely. There is a gravity which is not austere nor captious, which belongs not to melancholy, nor dwells in contraction of heart, but arises from tenderness and hangs upon reflection.

PARKER. Whatsoever may be the gravity of Mr. Milton, I have heard indistinctly that he has not always been the kindest

244

of husbands. Being a sagacious and a prudent man, he ought never to have taken a wife until he had ascertained her character.

MARVEL. Pray inform me whether the wisest men have been the most fortunate, or, if you prefer the expression, the most provident, in their choice. Of Solomon's wives (several hundreds) is it recorded that a single one sympathized with him, loved him, respected him, or esteemed him ? His wisdom and his poetry flowed alike on barren sand ; his cedar frowned on him ; his lily drooped and withered, before he had raised up his head from its hard cold glossiness, or had inhaled its fragrance with a second sigh. Disappointments sour most the less experienced. Young ladies are ready in imagining that marriage is all cake and kisses ; but very few of them are housewives long, before they discover that the vinous fermentation may be followed too soon by the acetous. Rarely do they discover, and more rarely do they admit, that such is the result of their own mismanagement. What woman can declare with sincerity, that she never in the calmer days of life has felt surprise, and shame also, if she is virtuous and sensible, at recollecting how nearly the same interest was excited in her by the most frivolous and least frivolous of her admirers ? The downy thistle-seed, hard to be uprooted, is carried by the lightest breath of air, and takes an imperceptible hold on what it catches : it falls the more readily into the more open breast, but sometimes the less open is vainly buttoned up against it.

Milton has, I am afraid, imitated too closely the authoritative voice of the patriarchs, and been somewhat too oriental (I forbear to say Scriptural) in his relations as a husband. But who, whether among the graver or less grave, is just to woman ? There may be moments when the beloved tells us, and tells us truly, that we are dearer to her than life. Is not this enough? is it not above all merit ? Yet, if ever the ardour of her enthusiasm subsides ; if her love ever loses, later in the day, the spirit and vivacity of its early dawn ; if between the sigh and the blush an interval is perceptible ; if the arm mistakes the chair for the shoulder ; what an outcry is there ! what a proclamation of her injustice and her inconstancy ! what an alternation of shrinking and spurning at the coldness of her heart ! Do we ask within if our own has retained all its ancient loyalty, all its own warmth, and all that was poured into it ? Often the true lover has little of true love compared with what he has undeservedly received and unreasonably exacts. But let it also be remembered that marriage is the metempsychosis of women ; that it turns them into different creatures from what they were before. Liveliness in the girl may have been mistaken for good temper : the little pervicacity which at first is attractively provoking, at last provokes without its attractiveness : negligence of order and propriety, of duties and civilities, long endured, often deprecated, ceases to be tolerable, when children grow up and are in danger of following the example. It often happens that, if a man unhappy in the married state were to disclose the manifold causes of his uneasiness, they would be found, by those who were beyond their influence, to be of such a nature as rather to excite derision than sympathy. The waters of bitterness do not fall on his head in a cataract, but through a colander; one however like the vases of the Danaides, perforated only for replenishment. We know scarcely the vestibule of a house of which we fancy we have penetrated into all the corners. We know not how grievously a man may have suffered, long before the calumnies of the world befell him as he reluctantly left his house-door. There are women from whom incessant tears of anger swell forth at imaginary wrongs ; but of contrition for their own delinquencies, not one.

Milton, in writing his treatise, of which probably the first idea was suggested from his own residence, was aware that the laws should provide, not only against our violence and injustice, but against our levity and inconstancy ; and that a man's capriciousness or satiety should not burst asunder the ties by which families are united. Do you believe that the crime of adultery has never been committed to the end of obtaining a divorce ? Do you believe that murder, that suicide, never has been committed because a divorce was unattainable ? Thus the most cruel tortures are terminated by the most frightful crimes. Milton has made his appeal to the authority of religion : we lower our eyes from him, and point to the miseries and guilt on every side before us, caused by the corrosion or the violent disruption of bonds which humanity would have loosened. He would have tried with a patient ear and with a delicate hand the chord that offended by its harshness ; and, when he could not reduce it to the proper tone, he would remove it for another.

PARKER. Mr. Marvel ! Mr. Marvel ! I can not follow you among these fiddlesticks. The age is notoriously irreligious.

MARVEL. I believe it ; I know it ; and, without a claim to extraordinary acuteness, I fancy I can discover by what means, and by whose agency, it became so. The preachers who exhibit most vehemence are the very men who support the worst corruptions ; corruptions not a portion of our nature, but sticking thereto by our slovenly supineness. Of what use is it to rail against our infirmities, of what use even to pity and bemoan them, if we help not in removing the evils that rise perpetually out of them ? Were every man to sweep the mire from before his house every morning, he would have little cause to complain of dirty streets. Some dust might be carried into them by the wind ; the tread of multitudes would make unsound what was solid ; yet, nothing being accumulated, the labour of removing the obstructions would be light. Another thing has increased the irreligion and immorality of the people, beside examples in elevated stations. Whatever is overconstrained will relax or crack. The age of Milton (for that was his age in which he was heard and honoured) was too religious, if anything can be called so. Prelaty now lays a soft and frilled hand upon our childishness. Forty years ago she stripped up her sleeve, scourged us heartily, and spat upon us—to remove the smart, no doubt ! This treatment made people run in all directions from her ; not unlike the primeval man described by Lucretius, fleeing before the fiercer and stronger animals :

> Viva videns vivo sepeliri viscera busto,
> At quos ecfugium servarat, corpore adeso
> Posterius, tremulas super ulcera tetra tenentes
> Palmas, horrificis adcibant vocibus orcum.[1]

PARKER. Dear me ! what a memory you possess, good Mr. Marvel ; you pronounce Latin verses charmingly. I wish you would go on to the end of the book.

MARVEL. Permit me to go on a shorter distance : to the conclusion of my remarks. As Popery caused the violence of the Reformers, so did Prelaty (the same thing under another name) the violence of the Presbyterians and Anabaptists. She treated them inhumanly : she reduced to poverty, she exiled, she maimed, she mutilated, she stabbed, she shot, she hanged, those who followed Christ in the narrow and quiet lane, rather than along the dust of the market-road, and who conversed with him rather in the cottage than the toll-booth. She would have nothing pass unless through her hands ; and she imposed a heavy and intolerable tax on the neces-

---

[1] Lucr. v. 991.

saries both of physical and of spiritual life. This baronial privilege our parliament would have suppressed : the king rose against the suppression, and broke his knuckles in the cogs of the mill.

PARKER. Sad times, Mr. Marvel ! sad times ! It fills me with heaviness to hear of them.

MARVEL. Low places are foggy first : days of sadness wet the people to the skin : they hang loosely for some time upon the ermine, but at last they penetrate it, and cause it to be thrown off. I do not like to hear a man cry out with pain ; but I would rather hear one than twenty. Sorrow is the growth of all seasons : we had much however to relieve it. Never did our England, since she first emerged from the ocean, rise so high above surrounding nations. The rivalry of Holland, the pride of Spain, the insolence of France, were thrust back by one finger each : yet those countries were then more powerful than they had ever been. The sword of Cromwell was preceded by the mace of Milton ; by that mace which, when Oliver had rendered his account, opened to our contemplation the garden-gate of Paradise. And there were some around not unworthy to enter with him. In the compass of sixteen centuries, you will not number on the whole earth so many wise and admirable men as you could have found united in that single day, when England showed her true magnitude, and solved the question, *Which is most, one or a million ?* There were giants in those days ; but giants who feared God, and not who fought against him. Less men, it appears, are braver. They show him a legal writ of ejectment, seize upon his house, and riotously carouse therein. But the morning must come ; and heaviness, we know, cometh in the morning.

PARKER. Wide is the difference between carousal and austerity. Your friend miscalculated the steps to fortune, in which, as we all are the architects of our own, if we omit the insertion of one or two, the rest are useless in farthering our ascent. He was too passionate, Mr. Marvel ! he was indeed.

MARVEL. Superficial men have no absorbing passion : there are no whirlpools in a shallow. I have often been amused at thinking in what estimation the greatest of mankind were holden by their contemporaries. Not even the most sagacious and prudent one could discover much of them, or could prognosticate their future course in the infinity of space ! Men like ourselves are permitted to stand near and indeed in the very presence of Milton : what do they see ?

ANDREW MARVEL AND BISHOP PARKER

dark clothes, grey hair, and sightless eyes !   Other men have better things : other men therefore are nobler !   The stars themselves are only bright by distance ; go close, and all is earthy.   But vapours illuminate these : from the breath and from the countenance of God comes light on worlds higher than they ; worlds to which he has given the forms and names of Shakespeare and of Milton.

PARKER. After all, I doubt whether much of his doctrine is remaining in the public mind.

MARVEL. Others are not inclined to remember all that we remember, and will not attend to us if we propose to tell them half.   Water will take up but a certain quantity of salt, even of the finest and purest.   If the short memories of men are to be quoted against the excellence of instruction, your lordship would never have censured them from the pulpit for forgetting what was delivered by their Saviour.   It is much, my lord bishop, that you allow my friend even the pittance of praise you have bestowed : for, if you will permit me to express my sentiments in verse, which I am in the habit of doing, I would say,

> Men like the ancient kalends, nones, and ides,
> Are reckoned backward, and the first stand last.

I am confident that Milton is heedless of how little weight he is held by those who are of none ; and that he never looks toward those somewhat more eminent, between whom and himself there have crept the waters of oblivion.   As the pearl ripens in the obscurity of its shell, so ripens in the tomb all the fame that is truly precious.   In fame he will be happier than in friendship.   Were it possible that one among the faithful of the angels could have suffered wounds and dissolution in his conflict with the false, I should scarcely feel greater awe at discovering on some bleak mountain the bones of this our mighty defender, once shining in celestial panoply, once glowing at the trumpet-blast of God, but not proof against the desperate and the damned, than I have felt at entering the humble abode of Milton, whose spirit already reaches heaven, yet whose corporeal frame hath no quiet or safe resting-place here below.   And shall not I, who loved him early, have the lonely and sad privilege to love him still ? or shall fidelity to power be a virtue, and fidelity to tribulation an offence ?

PARKER. We may best show our fidelity by our discretion.   It becomes my station, and suits my principles, to defend the English Constitution, both in church and state.

MARVEL. You highly praised the *Defence of the English People :* you called it a masterly piece of rhetoric and ratiocination.

PARKER. I might have admired the subtilty of it, and have praised the Latinity.

MARVEL. Less reasonably. But his godlike mind shines gloriously throughout his work ; only perhaps we look the more intently at it for the cloud it penetrates. Those who think we have enough of his poetry, still regret that we possess too little of his prose, and wish especially for more of his historical compositions. Davila and Bacon——

PARKER. You mean Lord Verulam.

MARVEL. That idle title was indeed thrown over his shoulders : but the trapping was unlikely to rest long upon a creature of such proud paces. He and Davila are the only men of high genius among the moderns who have attempted it ; and the greater of them has failed. He wanted honesty, he perverted facts, he courted favor : the present in his eyes was larger than the future.

PARKER. The Italians, who far excell us in the writing of history, are farther behind the ancients.

MARVEL. True enough. From Guicciardini and Machiavelli, the most celebrated of them, we acquire a vast quantity of trivial information. There is about them a sawdust which absorbs much blood and impurity, and of which the level surface is dry : but no traces by what agency rose such magnificent cities above the hovels of France and Germany : none

> Ut fortis Etruria crevit,

or, on the contrary, how the mistress of the world sank in the ordure of her priesthood.

> Scilicet et rerum facta est nequissima [1] Roma.

We are captivated by no charms of description, we are detained by no peculiarities of character : we hear a clamorous scuffle in the street, and we close the door. How different the historians of antiquity ! We read Sallust, and always are incited by the desire of

---

[1] Virgil, *Georg.,* ii. 534, which, however, reads " pulchrissima " for " nequissima."

reading on, although we are surrounded by conspirators and barbarians : we read Livy, until we imagine we are standing in an august pantheon, covered with altars and standards, over which are the four fatal letters that spell-bound all mankind.* We step forth again among the modern Italians : here we find plenty of rogues, plenty of receipts for making more ; and little else. In the best passages we come upon a crowd of dark reflections, which scarcely a glimmer of glory pierces through ; and we stare at the tenuity of the spectres, but never at their altitude.

Give me the poetical mind, the mind poetical in all things ; give me the poetical heart, the heart of hope and confidence, that beats the more strongly and resolutely under the good thrown down, and raises up fabric after fabric on the same foundation.

PARKER. At your time of life, Mr. Marvel ?

MARVEL. At mine, my lord bishop ! I have lived with Milton. Such creative and redeeming spirits are like kindly and renovating Nature. Volcano comes after volcano, yet covereth she with herbage and foliage, with vine and olive, and with whatever else refreshes and gladdens her, the Earth that has been gasping under the exhaustion of her throes.

PARKER. He has given us such a description of Eve's beauty as appears to me somewhat too pictorial, too luxuriant, too suggestive, too—I know not what.

MARVEL. The sight of beauty, in her purity and beatitude, turns us from all unrighteousness, and is death to sin.

PARKER. Before we part, my good Mr. Marvel, let me assure you that we part in amity, and that I bear no resentment in my breast against your friend. I am patient of Mr. Milton ; I am more than patient, I am indulgent, seeing that his influence on society is past.

MARVEL. Past it is indeed. What a deplorable thing is it that Folly should so constantly have power over Wisdom, and Wisdom so intermittently over Folly ! But we live morally, as we used to live politically, under a representative system ; and the majority (to employ a phrase of people at elections) carries the day.

PARKER. Let us piously hope, Mr. Marvel, that God in his good time may turn Mr. Milton from the error of his ways, and incline

* S. P. Q. R.—W. S. L.

his heart to repentance, and that so he may finally be prepared for death.

MARVEL. The wicked can never be prepared for it, the good always are. What is the preparation which so many ruffled wrists point out ? To gabble over prayer and praise and confession and contrition. My lord ! Heaven is not to be won by short hard work at the last, as some of us take a degree at the university, after much irregularity and negligence. I prefer a steady pace from the outset to the end, coming in cool and dismounting quietly. Instead of which, I have known many old play-fellows of the devil spring up suddenly from their beds and strike at him treacherously ; while he, without a cuff, laughed and made grimaces in the corner of the room.

XX. THE LADY LISLE AND ELIZABETH GAUNT *

(*Imag. Convers.*, iv., 1826 ; *Wks.*, i., 1846 ; v., 1876.)

LADY LISLE. Madam, I am confident you will pardon me ; for affliction teaches forgiveness.

ELIZABETH GAUNT. From the cell of the condemned we are going, unless my hopes mislead me, where alone we can receive it.

Tell me, I beseech you, lady ! in what matter or manner do you think you can have offended a poor sinner such as I am ? Surely we come into this dismal place for our offences ; and it is not here that any can be given or taken.

LADY LISLE. Just now, when I entered the prison, I saw your countenance serene and cheerful ; you looked upon me for a time with an unaltered eye : you turned away from me, as I fancied, only to utter some expressions of devotion ; and again you looked upon me, and tears rolled down your face. Alas that I should, by any circumstance, any action or recollection, make another unhappy ! Alas that I should deepen the gloom in the very shadow of death !

ELIZABETH GAUNT. Be comforted : you have not done it. Grief softens and melts and flows away with tears.

I wept because another was greatly more wretched than myself. I wept at that black attire—at that attire of modesty and of widowhood.

LADY LISLE. It covers a wounded, almost a broken, heart—an unworthy offering to our blessed Redeemer.

ELIZABETH GAUNT. In his name let us now rejoice ! Let us offer our prayers and our thanks at once together ! We may yield up our souls perhaps at the same hour.

LADY LISLE. Is mine so pure ? Have I bemoaned, as I should have done, the faults I have committed ? Have my sighs arisen for

---

* Burnet relates from William Penn, who was present, that Elizabeth Gaunt placed the faggots round her body with her own hands. Lady Lisle was not burned alive, though sentenced to it ; but hanged and beheaded.—W. S. L.

the unmerited mercies of my God ? and not rather for him, the beloved of my heart, the adviser and sustainer I have lost !

Open, O gates of Death !

Smile on me, approve my last action in this world, O virtuous husband ! O saint and martyr ! my brave, compassionate, and loving Lisle.

ELIZABETH GAUNT. And can not you too smile, sweet lady ? are not you with him even now ? Doth body, doth clay, doth air, separate and estrange free spirits ? Bethink you of his gladness, of his glory ; and begin to partake them.

O ! how could an Englishman, how could twelve, condemn to death, condemn to so great an evil as they thought it and may find it, this innocent and helpless widow !

LADY LISLE. Blame not *that* jury ! blame not the jury which brought against me the verdict of guilty. I was so : I received in my house a wanderer who had fought under the rash and giddy Monmouth. He was hungry and thirsty, and I took him in. My Saviour had commanded, my king had forbidden it.

Yet the twelve would not have delivered me over to death, unless the judge had threatened them with an accusation of treason in default of it. Terror made them unanimous : they redeemed their properties and lives at the stated price.

ELIZABETH GAUNT. I hope at least the unfortunate man, whom you received in the hour of danger, may avoid his penalty.

LADY LISLE. Let us hope it.

ELIZABETH GAUNT. I too am imprisoned for the same offence ; and I have little expectation that he who was concealed by me hath any chance of happiness, although he hath escaped. Could I find the means of conveying to him a small pittance, I should leave the world the more comfortably.

LADY LISLE. Trust in God ; not in one thing or another, but in all. Resign the care of this wanderer to *his* guidance.

ELIZABETH GAUNT. He abandoned that guidance.

LADY LISLE. Unfortunate ! how can money then avail him ?

ELIZABETH GAUNT. It might save him from distress and from despair, from the taunts of the hard-hearted and from the inclemency of the godly.

LADY LISLE. In godliness, O my friend ! there can not be inclemency.

254

LADY LISLE AND ELIZABETH GAUNT

ELIZABETH GAUNT. You are thinking of perfection, my dear lady ; and I marvel not at it ; for what else hath ever occupied your thoughts ! But godliness, in almost the best of us, often is austere, often uncompliant and rigid, proner to reprove than to pardon, to drag back or thrust aside than to invite and help onward.

Poor man ! I never knew him before : I can not tell how he shall endure his self-reproach, or whether it will bring him to calmer thoughts hereafter.

LADY LISLE. I am not a busy idler in curiosity ; nor, if I were, is there time enough left me for indulging in it ; yet gladly would I learn the history of events, at the first appearance so resembling those in mine.

ELIZABETH GAUNT. The person's name I never may disclose ; which would be the worst thing I could betray of the trust he placed in me. He took refuge in my humble dwelling, imploring me in the name of Christ to harbour him for a season. Food and raiment were afforded him unsparingly ; yet his fears made him shiver through them. Whatever I could urge of prayer and exhortation was not wanting : still, although he prayed, he was disquieted. Soon came to my ears the declaration of the king, that his majesty would rather pardon a rebel than the concealer of a rebel. The hope was a faint one : but it *was* a hope ; and I gave it him. His thanksgivings were now more ardent, his prayers more humble, and oftener repeated. They did not strengthen his heart : it was unpurified and unprepared for them. Poor creature ! he consented with it to betray me ; and I am condemned to be burnt alive. Can we believe, can we encourage the hope, that in his weary way through life he will find those only who will conceal from him the knowledge of this execution? Heavily, too heavily, must it weigh on so irresolute and infirm a breast.

Let it not move you to weeping.

LADY LISLE. It does not : oh ! it does not.

ELIZABETH GAUNT. What then ?

LADY LISLE. Your saintly tenderness, your heavenly tranquillity.

ELIZABETH GAUNT. No, no : abstain ! abstain ! It was I who grieved : it was I who doubted. Let us now be firmer : we have both the same rock to rest upon. See ! I shed no tears.

I saved his life, an unprofitable and (I fear) a joyless one : he, by

God's grace, has thrown open to me, and at an earlier hour than ever I ventured to expect it, the avenue to eternal bliss.

LADY LISLE. O my good angel ! that bestrewest with fresh flowers a path already smooth and pleasant to me, may those timorous men who have betrayed, and those misguided ones who have prosecuted us, be conscious on their death-beds that we have entered it ! and they too will at last find rest.

XXI. BISHOP BURNET AND HUMPHREY HARDCASTLE

(*Blackwood*, 1824 ; *Imag. Convers.*, i., 1824 ; i., 1826 ; *Wks.*, i., 1846 ; iv., 1876.)

HARDCASTLE. I am curious, my lord Bishop, to hear somewhat about the flight and escape of my namesake and uncle,[1] Sir Humphrey Hardcastle ; who was a free-spoken man, witty, choleric, and hospitable, and who cannot have been altogether an alien from the researches of your lordship into the history of the two late reigns.

BURNET. Why, Mr. Hardcastle, I do well remember the story of that knight, albeit his manners and morals were such as did entertain me little in his favour. For he hunted and drank and fornicated, and (some do aver) swore, which however, mark me, I do not deliver from my own knowledge, nor from any written and grave document. I the more wonder at him, since [2] he had lived among the Roundheads, as they were contemptuously called ; and the minister of his parish was Ezekiel Stedman, a Puritan of no ill-repute. Howbeit he was ensnared by his worldly-mindedness, and fell into evil courses. The Lord, who permitted him a long while to wallow in this mire, caught him by the heel, so to say, as he was coming out, and threw him into great peril in another way. For although he had mended his life, and had espoused [3] Margaret Pouncey, whose mother was a Touchet,—two staid women,—yet did he truly in a boozing-bout, such as some country gentlemen I could mention do hold after dinner, say of the Duke, " James,—a murrain on him !—is a Papist."

Now among his servants was one Will Taunton, a sallow shining-faced knave, sweaty with impudence. I do remember to have seen the said Taunton in the pillory, for some prominent part he had enacted under the doctor Titus Oates ; and a country wench, as I suppose her to have been from her apparel and speech, said unto me, plucking my sleeve, " Look, parson, Will's forehead is like a rank mushroom in a rainy morning ; and yet, I warrant you, they show it forsooth as the cleanest and honestest part about him."

---

[1] 1st and 2nd eds. read : " great-uncle."
[2] 1st and 2nd eds. read : " as he had."
[3] 1st and 2nd eds. read : " your great-aunt Margaret Pouncey."

To continue : Will went straightway and communicated the words of his master to Nicolas Shottery, the Duke's valet. Nick gave unto him a shilling, having first spatten thereon, as he, according to his superstition, said, for luck. The Duke ordered to be counted out unto him eight shillings more, together with a rosary, the which as he was afraid of wearing it (for he had not lost all grace) he sold at Richmond for two groats. He was missed in the family, and his roguery was scented. On which, nothing was foolisher, improperer, or unreasonabler, than the desperate push and strain Charles made, put upon it by his brother James, to catch your uncle Hum Hardcastle. Hum had his eye upon him, slipped the noose, and was over into the Low-Countries.

Abraham Cowley, one of your Pindaric [1] lyrists, a great stickler for the measures of the First Charles, was posted after him. But he played the said Abraham a scurvy trick, seizing him by his fine flowing curls, on which he prided himself mightily, like another Absalom, cuffing him, and, some do say, kicking him, in such dishonest wise as I care not to mention, to his, the said Abraham's great incommodity and confusion. It is agreed on all hands that he handled him very roughly, sending him back to his master with a flea in his ear, who gave him but cold comfort, and told him it would be an ill compliment to ask him to be seated.

" Phil White," added he, " may serve you, Cowley. You need not look back, man, nor spread your fingers like a fig-leaf on the place. Phil does not, like Dan Holroyd of Harwick, carry a bottle of peppered brine in his pocket ; he is a clever, apposite, upright little prig : I have often had him under my eye close enough, and I promise he may safely be trusted on the blind side of you."

Then, after these aggravating and childish words, turning to the Duke, as Abraham was leaving the presence, he is reported to have said, I hope untruly, " But, damn it, brother ! the jest would have been heightened [2] if we could have hanged the knave," meaning not indeed his messenger, but the above cited Hum Hardcastle. And on James shaking his head, sighing, and muttering his doubt of the King's sincerity, and his vexation at so bitter a disappointment,

---

[1] 1st and 2nd eds. read : " Pindarique." See the passage, in the second Conversation of Southey and Landor, on Milton's contempt for " the fashion in antique, Pindaricque, etc., affected by Cowley and others."
[2] 1st and 2nd eds. read : " heighthened."

BISHOP BURNET AND HARDCASTLE

"Oddsfish! Jim," said his Majesty, "the motion was Hum's own! I gave him no jog, upon my credit! His own choler did it, a rogue! and he would not have waited to be invested with the order, if I had pressed him ever so civilly. I will oblige you another time in anything, but we can hang only those we can get at."

It would appear that there was a sore and rankling grudge between them of long standing, and that there had been divers flings and flouts backward and forward, on this side the water, on the score of their mistress Poesy, whose favours to them both, if a man may judge from the upshot, left no such a mighty matter for heart-burnings and ill blood.

This reception had such a stress and stir upon the bile and spirits of doctor Spratt's friend (for such he was, even while writing about his mistresses) that he wooed his Pegasus another way, and rid gentlier. It fairly untuned him for Chloes and fantastical things of all sorts, set him upon anotherguess scent, gave him ever afterward a soberer and staider demeanour, and turned his mind to contentment.

HARDCASTLE. The pleasure I have taken in the narration of your lordship is for the greater part independent of what concerns my family. We [1] have only a few songs of our uncle [2]; and these too would have been lost, if the old coachman had not taught them to his grandson, still in my service. They are such as I forbid him to sing in our house, but connive at him doing it when he is in others, particularly at the inns, where they always obtain me the best wine and most gladsome attendance. In fact, I have ever found that, when my horses came out of a stable where he had been singing, they neighed the louder, and trotted the faster, and made a prouder display of their oats.

BURNET. I remember one of them from its being more reasonable than the invocations of a lover usually are. Either they talk of tears, which they ought to be ashamed of, as men and Christians; or of death, when the doctor has told them no such thing; or they run wild among the worst imps and devils of the gentiles: for in truth they are no better, whatever forms they assumed, Nymphs or Graces or what not.

HARDCASTLE. Pray, my lord Bishop, if there is no impropriety in asking it, might I request a copy of those verses?

[1] From " We " to " libertine but," p. 261, added in 2nd ed.
[2] 2nd ed. reads : " unkle."

259

BURNET. Truly, sir, I keep none of such a girl's-eye sampler. I
will attempt to recollect the words, which, I own it, pleased me by
their manfulness, as demonstrating that your uncle [1] Hum, though a
loosish man and slippery in foul proclivities, was stout and resolute
with the sluts in his wiser moments, calling them what they ought to
be called at the first word.

> Listen, mad girl! since giving ear
> May save the eyes hard work :
> Tender is he who holds you dear,
> But proud as pope or Turk.

Now Hum hated paganism and iniquity ; and nothing could stir
him from his church, though he attended it but seldom. He
proceeds thus :

> Some have been seen, whom people thought
> Much prettier girls than you,

Observe, he will be reasonable, and bring the creature to her
senses if he can :

> Setting a lover's tears at nought,
> Like any other dew ;

> And some too have been heard to swear,
> While with wet lids they stood,
> No man alive was worth a tear—
> *They* never wept—nor wou'd.

Resolute! aye! False creatures ; he sounded them, even the
deepest. There is something about these wantons black as hell, and
they can not help showing it.

HARDCASTLE. I thank your lordship, as much for your reflections
as for my uncle's poetry.

BURNET. I wish he had left behind him the experience he must
have paid dear for, that it might serve to admonish the sprigs and
sparks (as they are called) of our unhappy times, and purify the
pestilence they are breathing. Formerly, we know from Holy Writ,
the devils ran out of men into swine, and pushed down in those fit
bodies to the sea. It now appears that they were still snifting and
hankering after their old quarters ; and we find them rushing again

---

[1] 2nd ed. reads : " unkle."

BISHOP BURNET AND HARDCASTLE

into men, only the stronger and hungrier, the ungovernabler and uncleanlier, for so much salt-water bathing.

HARDCASTLE. I am afraid, my lord bishop, you have too much reason for this severe remark. My uncle I knew was somewhat of a libertine, but I [1] never had heard before that he was such a poet, and could hardly have imagined that he approached near enough to Mr. Cowley for jealousy or competition.

BURNET. Indeed they who discoursed on such matters were of the same opinion, excepting some few, who see nothing before them and everything behind. These declared that Hum would overtop Abraham, if he could only drink rather less, think rather more, and feel rather rightlier : that he had great spunk and spirit, and that not a fan was left upon a lap when anyone sang his airs. Lucretius [2] tells us that there is a plant on Helicon, so pestiferous that it kills by the odour of its flowers. It appears that these flowers are now collected by our young women for their sweet-pots, and that the plant itself is naturalised among us, and blossoming in every parlour-window. Poets, like ministers of state, have their parties, and it is difficult to get at truth, upon questions not capable of demonstration nor founded on matter of fact. To [3] take any trouble about them is an unwise thing. It is like mounting a wall covered with broken glass : you cut your fingers before you reach the top, and you only discover at last that it is, within a span or two, of equal height on both sides. To sit as an arbitrator between two contending poets, I should consider just as foolish, as to take the same position and office between two gamecocks, if it were at the same time as wicked. I say as wicked ; for I am firmly of opinion that those things are the foolishest which are the most immoral. The greatest of stakes, mundanely speaking, is the stake of reputation : hence he who hazards the most of it against a viler object, is the most irrational and insane. I do not understand rightly in what the greatness of your poets, and such like, may be certified to rest. Who would have imagined that the youth who was carried to his long home the other day, I mean my Lord Rochester's reputed child, Mr. George Nelly, was for several seasons a great poet ? Yet I remember the time when he was so

---

[1] 1st ed. reads : " concerns my family. I never knew that my uncle was a poet, and," etc.

[2] From " Lucretius " to " parlour-window " added in 2nd ed.

[3] From " To " to " rest " added in 2nd ed.

famous a [1] one, that he ran after Mr. Milton up Snow-hill, as the old gentleman was leaning on his daughter's arm from the Poultry, and, treading down the heel of his shoe, called him a rogue and a liar, while another poet sprang out [2], clapping his hands and crying " Bravely done, by Beelzebub ! the young cock spurs the blind buzzard gallantly ! " On a scrivener [3] representing to Mr. George the respectable character of Mr. Milton, and the probability that at some future time he might be considered as among our geniuses, and such as would reflect a certain portion of credit on his ward, and asking him withal why he appeared to him a rogue and a liar, he replied, " I have proofs known to few : I possess a sort of drama by him, entitled *Comus*, which was composed for the entertainment of Lord Pembroke, who held an appointment under the king, and this [4] John hath since changed sides, and written in defence of the Commonwealth."

Mr. George began with satirizing his father's friends, and confounding the better part of them with all the hirelings and nuisances of the age : with all the scavengers of lust and all the link-boys of literature ; with Newgate solicitors, the patrons of adulterers and forgers, who, in the long vacation, turn a penny by puffing a ballad, and are promised a shilling in silver for their own benefit, on crying down a religious tract. He soon became reconciled to them,[5] and they raised him upon their shoulders above the heads of the wittiest and the wisest. This served a whole winter. Afterward, whenever he wrote a bad poem, he supported his sinking fame by some signal act of profligacy, an elegy by a seduction, a heroic by an adultery, a tragedy by a divorce.[6] On the remark of a learned man that irregularity is no indication of genius, he began to lose ground rapidly, when on a sudden he cried out at the Haymarket, *there is no God.* It was then surmised more generally and more gravely that there was something in him, and he stood upon his legs almost to the last. Say what you will, once whispered a friend of mine, there are things in him strong as poison, and original as sin. Doubts however were entertained by some on more mature reflection, whether he earned all

---

[1] 1st and 2nd eds. read : " an one."
[2] 1st and 2nd eds. read : " out from a grocer's shop."
[3] 1st and 2nd eds. read : " On some neighbour."
[4] 1st and 2nd eds. read : " this very John."
[5] 1st and 2nd eds. read : " to the latter."
[6] 1st and 2nd eds. read : " divorse."

his reputation by his aphorism : for soon afterward he declared at the Cockpit, that he had purchased a large assortment of cutlasses and pistols, and that, as he was practising the use of them from morning to night, it would be imprudent in persons who were without them, either to laugh or to boggle at the Dutch vocabulary with which he had enriched our language. In fact, he had invented new rhymes in profusion, by such words as trackschuyt, Wageninghen, Skiermonikoog, Bergen-op-Zoom, and whatever is appertaining to the market-places of fish, flesh, fowl, flowers, and legumes, not to omit the dockyards and barracks and ginshops, with various kinds of essences and drugs.

Now, Mr. Hardcastle, I would not censure this : the idea is novel, and does no harm : but why should a man push his neck into a halter to sustain a catch or glee ?

Having had some concern in bringing his reputed father to a sense of penitence for his offences, I waited on the youth likewise, in a former illness, not without hope of leading him ultimately to a better way of thinking. I had hesitated too long : I found him far advanced in his convalescence. My arguments are not worth repeating : he replied thus. " I change my mistresses as Tom Southern his shirt, from economy. I can not afford to keep few ; and I am determined not to be forgotten till I am vastly richer. But I assure you, doctor Burnet, for your comfort, that if you imagine I am led astray by lasciviousness, as you call it, and lust, you are quite as much mistaken as if you called a book of arithmetic a bawdy book. I calculate on every kiss I give, modest or immodest, on lip or paper. I ask myself one question only ; what will it bring me ? " On my marvelling and raising up my hands, " You churchmen," he added with a laugh, " are too hot in all your quarters for the calm and steady contemplation of this high mystery."

He spake thus loosely, Mr. Hardcastle, and I confess I was disconcerted and took my leave of him. If I gave him any offence at all, it could only be when he said, " I should be sorry to die before I have written my life," and I replied, " Rather say, before you have mended it."

" But, doctor," continued he, " the work I propose may bring me a hundred pounds." Whereunto I rejoined, " That which I, young gentleman, suggest in preference, will be worth much more to you."

At last he is removed from among the living. Let us hope the best ; to wit, that the mercies which have begun with man's forget-fulness, will be crowned with God's forgiveness.[1]

HARDCASTLE. I perceive, my lord bishop, that writers of perishable fame may leave behind them something worth collecting. Repre-sented to us by historians like your lordship, we survey a light character as a film in agate, and a noxious one as a toad in marble.

BURNET. How near together, Mr. Hardcastle, are things which appear to us the most remote and opposite ! how near is death to life, and vanity to glory ! How deceived are we, if our expressions are any proofs of it, in what we might deem the very matters most subject to our senses ! the haze above our heads we call the heavens, and the thinnest of the air the firmament.

---

[1] The following footnote on Byron is inserted in 2nd ed. :—

" Little did I imagine that the extraordinary man, the worst parts of whose character are represented here, should indeed have been carried to the tomb so immaturely. If, before the dialogue was printed, he had performed those services to Greece which will render his name illustrious to eternity, those by which he merited such funereal honours as, in the parsimony of praise, knowing its value in republics, she hardly would have decreed to the most deserving of her heroes, if, I repeat it, he had performed those services, the performance of which I envy him from my soul, and as much as any other does the gifts of heaven he threw away so carelessly, never would I, from whatever provocation, have written a syllable against him. I had avoided him ; I had slighted him ; he knew it : he did not love me ; he could not. While he spoke or wrote against me, I said nothing in print or conversation : the taciturnity of pride gave way to other feelings, when my friends, men so much better, and (let the sincerity of the expression be ques-tioned by those who are unacquainted with us) so much dearer, so much oftener in my thoughts, were assailed by him too intemperately.

" Let any man who has been unfair or injurious to me, shew that he has been so to me only, and I offer him my hand at once, with more than mere forgiveness.

" Alas ! my writings are not upon slate : no finger, not of Time himself, who dips it in the clouds of years and in the storm and tempest, can efface the written. Let me be called what I may . . . I confess it, I am more inconsistent than he was. I do not talk of weeping or bewailing or lamenting, for I hate false words, and seek with care, difficulty, and moroseness, those that fit the thing . . . why then should I dissemble that, if I have shed no tears, they are at this moment in my eyes ! O that I could have clasped his hand before he died ! only to make him more enamoured of his own virtues, and to keep him with them always !

" A word to those who talk of inconsistency. There is as much of it in him who stands while another moves, as in him who moves while another stands. To condemn what is evil, and to commend what is good, is consistent : to retract an error, to soften an asperity, to speak all the good we can, after worse ill than we would, is that and more. If I must understand the word inconsistency as many do, I wish I may be inconsistent with all my enemies. I will take especial care that my inconsistency never makes me a worse man or a richer."—W. S. L.

This note was not reprinted after the 2nd ed., but was embodied in other Conversations.

XXII. STEELE AND ADDISON

(*Bk. of Beauty*, 1835 ; *Ablett's Lit. Hours*, 1837 ; *Wks.*, ii., 1846 ; v., 1876.)

ADDISON. Dick ! I am come to remonstrate with you on those unlucky habits which have been so detrimental to your health and fortune.

STEELE. Many thanks, Mr. Addison ; but really my fortune is not much improved by your arresting me for the hundred pounds ; nor is my health, if spirits are an indication of it, on seeing my furniture sold by auction to raise the money.[1]

ADDISON. Pooh, pooh, Dick ! what furniture had you about the house ?

STEELE. At least I had the arm-chair, of which you never before had dispossessed me longer than the evening ; and happy should I have been to enjoy your company in it again and again, if you had left it me.

ADDISON. We will contrive to hire another. I do assure you, my dear Dick, I have really felt for you.

STEELE. I only wish, my kind friend, you had not put out your feelers quite so far, nor exactly in this direction ; and that my poor wife had received an hour's notice ; she might have carried a few trinkets to some neighbour. She wanted her salts ; and the bailiff thanked her for the bottle that contained them, telling her the gold head of it was worth pretty nearly half-a-guinea.

ADDISON. Lady Steele then wanted her smelling-bottle ? Dear me ! the weather, I apprehend, is about to change. Have you any symptoms of your old gout ?

STEELE. My health has been long on the decline, you know.

ADDISON. Too well I know it, my dear friend, and I hinted it as delicately as I could. Nothing on earth beside this consideration

---

[1] Benjamin Victor's letter to Garrick, 1762, gives the facts. The motive professed for the execution was to arouse Steele to the error of his financial ways. The explanation was accepted, and the friendship between defaulting debtor and exacting creditor continued. For a discussion of the evidence see the *Examiner*, 6th May 1843. Hawkins was present when Steele himself told the story.

should have induced me to pursue a measure in appearance so unfriendly. You must grow more temperate—you really must.

STEELE. Mr. Addison, you did not speak so gravely and so firmly when we used to meet at Will's. You always drank as much as I did, and often invited and pressed me to continue, when I was weary, sleepy, and sick.

ADDISON. You thought so, because you were drunk. Indeed, at my own house I have sometimes asked you to take another glass, in compliance with the rules of society and hospitality.

STEELE. Once, it is true, you did it at your house ; the only time I ever had an invitation to dine in it. The Countess was never fond of the wit that smells of wine : her husband could once endure it.

ADDISON. We could talk more freely, you know, at the tavern. There we have dined together some hundred times.

STEELE. Most days, for many years.

ADDISON. Ah Dick ! Since we first met there, several of our friends are gone off the stage.

STEELE. And some are still acting.

ADDISON. Forbear, my dear friend, to joke and smile at infirmities or vices. Many have departed from us, in consequence, I apprehend, of indulging in the bottle ! When passions are excited, when reason is disturbed, when reputation is sullied, when fortune is squandered, and when health is lost by it, a retreat is sounded in vain. Some can not hear it, others will not profit by it.

STEELE. I must do you the justice to declare, that I never saw any other effect of hard drinking upon you, than to make you more circumspect and silent.

ADDISON. If ever I urged you, in the warmth of my heart, to transgress the bounds of sobriety, I entreat you, as a Christian, to forgive me.

STEELE. Most willingly, most cordially.

ADDISON. I feel confident that you will think of me, speak of me, and write of me, as you have ever done, without a diminution of esteem. We are feeble creatures ; we want one another's aid and assistance ; a want ordained by Providence, to show us at once our insufficiency and our strength. We must not abandon our friends from slight motives, nor let our passions be our interpreters in their own cause. Consistency is not more requisite to the sound Christian, than to the accomplished politician.

STEELE AND ADDISON

STEELE. I am inconsistent in my resolutions of improvement—no man ever was more so; but my attachments have a nerve in them neither to be deadened by ill treatment nor loosened by indulgence. A man grievously wounded, knows by the acuteness of the pain that a spirit of vitality is yet in him. I know that I retain my friendship for you by what you have made me suffer.

ADDISON. Entirely for your own good, I do protest, if you could see it.

STEELE. Alas! all our sufferings are so; the only mischief is, that we have no organs for perceiving it.

ADDISON. You reason well, my worthy sir; and relying on your kindness in my favour (for every man has enemies, and those mostly who serve their friends best) I say, Dick, on these considerations, since you never broke your word with me, and since I am certain you would be sorry it were known that only four-score pounds' worth could be found in the house, I renounce for the present the twenty yet wanting. Do not beat about for an answer: say not one word: farewell.

STEELE. Ah! could not that cold heart,* often and long as I reposed on it, bring me to my senses! I have indeed been drunken; but it is hard to awaken in such heaviness as this of mine is. I shared his poverty with him; I never aimed to share his prosperity. Well, well; I can not break old habits. I love my glass; I love Addison. Each will partake in killing me. Why can not I see him again in the arm-chair, his right hand upon his heart under the fawn-coloured waistcoat, his brow erect and clear as his conscience; his wig even and composed as his temper, with measurely curls and antithetical top-knots, like his style; the calmest poet, the most quiet patriot; dear Addison! drunk, deliberate, moral, sentimental, foaming over with truth and virtue, with tenderness and friendship, and only the worse in one ruffle for the wine.

* Doubts are now entertained whether the character of Addison is fairly represented by Pope and Johnson. It is better to make this statement than to omit a Conversation which had appeared elsewhere.—W. S. L.

XXIII. LORD CHESTERFIELD AND LORD CHATHAM

(*Imag. Convers.*, ii., 1824 ; ii., 1826 ; *Wks.*, ii., 1846 ; iii., 1876.)

CHESTERFIELD. It is true, my lord, we have not always been of the same opinion, or, to use a better, truer, and more significant expression, of the same *side* in politics ; yet I never heard a sentence from your lordship which I did not listen to with attention. I understand that you have written some pieces of advice to a young relative : they are mentioned as being [1] excellent : I wish I could have profited by them when I was composing mine on a similar occasion.

CHATHAM. My lord, you certainly would not have done it, even supposing they contained, which I am far from believing, any topics that could have escaped your penetrating view of manners and morals : for your lordship and I set out diversely from the [2] threshold. Let us then rather hope that what we both have written, with an equally good intention, may produce its due effect ; which indeed I am afraid may be almost as doubtful, if we consider how ineffectual were the cares and exhortations, and even the daily example and high renown, of the most zealous and prudent men, on the life and conduct of their children and disciples. We will however hope the best rather than fear the worst, and believe that there never was a right thing done or a wise one spoken in vain, although the fruit of them may not spring up in the place designated or at the time expected.

It [3] may be difficult, I fear indeed it is impossible, to give our young nobility the graces and the amenity of the French : therefore I would rather try to cultivate the virtues inherent in them than engraft such as are uncongenial with the stock. We have indeed some few among us who far excell in politeness the most polished of any

---

[1] 1st ed. reads : " truly excellent."

[2] 1st ed. reads : " very threshold."

[3] From " It " to " And now " added in 3rd ed. 1st and 2nd eds. read : " expected. CHESTERFIELD. Pray, if I am not taking too great a freedom give me the outline of your plan. CHATHAM. Willingly, my lord," etc.

other nation ; but the generality are as far surpassed, not merely by one nation, but by almost all.   There is in them an arrogance, a self-sufficiency, an exhibition of defiance, which turn away from them the attentions they would receive abroad.   Hence they call insincere those who actually did attempt to endure them, but were unable to keep pace with their professions and intentions.   Yet, my lord, I do not despair of your accomplishing what it would be hopeless to expect from any other.   For, since you were viceroy of Ireland, I have seen many natives of that country no less elegant in manners than the most accomplished of French gentlemen.

CHESTERFIELD. I look back with satisfaction to my residence among them.

CHATHAM. Well may your lordship.   Never since the conquest has Ireland passed so long a time in tranquillity and contentment. In this, my lord, you stand high above the highest of our kings : and by those who are right-minded, and who judge of men by the good they do and the difficulty of doing it, you will be placed by future historians in an elevated rank among the rulers of mankind.   Pardon me : for to praise a great man in his presence is no slight presumption.

CHESTERFIELD. My lord ! although I did not come to you for my reward, I receive it at your hands with humble gratitude, and may begin to think I have in part deserved it.   And now, if I am not taking too much freedom in requesting it, be pleased to give me the outline of your plan for education.

CHATHAM. Willingly, my lord : but since a greater man has laid down a more comprehensive one, containing all I could bring forward, would it not be preferable to consult it ?   I differ in nothing from Locke, unless it be that I would recommend the lighter as well as the graver part of the ancient classics, and the constant practice of imitating them in early youth.   This is no change in the system, and no larger an addition than a woodbine to a sacred grove.

CHESTERFIELD. I do not admire Mr. Locke.

CHATHAM. Nor I : he is too simply grand for admiration : I contemplate and revere him.   Equally deep and clear, he is both philosophically and grammatically [1] one among the most elegant of English writers.

CHESTERFIELD. If I expressed by any motion of limb or feature my

[1] 1st and 2nd eds. read : " grammatically the most."

surprise at this remark, your lordship I hope will pardon me a slight and involuntary transgression of my own precept. I must entreat you, before we move a step farther in our inquiry, to inform me whether I am really to consider [1] him so exquisite in style.

CHATHAM. Your lordship is capable of forming an opinion on this point, certainly no less correct than mine.

CHESTERFIELD. Pray assist me.

CHATHAM. Education and grammar are surely the two dryest of subjects on which a conversation can turn : yet, if the ground is not promiscuously sown, if what ought to be clear is not covered, if what ought to be covered is not bare, and above all if the plants are choice ones, we may spend a few moments on it not unpleasantly. It appears then to me, that elegance in prose composition is mainly this : a just admission of topics and of words ; neither too many nor too few of either ; enough of sweetness in the sound to induce us to enter and sit still ; enough of illustration and reflection to change the posture of our minds when they would tire ; and enough of sound matter in the complex to repay us for our attendance. I could perhaps be more logical in my definition, and more concise ; but am I at all erroneous ?

CHESTERFIELD. I see not that you are.

CHATHAM. My ear is well satisfied with Locke : I find nothing idle or redundant in him : and [2] I admire him particularly for his selection of plain and proper words. This I apprehend to be the prime essential of that eloquence which appeals solely to the reasoning faculties.

CHESTERFIELD. But in the opinion of you graver men, would not some of his principles lead too far ?

CHATHAM. The danger is that few will be led by them far enough : most who begin with him stop short, and, pretending to find pebbles in their shoes, throw themselves down and complain of their guide.

CHESTERFIELD. What then can be the reason why Plato, so much less intelligible, is so much more quoted and applauded ?

CHATHAM. The difficulties we never try are no difficulties to us. They who are upon the summit of a mountain know in some measure

---

[1] 1st and 2nd eds. read : " consider him in style the most elegant of our prose authors."
[2] From " and " to " faculties " added in 3rd ed.

its altitude, by comparing it with many objects around : but they who stand at the bottom and never mounted it, can compare it with few only, and with those imperfectly.[1]   Until a short time ago I could have conversed more fluently about Plato than I can at present : I had read all the titles to the dialogues and several scraps of commentary : these I have now forgotten, and am indebted to long attacks of the gout for what I have acquired instead.

CHESTERFIELD. A too severe schoolmaster ! I hope he allows a long vacation.

CHATHAM. Severe he is indeed: yet[2], although he sets no example of regularity, he exacts few observances and teaches many lessons[3]. Without him I should have had less patience, less reading, less reflection, less leisure ; in short, less of everything but of sleep.

CHESTERFIELD. Locke[4], from a deficiency of fancy, is not likely to attract so many listeners as Plato.

CHATHAM. And yet occasionally his language is both metaphorical and rich in images. In fact, all our great philosophers have this property, in a wonderful degree. Not to speak of the devotional, in whose writings one might expect it, we find it abundantly in Bacon, not sparingly in Hobbes ; the next to him in range of inquiry and potency of intellect. And what would you think, my lord, if you discovered in Newton a sentence in the spirit of Shakespeare ?

CHESTERFIELD. I should look upon it as upon a wonder, not to say a miracle : Newton, like Barrow, had no feeling or respect for poetry.

CHATHAM. His words are these : " I don't know what I may seem to the world ; but as to myself, I seem to have been only like a boy playing on the seashore, and diverting myself in now and then finding a smoother pebble or a prettier shell than ordinary, whilst the great ocean of Truth lay all undiscovered before me."

CHESTERFIELD. Surely Nature, who had given him the volumes of her greater mysteries to unseal ; who had bent over him and taken his hand, and taught him to decipher the characters of her sacred language ; who had lifted up her veil before him higher than ever yet for mortal, that she might impress her features and her fondness

---

[1] 1st ed. reads : " imperfectly : so fares it with Plato or his readers on one side, and with Plato and his talkers on the other. Until," etc.

[2] 1st ed. reads : " and although "; 2nd ed. reads : " and altho'."

[3] 1st and 2nd eds. read : " many things."

[4] From " Locke " to " upon her " added in 2nd ed.

on his heart ; threw it back wholly at these words, and gazed upon him with as much admiration as ever he had gazed with upon her.

Plato, I see from the Latin version, lies open on the table : the paragraphs marked with pencil, I presume, are fine passages.

CHATHAM. I have noted those only which appeared reprehensible, and chiefly where he is disingenuous and malicious.

CHESTERFIELD. They indeed ought to be the most remarkable in the works of a philosopher. If the malice is against those who are thought greater or as great, it goes toward the demonstration that they are so : if on the contrary the objects of it are inferior to himself, he can not take them up without raising them : unworthy of notice, they are more unworthy of passion. Surely no philosopher would turn to an opposite conclusion from that which in the commencement he had designed to prove : as here he must do.

CHATHAM. He avoids an open hostility to Democritus and Xenophon and Aristoteles ; yet [1] I have detected in him more than one dark passage, with a dagger in his hand and a bitter sneer on his countenance. I know not whether it has been observed before that these words are aimed at the latter, the citizen of another state and the commentator of other laws.

Οὐδ' ἐπιθυμία σε ἄλλης πόλεως οὐδ' ἄλλων νόμων ἔλαβεν εἰδέναι, ἀλλ' ἡμεῖς σοι ἱκανοὶ ἦμεν καὶ ἡ ἡμετέρα πόλις.

The compliment is more injurious to Socrates, for whom it was intended, than the insinuation to Aristoteles. But the prime object of his hatred, open here and undissembled, is Prodicus ; author of the beautiful allegory in which Pleasure and Virtue offer themselves to the choice of Hercules. In one place he mentions him with Polus *and many others :* the least difficult and least clever of malignant expressions, where genius is the subject of calumny and invective. One hardly could imagine that he had the assurance and effrontery to call Epicharmus the chief of comic writers, before a people who that very day perhaps had been at a comedy of Aristophanes. The talent of Epicharmus lay in puns and ribaldry, and Hiero punished him for immodest conversation.

CHESTERFIELD. I have read somewhere that, when Plato was young, it was predicted of him, from his satirical vein, that he would become in time a substitute for Archilochus.

---

[1] 1st and 2nd eds. read : " but I fancy."

CHESTERFIELD AND CHATHAM

CHATHAM. Athenæus, I think, has recorded it. I do not find so much wit as I expected ; and, to speak plainly, his wit is the most tiresome and dull part of him ; for who can endure a long series of conversations full of questions to entrap a sophist ? Why not lead us to the trap at once by some unexpected turn ? Yet [1] Plato ought to be more powerful in wit than in argument, for, it is evident, he labours at it more. There is more applicable good-sense, more delicate wit, more urbanity, more gracefulness, in a single paper of the *Spectator*, than in six or eight among the minor of these dialogues ; in all which, not excepting the *Phædo*, I was disappointed.

CHESTERFIELD. The language is said to be masterly and sonorous.

CHATHAM. *Αὐτὸ καθ' αὑτὸ ὡσαύτως κατὰ ταῦτα ἔχει, καὶ οὐδέποτε οὐδαμῶς ἀλλοίωσιν οὐδεμίαν ἐνδέχεται.** And [2] again are several of the like sounds and words. *Σμικρα φυσις ουδεν μεγα ουδεποτε ουτε ιδιωτην ουτε πολιν δρᾶ.*

CHESTERFIELD. Come, come, my lord ; do not attempt to persuade me that an old woman's charm to cure a corn or remove a wart, or a gipsy-girl's to catch a sixpence, is Plato's Greek.

CHATHAM. Look yourself.

CHESTERFIELD. I have forgotten the characters pretty nearly : faith ! they appear to me, from what I can pick up, to correspond with the sounds you gave them. Jupiter, it is said by the ancients, would have spoken no other language than Plato's. If ever Jupiter uttered such sounds as these, it could be only when he was crossing the Hellespont.

CHATHAM. What do you think of this jingle ? *Πρῶτον εὐλαβη-θῶμέν τι πάθος μὴ παθῶμεν.*

CHESTERFIELD. I really thought that his language was [3] harmonious to the last degree.

CHATHAM. Generally it is so : his language is the best of him. We moderns are still children in our tongues, at least we English. For my own part, I always spoke in Parliament what I considered the most effectual to persuade my hearers, without a care or a thought touching the structure of my sentences : but knowing that the ancient orators and writers laid the first foundation of their glory

---

[1] From " Yet " to " more " added in 2nd ed.

* *Phædo.*—W. S. L.   [2] From "And " to " δρᾶ " added in 3rd ed.

[3] 1st and 2nd eds. read : " was accurate and harmonious," etc.

upon syllables, I was surprised to find no fewer than nine short ones together in this eloquent author, ἄνδρας ἀποδεδοκιμακότες.* The accents which were guides to them, although unwritten, may have taken off somewhat from this peculiarity, and may have been a sort of support to the feebleness of the sound. No modern language can admit the concourse of so many such; and the Latin was so inadequate to the supply of them, that it produced, I believe, but one galliambic in the times of its strength and fertility; which poem required them in greater numbers and closer together than any other, but did not receive nine conjointly.

CHESTERFIELD. Cicero was himself a trifler in cadences, and whoever thinks much about them will become so, if indeed the very thought when it enters is not trifling.

CHATHAM. I am not sure that it is; for an orderly and sweet sentence, by gaining our ear, conciliates our affections; and the voice of a beggar has often more effect upon us than his distress. Your mention of Cicero on this occasion, reminds me of his *O fortu natam natam me consule Romam.* Playful as he was in his vanity, I do not believe the verse is his: but Plato wrote ἀλλὰ παρ᾽ αὐτοὺς αὖ τοὺς δεῖν οὓς ὄντας ταῦτα, &c. We[1] may be too fastidious and fantastic in sounds and syllables; but a frequent recurrence of the same is offensive to the ear, and particularly in poetry. Nevertheless, he who appears to have had a more delicate one than almost any of the moderns, and indeed whose latinity surpasses in elegance that of any of the Romans themselves, excepting Cicero and Cæsar, was persuaded that Tibullus was fond and studious of syllabic repetitions. It appears that this poet, says Muretus, thought it elegant to continue them, and that such as the following did not happen by accident, but were produced by application and design. "*Me*[2] *mea.* Ip*se* *se*ram. Po*ma ma*nu. Mul*ta ta*bella. Sic*ca ca*nis."

CHESTERFIELD.[3] The Latin of Muretus may be elaborate and elegant, but he, like nearly all the best modern latinists, was conceited, fantastical, and weakly-minded. And now I remember having been present at a discussion between two scholars on his merits in style. It was doubted whether he or Bembo is the most accurate: the beauties and faults of each were brought forward: and the

---

* *Phædo.*—W. S. L.   [1] From " We " to " *canis* " added in 2nd ed.
[2] Tib., i. i. 5, 7, 8 ; i. iii. 28 ; i. iv. 6.
[3] From " CHESTERFIELD " to " tongue " added in 3rd ed.

sentence was given in favour of Bembo, for two or three reasons, of which the only one I can recollect is, that Muretus wrote *sinceritas*, never doubting its latinity, whereas Bembo, when he employed it, said " *Si verbo uti liceat.*"

CHATHAM. I should never have suspected that a word so requisite was wanting to the Latin tongue. Let [1] me turn over my scrap of paper, which however would best perhaps have kept its place between the leaves here.

CHESTERFIELD. No, my lord, if you thought anything worth noticing and writing down, surely I may well think it worth knowing.

CHATHAM. First then I find a mark of admiration, that this most learned and eloquent man, Ciceronian as he was and enraptured by Virgil, should not have remarked in him or Cicero what he notices as a peculiarity in Tibullus. " *Sin* [2] *in* processu. *Sin in* sua. Qu*in intra* portas. Comprend*ere refert. Ore re*ferret. Quæ*rere regna.* Crines effu*sa sa*cerdos. A fra*tre re*cepi. Surg*ere regna. Ære re*nidenti. Serva*re re*cursus. Sub au*re re*liquit. Mitt*êre re*lictâ. String*ere re*mos. Curr*ere re*mis." In Cicero I found after an evening's reading " Si plus adipisca*re re* (where certainly it could as easily have been avoided as committed). Neque excludentes ab ej*us us*u *su*os. Meo j*ure re*spondeo. Observa*re re*stricte. *Me me*tu libero. Reli*qui qui.* Maxi*me me* tuto. Non es*se se se*natorem " ; and a few words lower " illos enim bonos du*ces esse, se* jam confectum *se*nectute." Such a concourse of *es* and *se* is perhaps not to be found again in all the books of my library. Our own language is comparatively poor in sibilants, and would refuse the supplies on this occasion. Similar sounds repeated, not indeed consecutively, but closely, are in Homer and Anacreon.

Οἷοι τρώϊοι ἵπποι ἐπιστάμενοι πεδίοιο.   *Il. E.*
Δέποινα, σοὶ μὲν ἵπποι.   *Anac. Frag.*

In the former you have the same six times in six feet ; in the latter thrice in three. Yet the sound of neither verse is so unpleasant as that of Horace, where the repetition comes but once :

" Dirus per urbes Afer *it It*alas." [3]

---

[1] From " Let " to " language from Plato's " added in 2nd ed.
[2] *Georg.*, II., III., chiefly.
[3] As the true reading is " ut Italas," the complaint is pointless.

We have slided into Cicero's language from Plato's. As for his [1] wit, what think you of this ? " I am ready, O Socrates, to give myself up to the strangers, to flay me worse than they flay me now, if the flaying ends not in a hide, as that of Marsyas did, but in virtue." Or what think you of a project to make a doll and dedicate it to Memory ? The stuff that follows is worse still. Toward the end of the volume, in the *Gorgias*, Polus says to Socrates, " Do not you see Archeläus, son of Perdiccas, reigning over the Macedonians ? " to which Socrates replies, " If I do not see him, I hear of him."

In the beginning of the same dialogue, Gorgias, at the request of Socrates to be brief, assents to his proposition twice, by using the monosyllable : whereupon Socrates says, " I admire your replies, Gorgias ; they are as short as they can be." If the same monosyllable had been the answer to several questions in succession, and if those questions had been complicated and intricate, then, and then only, the remark had been well-placed.

You remember, my lord, the derivations made by Swift, of Agamemnon,[2] Ajax, Achilles, Andromache, and other names of heroes and heroines. These are hardly more absurd and ridiculous than almost all made by Plato and attributed with great complacency to Socrates, of the same and similar; and are much less literal. It is incredible how erroneous were the most learned, both among the Greeks and Romans, on the origin of words.

CHESTERFIELD. I have heard it reported that our own lexicographers are subject, in some degree, to the same animadversion : but I can judge more adequately of bad reasoning or bad wit.

CHATHAM. A little of the latter tires and nauseates, while in the former there is generally something to exercise the ingenuity. I have seen persons who could employ a moment or two unreluctantly in straightening a crooked nail : with about the same labour and interest I would hammer upon an inexact thought. Here is one which I wonder that Cicero, in mentioning the dialogue, has failed to remark. Our philosopher divides rhetoric into the true and the false ; as if any part of a definition or description were to be founded on the defects of what is defined or described. Rhetoric may be turned to good or bad purposes ; but this is no proof or indication

---

[1] 1st ed. reads : " As for wit."
[2] 1st and 2nd eds. read : " Agamemnon, and other . . . heroes. These," etc.

that it must be divided into good and bad. The use of a thing is not the thing itself; how then is the abuse?

The wit of Plato's dialogues is altogether of a single kind, and of that which in a continuance is the least welcome. For irony is akin to cavil; and cavil, as the best wit is either good-natured or wears the appearance of good-nature, is nearly its antipode. Plato has neither the grace of Xenophon nor the gravity of Cicero, who tempers it admirably with urbanity and facetiousness. Although [1] he is most celebrated for imagination, and for an eloquence highly poetical, there are incomparably more, both in quantity and quality, of poetical thoughts and images, in Bacon than in Plato. The language of Plato is vastly more sonorous: he is called, and nobody questions that he is, eloquent: but there is no eloquence which does not agitate the soul: he never does. Demosthenes effects it by strong appeals, and through the reason. Rousseau effects it sometimes in despite of the reason, and by uniting the Graces with the Passions. We often say we hate Rousseau; but how often does the lover say (or wish to say) he hates the beloved! In fact, the moral part of Rousseau was odious, and much of the intellectual was perverse and depraved: there was, however, a noble instrument of harmony, sounding along high and intricately vaulted arches. The characteristic of [2] Plato is, the dexterity and ease with which he supports and shifts an argument, and exhibits it in all its phases. Nevertheless, a series of interrogations, long as he draws them out for this purpose, would weary me in one dialogue: he continues them in twenty, with people of the same description, on the same subjects.

CHESTERFIELD. It is rather an idle thing for an old gentleman in a purple robe to be sticking pins in every chair on which a sophist is likely to sit down; and rather a tiresome and cheerless one to follow and stand by him, day after day in the cold, laying gins for tom-tits.

CHATHAM. In general, I own, he did so: but both he and Aristoteles turned occasionally their irony (of which indeed the latter had little) where irony is best employed: against false piety, against that which would be the substitute and not the support of morality. When [3] a high sound issues from a high soul, our ears and hearts are opened to it; otherwise we let " the wind blow where it listeth."

---

[1] From " Although " to " arches " added in 3rd ed.
[2] 1st and 2nd eds. read : " of my author."
[3] From " When " to " inference of mine " added in 3rd ed.

He jokes on grave subjects, and such as he himself thinks to be grave ; and he is grave on light ones. Can anything be flatter and duller than : " ' It seems becoming,' said Glauco, ' that we should stay.' ' Then, if it do seem so,' said I, ' we ought to stay.' "

CHESTERFIELD. Here at least is no quibbling.

CHATHAM. Do you want a little of that ? Let me open almost any page whatever, and I can supply abundantly the most capricious customer. Take for specimen a pinch of the *Polity.* Here he carries his quibbles to such an extent as to demonstrate that *Justice is a sort of thief.* These are his very words, positive and express ; no mere inference of mine.

The Greek language, more courteous than the Roman or the French or ours, and resembling in this property the Italian, in addressing a person, had ready among other terms, ὦ θαυμάσιε and ὦ βέλτιστε. Socrates meets an orderly good man, who, from respect to the laws, is going to accuse his own father of a capital crime, as he imagines it to be ; and, doubting if he understood him, asks ὁ σὸς, ὦ βέλτιστε. Aristoteles, in the eighth book of his *Ethics,* gravely says that children ought to see no indecent statue or picture, unless it represents some God committing the obscenity.

Such [1] are the two best pieces of wit in the two authors : and I suspect that Plato was as unaware in this place of being witty as he was in others of not being so.

In regard to their philosophy, and indeed to that of the ancients in general, there was little of sound and salutary which they did not derive from Democritus or from Pythagoras : from the former Aristoteles drew most, from the latter Plato. Cicero says improperly of Socrates, what is repeated every day in schools and colleges, that he first drew down Philosophy into private houses : Pythagoras had done [2] it more systematically and more extensively. Upon his tenets and his discipline were founded many institutions of the earlier and quieter converts to Christianity.

CHESTERFIELD. There is, I remember, a very dangerous doctrine attributed to this Democritus, whom you mentioned before him : he said that governments should have two supporters, rewards and punishments. Now twelve hangmen, and even twelve judges, may be paid : but Mansfield, I suspect, would commit any man to Bride-

---

[1] From " Such " to " so " added in 3rd ed.
[2] 1st and 2nd eds. read : " done so."

well or the pillory, who had broached a declaration so seditious, as that people of ordinary business, unhired for it, should be paid for doing their duty. National debts, he would inform the jury, are not to be aggravated by such idle and superfluous expenditure, increased at any man's option.

CHATHAM. I know not what my lord Mansfield, a worse enemy to our constitution than even that degraded and despicable prince for whose service he was educated, may think or dictate on the subject : but among all the books I ever read in which rewards and punishments are mentioned, I never found one where the words come in any other order than this : rewards first, then punishments. A plain evidence and proof to my humble understanding, that in the same succession they present themselves to the unperverted mind. We mention them not only in regard to our polity, but in contemplation of a better state hereafter ; and there too they occur to us as upon earth.

CHESTERFIELD. In the pleadings of Mansfield, in his charges, in his decisions, in his addresses to parliament, I have heard nothing so strikingly true as these observations of your lordship, and I wish I had heard nothing so novel.

CHATHAM. I, in the name of our country, unite with you, my lord, in this wish. Let us trace again the more innocent wanderings of a greater man, I know not whether less prejudiced, but certainly less profligate and corrupt.

Socrates in the *Gorgias* is represented as saying that he believes the soul and body both to exist in another state, although separately ; the body just as it was in life, with its infirmities, wounds, and distortions. This would be great injustice ; for hence a long life, rendered so by frugality and temperance, would acquire, in part of its recompense, the imbecility of age, with deafness, blindness, and whatever else is most afflictive and oppressive in that condition. The soul carries upon its back, he says, the marks of floggings and bruises and scars, contracted by perjuries upon earth, and by the delivery *in court* of unjust sentences ; such I believe, in this place, is the meaning of ἀδικίαι, and not merely any common acts of injustice. The utility of exposures in another life, he says, arises from example to others. But in what manner can they profit by this example ? From what wickedness can they be deterred by these scenes of terror ? Ideas as idly fanciful and childishly silly are in his description of the infernal rivers, which he derived from the poets, and which, without line or level, he led over places just as unfruitful afterward as before. Returning to this strange body of his, it cannot be supposed an inert substance : the words *after death* mean *after this life upon earth*. If he would say that it is inert, he must suppose it to be motionless : when did it become so ? Strange that it should have motion to reach Tartarus and should then lose it. If so, of what use could it be ? He does not say it, nor mean it, I imagine.

CHESTERFIELD. On some occasions, it appears, he leaves off meaning very abruptly. Men [1] leap awkwardly in long flowing dressing-gowns, and, instead of clearing the thorns and stakes, expose God knows what.

CHATHAM. It is not wonderful or strange that Aristoteles should ridicule his vagaries. Nothing can be more puerile and contemptible than the ideas he attributes to Socrates on future punishments : among the rest, that the damned appeal by name to those whom they have slain or wronged, and are dragged backward and forward from Tartarus to Cocytus and Periphlegethon, until the murdered or injured consent to pardon them. So the crime is punished, not according to its heinousness, but according to the kindness or severity of those who suffered by it. Now the greater crime is committed in having slain or injured the generous and kind man ; the greater punishment is inflicted for injuring or slaying the ungenerous and unkind. Plato [2] tells us in the *Timæus*, that God created time and the heavens at the same moment, in order that, being born together, they should cease together.

CHESTERFIELD. Does he inform us also that the Creator in the beginning separated the light from the darkness ? an idea very Platonic.

CHATHAM. No.

CHESTERFIELD. What other passage amuses your lordship ?

CHATHAM. Nothing peculiar to this author. Turning over the leaves, I am reminded of what occurs often in the Athenian law-procedures, that while the *prosecutor* has the same appellation as with us, the *defendant* is called the *flyer*, ὁ φεύγων : a proof, shall I say, that the Athenians were a wiser people, or a less firm one, than we are ?

---

[1] From " Men " to " what " added in 3rd ed.
[2] From " Plato " to " poetry " (" now Balder . . . poetry ") added in 2nd ed., where the passage ends : " poetry and eloquence."

They, as we do, say *to give judgment :* but they really did give it, and gratuitously : we must drop a purse of gold on every step of the judgment-seat, or be kicked down headlong.

It is very amusing to trace the expressions of different nations for the same thing. What we, half a century ago, called to *banter*, and what, if I remember the word, I think I have lately heard called to *quiz*, gives no other idea than of coarseness and inurbanity. The French convey one of buzz and bustle in *persiffler ;* the Italians, as naturally, one of singing, and amusing and misleading the judgment, by *canzonare*, or, as Boccaccio speaks, *uccellare ;* the Athenians knew that the Graces and childhood had most power of this kind upon the affections, and their expressions were χαριεντίζειν and παιδεύειν.

In manifestoes or remonstrances we English say to *draw up*, from our love of conciseness ; the Frenchman says *dresser*, very characteristically ; and the Italian, the most verbose of men, *stendere*. Many words have degenerated. Who would imagine that a singer or tippler should derive his appellation from Jupiter ? his fellows call him *jovial*. Our northern Gods are respected as little. The vilest of prose or poetry is called *balderdash :* now Balder was among the Scandinavians the presiding God of poetry. Braga was the Goddess of eloquence : and she has left us *brag* and *braggart*.

I [1] am reminded by the mention of poetry, that Plato is offended in the *Iliad* at the undignified grief of Achilles and of Priam. To clasp the knee is going too far : and to roll in the dust is beastly. I am certain that he never was a father or a friend : not that among us the loss of friends is accompanied by such violence of affliction, but because I have observed that grief is less often in proportion to delicacy, and even to tenderness, than to the higher energies of our nature and the impetuosity of our nobler passions. The intemperate and wild resentment of Achilles at the injustice of Agamemnon, and his self-devotion, certain as he was of his fate, prepare us for intensity and extravagance of feeling, and teach us that in such a character diversity is not incongruity. This censure of the philosopher on the poet, convinces me that the wisest of his works was the burning of his tragedies. Heroism, as Plato would have had it, would be afraid to soil his robe, and Passion would blush to unfold her handkerchief. He who could censure the two most admirable passages in Homer, could indeed feel no reluctance at banishing the

---

[1] From " I " to " contingency " added in 2nd ed.

poets from his republic : and we can not wonder that he strays wide
from sound philosophy, who knows so little of the human heart, as to
be ignorant that the poet is most a poet in the midst of its varieties and
its excesses.   Only with God can greatness exist without irregularity :
that of Achilles was a necessary and essential part of him.   Without
it, no resentment at Agamemnon, no abandonment of his cause
and of his countrymen, no revenge for Patroclus, no indignity to
the body of his bravest enemy, no impatience at the first sight of
Priam, no effusion of tears at his paternal sorrows, no agony stronger
than his vows or than his vengeance forcing him to deliver up the
mangled hero : in short, no *Iliad*, no Homer.   We are all little before
such men, and principally when we censure or contend with them.
Plato on this occasion stands among the ringers of the twelve un-
changeable French bells ; among the apes who chatter as they pick
out the scurf of Shakspeare.   These two poets divide the ages of the
world between them, and will divide the ages of eternity.   Prudent
men, who wish to avoid the appearance of pygmies, will reverently
keep at some distance, laying aside here their cruet of vinegar and
here their cake of honey.   Plato is the only one of the ancients who
extols the poetry of Solon ; of whom he says that, if he had written
his poem on the war of the Athenians against the island of Atalantis,
undistracted by the business of the state, he might have rivalled the
glory of Hesiod and Homer.   No man of sound judgment ever placed
these names together, unless as contemporaries ; and he must possess
a very unsound one indeed, who calculates thus on the contingency [1]
of Homer's rival in any statesman.

    " Poetical expression," Plato tells you, " is a copy of the poet's
own conception of things ; and things, of the archetype existing in
the divine mind ; thus the poet's expression is a copy at the third
hand."   And this argument he adduces to prove that poetry is far
distant from truth.   It proves no such thing ; and if it did, it would
not prove that poetry is not delightful ; and delight, we know, is its
aim and end.   But that truths also, and most important ones, are
conveyed by poetry, is quite as certain as that fallacies, and the most
captious and quibbling fallacies, are conveyed by Plato :   more

----

    [1] 2nd ed. reads : " contingency of rivalling Homer.   CHESTERFIELD. I myself
love genteel poetry, and read Hammond's elegies rather than the *Iliad* : at the
same time I confess I have reason to think my choice a wrong one and that poetry
like religion," etc.   For Hammond, consult Landor's lines to Lord Nugent,
Dry Sticks.

certain nothing can be. If the poet has a conception of things as they emanate from the divine mind, whether it is at third hand or at thirtieth, so long as nothing distorts or disturbs them, what matters it ? The image or archetype is God's : he impresses it on things : the poet represents the things as they are impressed on his mind by the hand of the Creator. Now, if this is done, the distance from truth is not remote. But there is a truth, accommodated to our nature, which poetry best conveys. There is a truth for the reason ; there is a truth for the passions; there is a truth for every character of man. Shakspeare has rendered this clear and luminous, over all the stumps and stumbling-blocks and lighter brush-wood and briars thrown across the path by the puerile trickery of Plato.

CHESTERFIELD. I have reason to think that [1] poetry like religion levels the intellects of men, the wise talking on that subject as absurdly as the ignorant. Great poets are the only judges of great poets : and their animosities and prejudices I will not say pervert their judgment, but blot, interline, and corrupt the copies we receive of it. I have as little faith in Plato's love as you have in his philosophy.

CHATHAM. In his disquisition on love is a receipt to cure the hiccup. "If you will hold your breath a little, it will go : if that should be disagreeable, take a good draught of water : but if the hiccup is very vehement, tickle your nose to sneezing, and when that has happened once or twice, be the hiccup obstinate as it may, it will be removed."

CHESTERFIELD. Who would buy a village cookery book, or a two-penny almanack, if the author stuffed into it such silliness as this ?

CHATHAM. In the same dialogue is a piece of sophistry more trivial than the receipt. "If all pleasures are weaker than love, they are the conquered, he the conqueror : Love then, *who predominates over lusts and pleasures*, is temperate to a wonderful degree." It is fair however to remark, that Agatho, here introduced as the speaker, says a part of what is spoken is serious, a part is joke. I wish Plato had left some indication by which we might distinguish the one from the other ; but neither he nor the acutest of his commentators has done it. Sound [2] sense, in my opinion, is preferable to bodiless incomprehensible vagaries : and if ever I become an author and am praised

---

[1] From " that " to " it " added in 2nd ed.
[2] From " Sound " to " meaning " added in 3rd ed.

at all, I trust it will be not because I am so sublime an intelligence as to be unreadable without help, or without a controversy of clever and acute men about my meaning.

He[1] has here also given us a sort of dithyrambic, than which, as it appears to me, nothing is more redundantly verbose ; yet Socrates is introduced as praising it to the skies. His knowledge of poetry, I suspect, did not carry him beyond a fable. To stick there is better than to follow (as Plato exhibits him doing) an old woman, and to relate as his own opinion that the business of genii or demons is to carry prayer and sacrifice from men to the Gods, and precepts from the Gods again to men. I am not so idle as to run far into his theories, and to examine what never has been and never will be brought into use; which alone is a sufficient proof of utter worthlessness. Nothing can be more absurd than his regulations for the order of succession to property. Even those of a certain Irish lord are more provident, who, about to die childless, ordered that his money should go to the elder son of his brother, and, if he had no elder son, to the second. As for marriages, on the outset he would appoint a judge to examine the males stark-naked, in order to decide on their fitness for that condition ; females only to a certain point.

CHESTERFIELD. I am astonished at the enormous proportion of fancy to philosophy, of folly to fancy, and of impudence to folly, in this moralist, theologian, and legislator.

CHATHAM. You are not then disposed to look at the other places marked ?

CHESTERFIELD. In truth, no.

CHATHAM. He was fond of puns too, and the silliest and commonest, those on names. Ἤρεσεν οὖν μοι καὶ ἐν τῷ μύθῳ ὁ Προμηθεὺς μᾶλλον τοῦ Ἐπιμηθέως ᾧ χρώμενος ἐγὼ καὶ προμηθούμενος, &c., and below ἀλλὰ Καλλίᾳ τῷ καλῷ, &c.

The worst is, that he attributes the vainest of sophistry and the basest of malignity to Socrates. A wise and virtuous man may have the misfortune to be at variance with a single great author among his contemporaries, but neither a virtuous nor a wise one can be drawn into hostilities against all the best: he to whom this happens must be weak or wicked. Impudence may prompt some to asseverate that, with prodigious manliness and self-devotion, they hazard to cut their feet and break their shins by stemming the current ; that the perilous

---

[1] From " He " to " In truth, no," added in 2nd ed.

state of literature calls aloud on them, and that they encounter it equally for the public good and the correction of the faulty writer. But the public good, in my opinion, is ill promoted by telling men that all their other teachers are worth nothing, and that to be contented is to be dull, to be pleased is to be foolish ; nor have I remarked or heard of any instance where morals have been improved by scurrility, diffidence calmed, encouraged, sustained, led forth, by violence, or genius exalted by contempt.   I am sorry that a great man should have partaken the infirmities of the least, in their worst propensities.   This principally has induced me to show you that, within the few pages you see between my fingers, he has committed as grave faults in style and sentiment, not only as Prodicus, but (I must believe) as Polus.   We hear from the unprejudiced that Prodicus, like our Locke, was exact in his definitions ; we know that he arrived at the perfection of style ; and our gratitude is due to him for one of the most beautiful works delivered down to us from antiquity.

CHESTERFIELD. Your lordship has proved to me that a divine man, even with a swarm of bees from nose to chin, may cry aloud and labour hard, and lay his quarter-staff about him in every direction, and still be an indifferent buffoon.

CHATHAM. Buffoonery is hardly the thing wherein a man of genius would be ambitious to excell ; but, of all failures, to fail in a witticism is the worst ; and the mishap is the more calamitous in a drawn-out and detailed [1] one.

He [2] often fails in a contrary extreme.   The soundest of those great critics whom we call grammarians, Dionysius of Halicarnassus, censures him for bringing bombast into philosophical disquisitions : and Dr. Hurd, neither a severe judge nor an incompetent one, quoting the passage, adds " The *Phædrus*, though the most remarkable, is not the only example."

CHESTERFIELD. Better a little idle play with bubbles and bladders, than cut and dry dogmas and indigestible sophisms.   Plato falls over his own sword ; not by hanging it negligently or loosely, but by stepping with it awkwardly ; and the derision he incurs is proportionate to the gravity of his gait.   Half the pleasure in the world arises from malignity ; and little of the other half is free from its encroachments. Those who enjoyed his smartness and versatility of attack, laugh as

[1] 1st and 2nd eds. read : " detailed, and written one."
[2] From " He " to " sophisms " added in 3rd ed.

heartily at him as with him, demonstrate that a great man upon the ground is lower than a little man upon his legs, and conclude that the light of imagination leads only to gulfs and precipices.

CHATHAM. We, however, with greater wisdom and higher satisfaction, may survey him calmly and reverentially, as one of lofty, massy, comprehensive mind, whose failings myriads have partaken, whose excellences few ; and we may consider him as an example, the more remarkable and striking to those we would instruct, for that very inequality and asperity of character, which many would exaggerate, and some conceal. Let us however rather trust Locke and Bacon : let us believe the one to be a wiser man, and the other both a wiser and better. There [1] is as much difference between Plato and Bacon as there is between a pliant luxuriant twig, waving backward and forward on the summit of a tree, and a sound stiff well-seasoned walking-stick, with a ferrule that sticks as far as is needful into the ground and makes every step secure. Hearing much of the poetry that is about him, I looked for it in vain : and I defy any man to fill with it, pure and impure, a couple of such pages as are usually meted out, with honest exactness and great marginal liberality, three hundred to the volume. Florid prose-writers are never tolerable poets. Jeremy Taylor is an example among many : his poetry is even worse, if possible, than the austere Hobbes's.

CHESTERFIELD. It is generous in you to countenance the persecuted Locke ; and to examine the skull of Bacon, undeterred by a heart so putrid.

CHATHAM. I declare to you, I should have the courage to say the same thing if they were living, and expelled from court and Christchurch.

CHESTERFIELD. We think more advantageously of artificial dignities while the bearers are living, more advantageously of real when they are dead.

CHATHAM. The tomb is the pedestal of greatness. I make a distinction between God's great and the King's great.[2]

" Non bene conveniunt nec in unâ sede morantur."

CHESTERFIELD. So much the worse for both parties. Compliments are in their place only where there is full as much of weakness as of

---

[1] From " There " to " CHATHAM " added in 3rd ed.
[2] 1st ed. reads : " great. CHESTERFIELD. ' Non . . . morantur,' So much," etc.

merit ; so that when I express my admiration to your lordship, all idea of compliment must vanish. Permit me then to say that I have always been gratified at this among your other noble qualities, that, possessing more wit than perhaps any man living, you have the moderation to use it rarely, and oftener in friendship than in enmity.

CHATHAM. Profligate men and pernicious follies may fairly and reasonably be exposed ; light peculiarities may also be exhibited ; but only in such a manner that he who gave the prototype would willingly take the copy. But in general he who pursues another race of writers is little better than a fox-hunter who rides twenty miles from home for the sport : what can he do with his game when he has caught it ? As he is only the servant of the dogs, so the satirist is only a caterer to the ferocious or false appetites of the most indiscriminating and brutal minds. Does he pretend that no exercise else is good for him ? He confesses then an unsoundness in a vital part.

CHESTERFIELD. Reflections such as these induced me long ago to prefer the wit of Addison and La Fontaine to other kinds : it is more harmless, more gay, and more insinuating.

CHATHAM. Our own language contains in it a greater quantity and a greater variety of wit and humour, than all the rest of all ages and countries ; closing only Cervantes, the Homer of irony, and not only of sharper and better-tempered wit than he who lies before me, but even of an imagination more vivid and poetical, a sounder too and shrewder philosopher. The [1] little volume of Bacon's *Essays*, in my opinion, exhibits not only more strength of mind, not only more true philosophy, but more originality, more fancy, more imagination, than all these volumes of Plato ; supposing even that he drew nothing from others ; whereas we must receive the authority of antiquity, and believe that he owed to them the greater part, and almost the whole. Without this authority, we should perceive it in the absence of fixed principles, and in the jarring of contradictory positions. It must be conceded that we moderns are but slovens in composition, or ignorant for the most-part of its regulations and laws ; yet we may insist that there have been among us those to whom, in all the higher magistratures of intellect, the gravest of the ancients would have risen up, and have placed with proper deference at their side.

[1] From " The " to " positions " added in 2nd ed.

CHESTERFIELD.[1] I never have found anyone so unprejudiced and so unprepossessed on Plato.

CHATHAM. My lord, I do not know that I am entirely.

CHESTERFIELD. How ! my lord.

CHATHAM. I know that everything I have said is just and incontrovertible, and that I could add ten times as much and as fairly ; but I can not take to myself a praise that does not belong to me, any more than I could a purse. I dislike, not to say detest, the character of Plato, as I collect it from his works, and the worst part of it I conceive to be his coldness and insincerity in friendship. He pretended to have been sick during the imprisonment of Socrates : was he so very sick that he could not have been carried to receive the last words of his departing friend ? the last counsels of a master so affectionate and impressive ? He was never sick when a prince was to be visited on his throne, insolent and tyrannical as that prince might be.

CHESTERFIELD. A throne is to few so frightful a thing as a death-bed.

CHATHAM. My lord, it is a more frightful thing to any man who knows it well, than the death-couch of Socrates was to himself, or to those who from their hearts could reason as he did on it.

CHESTERFIELD. I am happy, my lord, and grateful to you, that the conversation has taken a different turn from what I had expected. I came to receive some information from you on what might be profitable in the education of the young, and you have given me some which would be greatly so in that of the old. My system, I know, can not be quite according to your sentiments ; but as no man living hath a nobler air or a more dignified demeanour than your lordship, I shall be flattered by hearing that what I have written on politeness meets in some degree your approbation.

CHATHAM. I believe you are right, my lord. What is superficial in politeness, what we see oftenest and what people generally admire most, must be laid upon a cold breast or will not stand : so far we agree : but whatever is most graceful in it can be produced only by the movements of the heart.

CHESTERFIELD. These movements, I contend, are to be imitated, and as easily as those of the feet ; and that good actors must beware of being moved too much from within. My lord, I do not inquire of

[1] From " CHESTERFIELD " to " did on it " added in 2nd ed.

288

you whether that huge quarto is the Bible : for I see the letters on the back. Permit me.

CHATHAM. I did not imagine your lordship was such an enthusiast in religion : I am heartily glad to witness your veneration for a book which, to say nothing of its holiness or authority, contains more specimens of genius than any other volume in existence.

CHESTERFIELD. I kissed it from no such motive : I kissed it preparatorily to swearing on it, as your lordship's power and credit is from this time forward at my mercy, that I never will divulge the knowledge I possess of your reading Greek and philosophy.[1]

[1] 1st ed. has the following terminal note :—

" Lord Chatham left two sons : one inherited his passion, the other his power, neither of them his virtues, his manners, or his abilities ; yet each fancied he had the better part of the inheritance."

The criticisms of Plato exhibit Landor's failure to understand sometimes the meaning and usually the significance of the cited passages.

XXIV. DAVID HUME AND JOHN HOME

(*Imag. Convers.*, ii., 1824 ; ii., 1826 ; *Wks.*, i., 1846 ; *Wks.*, iv., 1876.)

HUME. We Scotchmen, sir, are somewhat proud of our families and relationships : this is however a nationality which perhaps I should not have detected in myself, if I had not been favoured with the flattering present of your tragedy. Our names, as often happens, are spelled differently ; but I yielded with no reluctance to the persuasion, that we are, and not very distantly, of the same stock.

HOME. I hope, sir, our mountains will detain you among them some time, and I presume to promise you that you will find in Edinburgh a society as polished and literate as in Paris.

HUME. As literate I can easily believe, my cousin, and perhaps as polished, if you reason upon the ingredients of polish : but there is certainly much more amenity and urbanity at Paris than anywhere else in the world, and people there are less likely to give and take offence. All topics may be discussed without arrogance and super ciliousness : an atheist would see you worship a stool or light a candle at noon without a sneer at you ; and a bishop, if you were well-dressed and perfumed, would argue with you calmly and serenely, though you doubted the whole Athanasian creed.

HOME. So much the worse : God forbid we should ever experience this lukewarmness in Scotland.

HUME. God, it appears, has forbidden it : for which reason, to show my obedience and submission, I live as much as possible in France, where at present God has forbidden no such thing.

HOME. Religion, my dear sir, can alone make men happy and keep them so.

HUME. Nothing is better calculated to make men happy than religion, if you will allow them to manage it according to their minds ; in which case the strong men hunt down others, until they can fold them, entrap them, or noose them. Here however let the discussion terminate. Both of us have been in a cherry orchard, and have observed the advantages of the jacket, hat, and rattle.

DAVID HUME AND JOHN HOME

HOME. Our reformed religion does not authorise any line of conduct diverging from right reason : we are commanded by it to speak the truth to all men.

HUME. Are you likewise [1] commanded to hear it from all men ?

HOME. Yes, let it only be proved to be truth.

HUME. I doubt the observance [2] : you will not even let the fact be proved : you resist the attempt : you blockade the preliminaries. Religion, as you practise it in Scotland, in some cases is opposite to reason and subversive of happiness.

HOME. In what instance ?

HUME. If you had a brother whose wife was unfaithful to him without his suspicion ; if he lived with her happily ; if he had children by her ; if others of which he was fond could be proved by you, and you only, not to be his ; what would you do ?

HOME. O the harlot [3] ! we have none such here, excepting the wife indeed (as we hear she is) of a little lame blear-eyed lieutenant, brought with him from Sicily, and bearing an Etna of her own about her, and truly no quiescent or intermittent one, which Mungo Murray (the apprentice of Hector Abercrombie) tells me has engulfed [4] half the dissolutes in the parish. Of [5] the married men who visited her, there was never one whose boot did not pinch him soon after, or the weather was no weather for corns and rheumatisms, or [6] he must e'en go to Glasgow to look after a bad debt, the times being too ticklish to bear losses. I [7] run into this discourse, not fearing that another philosopher will, like Empedocles, precipitate himself into the crater, but merely to warn you against the husband, whose intrepidity on entering the houses of strangers has caught many acute and wary folks. After the first compliments, he will lament to you that elegant and solid literature is more neglected in our days than it ever was. He will entreat you to recommend him to your bookseller ; his own having been too much enriched by him had grown insolent. It is desirable that it should be one who could advance three or four guineas : not that he cares about the money, but that it is always

---

[1] 1st ed. reads : " also."
[2] 1st ed. reads : " fact : on the contrary, you," etc.
[3] 1st ed. reads : " strumpet."
[4] 1st ed. reads : " boiled over upon half."
[5] From " Of " to " rheumatisms " added in 2nd ed.
[6] From " or " to " losses " added in 3rd ed.
[7] From " I " to " fish out of water " added in 2nd ed.

best to have a check upon these people. You smile : he has probably joined you in the street already, and found his way into your study, and requested of you *by the bye* a trifling loan, as being the only person in the world with whom he could take such a liberty.

HUME. You seem to forget that I am but just arrived, and never knew him.

HOME. That is no impediment : on the contrary, it is a reason the more. A new face is as inviting to him as to the mosquitoes in America. If you lend him a guinea to be rid of him, he will declare the next day that he borrowed it at your own request, and that he returned it the same evening.

HUME. Such men perhaps may have their reasons for being here ; but the woman must be, as people say, like a fish out of water. Again [1] to the question. Come now, if you had a brother, I was supposing, whose wife——

HOME. Out upon her ! should my brother cohabit with her ? should my nephews be defrauded of their patrimony by bastards ?

HUME. You would then destroy his happiness, and his children's : for, supposing that you preserved to them a scanty portion more of fortune (which you could not do), still the shame they would feel from their mother's infamy would much outweigh it.

HOME. I do not see clearly that this is a question of religion.

HUME. All the momentous actions of religious men are referable to their religion, more or less nearly ; all the social duties, and surely these are implicated here, are connected with it. Suppose again that you knew a brother and sister, who, born in different countries, met at last, ignorant of their affinity, and married.

HOME. Poor blind sinful creatures ! God be merciful to them !

HUME. I join you heartily in the prayer, and would only add to it, man be merciful to them also ! Imagine them to have lived together ten years, to have a numerous and happy family, to come and reside in your parish, and the attestation of their prior relationship to be made indubitable to you by some document which alone could establish and record it : what would you do ?

HOME. I would snap asunder the chain that the devil had ensnared them in, even if he stood before me ; I would implore God to pardon them, and to survey with an eye of mercy their unoffending bairns.

[1] 1st ed. reads : " But if you had one such—— HOME. Out on her," etc.

DAVID HUME AND JOHN HOME

HUME. And would not you be disposed to behold them with an eye of the same materials ?

HOME. Could I leave them in mortal sin ? a prey to the ensnarer of souls ! No ; I would rush between them as with a flaming sword ; I would rescue them by God's help from perdition.

HUME. What misery and consternation would this rescue bring with it !

HOME. They would call upon the hills to cover them, to crush and extinguish their shame.

HUME. Those who had lived together in love and innocence and felicity ? A word spoken to them by their pastor brings them into irremediable guilt and anguish. And you would do this ?

HOME. The laws of God are above all other laws : his ways are inscrutable : thick darkness covers his throne.

HUME. My cousin, you who have written so elegant and pathetic a tragedy, cannot but have read the best-contrived one in existence, the *Œdipus* of Sophocles.

HOME. It has wrung my heart ; it has deluged my eyes with weeping.[1]

HUME. Which would you rather do ; cause and excite those sufferings, or assuage and quell them ?

HOME. Am I a Scotchman or an islander of the Red Sea, that a question like this should be asked me ?

HUME. You would not then have given to Œdipus that information which drove him and Jocasta to despair ?

HOME.[2] As a Christian and a minister of the gospel, I am commanded to defy the devil, and to burst asunder the bonds of sin.

HUME. I am certain you would be greatly pained in doing it.

HOME. I should never overcome the grief and anxiety so severe a duty would cause me.

HUME. You have now proved, better than I could have done in twenty *Essays*, that, if morality is not religion, neither is religion morality. Either of them, to be good (and the one must be and the other should be so), will produce good effects from the beginning to the end, and be followed by no remorse or repentance.

It [3] would be presumptuous in me to quote the Bible to you, who

---

[1] 1st ed. ends the sentence at " eyes."
[2] 1st ed. reads : " To him no. As a Christian," etc.
[3] From " It " to " effect " added in 2nd ed.

are so much more conversant in it : yet I cannot refrain from repeating, for my own satisfaction, the beautiful sentence on Holiness ;
that " all her ways are pleasantness, and all her paths are peace."
It says, not one or two paths, but *all :* for vice hath one or two
passably pleasant in the season, if we could forget that, when we
would return, the road is difficult to find, and must be picked out in
the dark.   Imagine anything in the semblance of a duty attended by
regret and sorrow, and be assured that Holiness has no concern in it.
Admonition, it is true, is sometimes of such a nature, from that of the
irregularity it would correct, as to occasion a sigh or a blush to him
who gives it ; in this case, the sensation so manifested adds weight to
the reproof and indemnifies the reprover.   He is happy to have done,
what from generosity and tenderness of heart he was sorry and slow
to do ; and the person in whose behalf he acted must be degraded
beneath the dignity of manhood, if he feels less for himself than
another has felt for him.   The regret is not at the performance of his
duty, but at the failure of its effect.

To produce as much happiness as we can, and to prevent as much
misery, is the proper aim and end of true morality and true religion.
Only give things their right direction [1] ; do but place and train them
well, and there is room to move easily and pleasantly in the midst
of them.

HOME. What ! [2] in the midst of vice and wickedness ? and must
we place and train those ?

HUME. There was a time when what is wine was not wine, when
what is vinegar was not vinegar, when what is corruption was not
corruption.   That which would turn into vice, may not only not turn
into it, but may, by discreet and attentive management, become the
groundwork of virtue.   A little watchfulness over ourselves will save
us a great deal of watchfulness over others, and will permit the
kindliest of religions to drop her inconvenient and unseemly talk,
of enmity and strife, cuirasses and breastplates, battles and exter-
minations.

HOME. These carnal terms are frequent in the books of the Old
Testament.

---

[1] 1st ed. reads (after " direction ") : " there is room "; from " and there " to
" midst of them " added in 2nd ed.

[2] 1st ed. reads : " What ! room for vice and wickedness ? HUME. There
was," etc.

DAVID HUME AND JOHN HOME

HUME. Because the books of the Old Testament were written when the world was much more barbarous and ferocious than it is at present ; and legislators must accommodate their language to the customs and manners of the country.

HOME. Apparently you would rather abolish the forcible expressions of our pious reformers than the abominations at which their souls revolted. I am afraid you would hesitate as little to demolish kirks as convents, to drive out ministers as monks.

HUME. I would let ministers and their kirks alone. I would abolish monasteries ; but gradually and humanely ; and not until I had discovered how and where the studious and pious could spend their time better. I hold religion in the light of a medal which has contracted rust from ages. This rust seems to have been its preserver for many centuries, but after some few more will certainly be its consumer, and leave no vestige of effigy or superscription behind : it should be detached carefully and patiently, not ignorantly and rudely scoured off. Happiness may be taken away from many with the design of communicating it to more : but that which is a grateful and refreshing odor in a limited space, would be none whatever in a larger ; that which is comfortable warmth to the domestic circle, would not awaken the chirping of a cricket, or stimulate the flight of a butterfly, in the forest ; that which satisfies a hundred poor monks, would, if thrown open to society at large, contribute not an atom to its benefit and emolument. Placid tempers, regulated habitudes, consolatory visitations, are suppressed and destroyed, and nothing rises from their ruins. Better let the cell be standing, than level it only for the thorn and nettle.

HOME. What good do these idlers, with their cords and wallets, or, if you please, with their regularities ?

HUME. These have their value, at least to the possessor and the few about him. Ask rather, what is the worth of his abode to the prince or to the public ? who is the wiser for his cowl, the warmer for his frock, the more contented for his cloister, when they are taken from him ? Monks, it is true, are only as stars that shine upon the desert : but tell me, I beseech you, who caused such a desert in the moral world ? And who rendered so faint a light, in some of its periods, a blessing ? Ignorant rulers, must be the answer, and inhuman laws. They should cease to exist some time before their antidotes, however ill-compounded, are cast away.

If we had lived seven or eight centuries ago, John Home would probably have been saying mass at the altar, and David Hume, fatter and lazier, would have been pursuing his theological studies in the convent. We are so much the creatures of times and seasons, so modified and fashioned by them, that the very plants upon the wall, if they were as sensible as some suppose them to be, would laugh at us.

Home. Fantastic forms and ceremonies are rather what the philosopher will reprehend. Strip away these, reduce things to their primitive state of purity and holiness, and nothing can alter or shake us, clinging, as we should, to the anchor of Faith.

Hume. People clung to it long ago ; but many lost their grasp, benumbed by holding too tightly. The church of Scotland brings close together the objects of veneration and abhorrence. The evil principle, or devil, was, in my opinion, hardly worth the expense of his voyage from Persia ; but, since you have him, you seem resolved to treat him nobly, hating him, defying him, and fearing him never-theless. I would not however place him so very near the Creator, let his pretensions, from custom and precedent, be what they may.

Home. He is always marring the fair works of our heavenly Father : in this labour is his only proximity.

Hume. You represent him as spurring men on to wickedness, from no other motive than the pleasure he experiences in rendering them miserable.

Home. He has no other, excepting his inveterate spite and malice against God ; from which indeed, to speak more properly, this desire originates.

Hume. Has he lost his wits, as well as his station, that he fancies he can render God unhappy by being spiteful and malicious ? You wrong him greatly ; but you wrong God more. For in all Satan's attempts to seduce men into wickedness, he leaves everyone his free will either to resist or yield ; but the heavenly Father, as you would represent him, predestines the greater part of mankind to everlasting pains and torments, antecedently to corruption or temptation. There is no impiety in asking you which is the worst : for impiety most certainly does not consist in setting men right on what is demon-strable in their religion, nor in proving to them that God is greater and better than, with all their zeal for him, they have ever thought him.

DAVID HUME AND JOHN HOME

HOME. This is to confound religion with philosophy, the source of nearly [1] every evil in conduct and of every error in ethics.

HUME. Religion is the eldest sister of Philosophy : on whatever subjects they may differ, it is unbecoming in either to quarrel, and most so about their inheritance.

HOME. And have you nothing, sir, to say against the pomps and vanities of other worships, that you should assail the institutions of your native country ? To fear God, I must suppose then, is less meritorious than to build steeples, and embroider surplices, and compose chants, and blow the bellows of organs.

HUME. My dear sir, it is not because God is delighted with hymns and instruments of music, or prefers base to tenor or tenor to base, or Handel to Giles Halloway, that nations throng to celebrate in their churches his power and his beneficence : it is not that Inigo Jones or Christopher Wren could erect to him a habitation more worthy of his presence than the humblest cottage on the loneliest moor : it is that the best feelings, the highest faculties, the greatest wealth, should be displayed and exercised in the patrimonial palace of every family united. For such are churches both to the rich and poor.

HOME. Your hand, David ! Pardon me, sir ; the sentiment carried me beyond custom ; for it recalled to me the moments of blissful enthusiasm when I was writing my tragedy, and charmed me the more as coming from you.

HUME. I explain the causes of things, and leave them.

HOME. Go on, sir, pray go on ; for here we can walk together. Suppose that God never heard us, never cared for us : do those care for you or hear you whose exploits you celebrate at public dinners, our Wallaces and Bruces ? yet are not we thence the braver, the more generous, the more grateful ?

HUME. I do not see clearly how the more grateful : but I would not analyse by reducing to a cinder a lofty sentiment.

HOME. Surely [2] we are grateful for the benefits our illustrious patriots have conferred on us : and every act of gratitude is rewarded by reproduction. Justice is often pale and melancholy ; but Gratitude, her daughter, is constantly in the flow of spirits and the bloom of loveliness. You call out to her when you fancy she is

---

[1] 1st ed. reads : " of every evil, and of every error."
[2] From " Surely " to " conferred on us " added in 3rd ed. ; 1st ed. reads : " Every act," etc.

passing ; you want her for your dependents, your domestics, your friends, your children. The ancients, as you know, habitually asked their Gods and Goddesses by which of their names it was most agreeable to them to be invoked : now let Gratitude be, what for the play of our fancy we have just imagined her, a sentient living power ; I can not think of any name more likely to be pleasing to her, than Religion. The simplest breast often holds more reason in it than it knows of, and more than Philosophy looks for or suspects. We almost as frequently despise what is not despicable as we admire and reverence what is. No nation in the world was ever so enlightened, and in all parts and qualities so civilised, as the Scotch. Why would you shake or unsettle or disturb those principles which have rendered us peaceable and contented ?

HUME. I would not by any means.

HOME. Many of your writings have evidently such a tendency.

HUME. Those of my writings to which you refer will be read by no nation : a few speculative men will take them ; but none will be rendered more gloomy, more dissatisfied, or more unsocial by them. Rarely will you find one who, five minutes together, can fix his mind even on the surface : some new tune, some idle project, some light thought, some impracticable wish, will generally run, like the dazzling haze of summer on the dry heath, betwixt them and the reader. A bagpipe will swallow them up, a strathspey will dissipate them, or Romance with the death-rattle in her throat will drive them away into dark staircases and charnel-houses.

You and I, in the course of our conversation, have been at variance, as much as discreet and honest men ought to be : each knows that the other thinks differently from him, yet each esteems the other. I can not but smile when I reflect that a few paces, a glass of wine, a cup of tea, conciliate those whom Wisdom would keep asunder.

HOME. No wonder you scoff emphatically, as you pronounce the word *wisdom*.

HUME. If men would permit their minds, like their children, to associate freely together, if they would agree to meet one another with smiles and frankness, instead of suspicion and defiance, the common stock of intelligence and of happiness would be centupled. Probably those two men who hate each other most, and whose best husbandry is to sow burs and thistles in each other's path, would, if

298

they had ever met and conversed familiarly, have been ardent and inseparable friends. The minister who may order my book to be burnt to-morrow by the hangman, if I, by any accident, had been seated yesterday by his side at dinner, might perhaps in another fortnight recommend me to his master, for a man of such gravity and understanding as to be worthy of being a privy councillor, and might conduct me to the treasury-bench.